CRYSTAL SYMMETRY

AND

PHYSICAL PROPERTIES

CRYSTAL SYMMETRY

AND

PHYSICAL PROPERTIES

S. BHAGAVANTAM

Scientific Adviser to the Minister of Defence, New Delhi, India

1966

ACADEMIC PRESS
London and New York

ACADEMIC PRESS INC. (LONDON) LTD
Berkeley Square House
Berkeley Square
London, W.1

U.S. Edition published by
ACADEMIC PRESS INC.
111 Fifth Avenue
New York, New York 10003

Library of Congress Catalog Card Number: 66–16697

Printed in Great Britain by
JOHN WRIGHT & SONS LTD., THE STONEBRIDGE PRESS, BRISTOL

Preface

The author has been engaged for quite some years now in the application of group theoretical methods to the solution of problems in crystal physics, particularly those involving the effect of symmetry on the physical properties of single crystals. The results obtained have been published from time to time in different journals. The object of this book is to give a connected account of these results in respect of widely varying physical properties and with an introduction to the methods employed. The necessary background mathematics, such as that dealing with tensors, matrices and groups, and some geometrical crystallography, such as that dealing with the derivation of crystal classes, are included. These are, however, severely limited, and do not go beyond what is necessary for the reader to understand the main theme of the book. The book is primarily intended to interest students of solid state physics, and it is hoped that it will prove useful to the experimenter interested in studying the properties of single crystals.

Since the book is largely based on work carried out earlier by the author, either by himself or in conjunction with collaborators, only a small number of references is given in the text and no attempt has been made to append a complete bibliography.

Finally, the author wishes to record his appreciation of the help given by Mr. P. V. Pantulu during discussions while preparing the manuscript and while reading the final proofs. The author is deeply indebted to his wife, Mrs. Sita Bhagavantam, who is responsible in no small measure for enabling him to undertake a task of this magnitude and find the time to fulfil it.

S. BHAGAVANTAM

New Delhi
February 1966

Contents

vii

CHAPTER 5
Crystallographic Groups

CHAPTER 6
Symmetry and Physical Properties

CHAPTER 7
Group Theoretical Method

CHAPTER 8
Classification of Physical Properties

CHAPTER 9
Strain

CHAPTER 10
Stress

CHAPTER 11
Elasticity

CHAPTER 12
Large Stresses and Strains

CHAPTER 13
Thermal Expansion

CHAPTER 14
Electrical Properties

CHAPTER 15
Magnetic Properties

CHAPTER 16
Optical Properties

CHAPTER 17
Transport Phenomena

CHAPTER 18
Single Crystal Illustrations

CHAPTER 1

Linear Transformations

1.1 Linear Orthogonal Transformations

Let us assume that a rectangular cartesian system of coordinates is set up in three-dimensional space. Let OX_1, OX_2, OX_3 be the axes and the system of coordinates referred to as the X-system. Any point P in the space can now be described by its coordinates x_1, x_2, x_3. Conversely, to any ordered triplet of numbers x_1, x_2, x_3 corresponds a point in the space. If OX_1', OX_2', OX_3' be another system of rectangular cartesian coordinates with the same origin O, all points in the space can equally well be described by coordinates appropriate to this X'-system. Let the direction cosines of OX_1' with respect to the axes OX_1, OX_2, OX_3 be a_{11}, a_{12}, a_{13}, those of OX_2' be a_{21}, a_{22}, a_{23}, and those of OX_3' be a_{31}, a_{32}, a_{33} respectively. The following scheme is a convenient way of describing the relation between the axes in the X-system and the axes in the X'-system.

	X_1	X_2	X_3
X_1'	a_{11}	a_{12}	a_{13}
X_2'	a_{21}	a_{22}	a_{23}
X_3'	a_{31}	a_{32}	a_{33}

$$\text{(1)}$$

In the scheme of coefficients given as (1), the rows give the direction cosines of the X'-axes with respect to the X-axes and it is evident that the columns give the direction cosines of the X-axes with respect to the X'-axes. It is readily seen that if the coordinates of a point P with respect to the X-system are x_1, x_2, x_3 and if the coordinates of the same point with respect to the X'-system are x_1', x_2', x_3' the following relations hold good.

$$x_1' = a_{11} x_1 + a_{12} x_2 + a_{13} x_3$$
$$x_2' = a_{21} x_1 + a_{22} x_2 + a_{23} x_3$$
$$x_3' = a_{31} x_1 + a_{32} x_2 + a_{33} x_3. \tag{2}$$

The set of equations (2) may be concisely written as

$$x_i' = \sum_{j=1}^{3} a_{ij} x_j \quad (i, j = 1, 2, 3). \tag{3}$$

Further, we can drop the summation sign by adopting the *summation convention*, namely, *when a suffix is repeated in the same term, it is to be understood that summation with respect to that suffix has to be carried out over all the values that the suffix takes.* Thus (3) can be written as

$$x'_i = a_{ij} x_j \quad (i, j = 1, 2, 3). \tag{4}$$

It follows that it does not matter what letter we use for a repeated suffix. Thus $x'_i = a_{ij} x_j = a_{ik} x_k$. In the above equations, i is called the *free suffix* and j is called the *dummy suffix*.

The equations (2), (3) and (4) are different ways of writing the same transformation for the coordinates of a point when a change is made from one rectangular cartesian system (X-system) to another (X'-system). From what has been stated above regarding the direction cosines of the X-axes with reference to the X'-axes, it follows that the transformation inverse to (2) is obtained by changing the rows into columns and columns into rows in the scheme of coefficients given as (1) and interchanging x with x'. The inverse transformation equations read

$$x_i = a_{ji} x'_j \quad (i, j = 1, 2, 3). \tag{5}$$

In what follows, we shall understand that suffixes like i and j run from 1 to 3 unless otherwise stated.

From the very fact that each row in the scheme of coefficients in (1) gives the direction cosines of a straight line (one of the axes in the X'-system) with respect to the rectangular axes OX_1, OX_2, OX_3, relations (6) follow.

$$a_{11}^2 + a_{12}^2 + a_{13}^2 = 1$$
$$a_{21}^2 + a_{22}^2 + a_{23}^2 = 1$$
$$a_{31}^2 + a_{32}^2 + a_{33}^2 = 1. \tag{6}$$

Again, since the axes in the X'-system are mutually perpendicular, the following relations between the direction cosines of any pair of them hold good.

$$a_{21} a_{31} + a_{22} a_{32} + a_{23} a_{33} = 0$$
$$a_{31} a_{11} + a_{32} a_{12} + a_{33} a_{13} = 0$$
$$a_{11} a_{21} + a_{12} a_{22} + a_{13} a_{23} = 0. \tag{7}$$

Making use of the summation convention, the above relations between the coefficients a_{ij} can be written concisely as in (8).

$$a_{ik} a_{jk} = \begin{cases} 1 & \text{if } i = j \\ 0 & \text{if } i \neq j. \end{cases} \tag{8}$$

Introducing the symbol δ_{ij} called the *Kronecker delta* defined by

$$\delta_{ij} = \begin{cases} 1 & \text{if} \quad i = j \\ 0 & \text{if} \quad i \neq j \end{cases}$$

the relations (8) are written as (9).

$$a_{ik} a_{jk} = \delta_{ij}. \tag{9}$$

Since the columns in the scheme of coefficients in (1) represent the direction cosines of the X-axes with respect to the X'-axes, similar arguments as above give (10).

$$a_{ki} a_{kj} = \delta_{ij}. \tag{10}$$

The relations (8) and (9) are called *orthogonality relations*. Transformations in which the coefficients satisfy the orthogonality relations are called linear orthogonal transformations.

If two linear orthogonal transformations of coordinates are applied successively, the resulting transformation from the initial to final coordinates is also linear orthogonal. Let the transformations be

$$x_i' = a_{ij} x_j \quad \text{and} \quad x_i'' = b_{ij} x_j'. \tag{11}$$

We want to find expressions for the coefficients c_{ij} of the transformation

$$x_i'' = c_{ij} x_j \tag{12}$$

in terms of a_{ij} and b_{ij}. Substituting for x_j' in (11) and comparing with (12), we obtain

$$c_{ij} = b_{ik} a_{kj}. \tag{13}$$

Transformation (13) is called the product of transformations contained in (11). The result may be readily extended to the product of any number of transformations. Equations (13) show that c_{ij} satisfy the orthogonality relations.

1.2 The Determinant of the Transformation

The determinant of the scheme of coefficients given in equation (1) may be called the determinant of the transformation and denoted by $|a_{ij}|$. This is written explicitly as

$$\begin{vmatrix} a_{11} & a_{12} & a_{13} \\ a_{21} & a_{22} & a_{23} \\ a_{31} & a_{32} & a_{33} \end{vmatrix}.$$

We denote the value of the determinant by Δ. It may be noted from equation (13) that the determinant of the product of two transformations is the product of the determinants of the transformations.

We shall obtain an important property of the determinant of an orthogonal transformation. Taking the orthogonality relations in the form

$$a_{ij} a_{ik} = \delta_{jk}$$

and forming the determinants on both sides, we obtain the relation (14).

$$|a_{ij} a_{ik}| = |\delta_{jk}| = \begin{vmatrix} 1 & 0 & 0 \\ 0 & 1 & 0 \\ 0 & 0 & 1 \end{vmatrix} = 1. \tag{14}$$

By writing the determinant $|a_{ij} a_{ik}|$ in the expanded form, it is easily seen that it equals the product

$$\begin{vmatrix} a_{11} & a_{21} & a_{31} \\ a_{12} & a_{22} & a_{32} \\ a_{13} & a_{23} & a_{33} \end{vmatrix} \begin{vmatrix} a_{11} & a_{12} & a_{13} \\ a_{21} & a_{22} & a_{23} \\ a_{31} & a_{32} & a_{33} \end{vmatrix}.$$

Because the rows and columns of a determinant can be interchanged without altering its value, the above product is equal to

$$|a_{ij}| . |a_{ij}| = \Delta^2 = 1.$$

Therefore $\Delta = \pm 1$. Thus for all transformations from one rectangular cartesian system to another with the same origin, the determinant of the transformation coefficients is equal to ± 1.

As is well known, there are two possible orientations for the cartesian system, each of which cannot be made to coincide with the other by a rigid body rotation, one of them being recognized as the right-handed system and the other as the left-handed system. The determinant of the transformation is ± 1 according as the original and the transformed axes have the same sense or the opposite sense respectively. This can be shown in the following way. If it is possible to obtain the X'-system from the X-system by a rigid body rotation only, then both systems of axes must have the same sense. Since a rigid body rotation from the initial to final positions takes place continuously, the a_{ij} should vary continuously. The determinant $|a_{ij}|$ is a continuous function in the variables a_{ij} and therefore it cannot change its value discontinuously when a_{ij} vary continuously. The identity transformation which is the transformation $x_i' = x_i$ has $|a_{ij}| = +1$. It follows that all transformations which are obtained by rigid body rotations, i.e. all transformations which preserve the sense of the axes have $|a_{ij}| = +1$. The transformation $x_1' = -x_1$; $x_2' = -x_2$; $x_3' = -x_3$, which is an inversion of the sign in each case, may be denoted by i and has $\Delta = -1$. It obviously changes the sense of the coordinate system. Any transformation that changes the sense can be interpreted as the result of the application of a transformation which preserves the sense followed by i. Since every transformation which preserves the sense has $\Delta = +1$ and i has $\Delta = -1$, it follows that every transformation that changes sense has $\Delta = -1$.

The converse proposition that all the transformations which have $\Delta = \pm 1$ preserve or change the sense respectively follows.

1.3 Transformation of Space

The transformation equations (2) can be interpreted in two essentially different ways. The first one is to regard the two sets of numbers x_1, x_2, x_3 and x_1', x_2', x_3' as the coordinates of the same point when it is referred to two different sets of coordinate systems. In this interpretation, equations (2) give a transformation of coordinate axes. The second one is to regard the set of numbers x_1, x_2, x_3 as the coordinates of a point P, and the set of numbers x_1', x_2', x_3' as coordinates of another point Q where P and Q are both referred to the same coordinate system. In this interpretation, equations (2) give a transformation of the point P into another point Q, and thus it constitutes a transformation of space. The linear orthogonal transformations have the important property that they are distance-preserving, i.e. they leave the distance between any two points in the space unaltered. This is verified by showing that all linear orthogonal transformations leave the expression $(x_1^2 + x_2^2 + x_3^2)$ invariant. Using the relations $x_i = a_{ji} x_j'$ and $a_{ij} a_{ik} = \delta_{jk}$, one can show that $x_1^2 + x_2^2 + x_3^2 = x_1'^2 + x_2'^2 + x_3'^2$. It may be mentioned here that the operations which transform a crystal into a geometrically identical position with itself are linear orthogonal transformations. These are referred to as the symmetry operations characteristic of the crystal. Following the same arguments as in the previous Section, transformations whose determinant equals $+1$ can be interpreted as rigid body rotations of space. The symmetry operations of a crystal which are pure rotations are among these. Transformations whose determinant equals -1 can be interpreted as rigid body rotations of space followed by an inversion of space about the origin. Such a combined transformation may be referred to as rotation-inversion or rotation-reflection. We will see later that transformations of space which are not linear orthogonal effect a distortion of space. Such transformations are useful in describing deformations of bodies.

1.4 Eulerian Angles

It has been shown that the nine coefficients a_{ij} of a linear orthogonal transformation are related by six orthogonality relations. It follows that the coefficients a_{ij} can be expressed in terms of three independent parameters. Such a parametric representation of the rotation of a rigid body about a point by what are known as Eulerian angles is given here.

In Fig. 1, let O be the fixed point about which the rotation takes place and let OX_1, OX_2, OX_3 form a right-handed rectangular cartesian system fixed in space. Let OX_1', OX_2', OX_3' form a system of rectangular

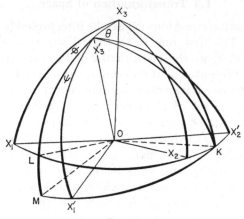

Fig. 1.

cartesian coordinates fixed relative to the rigid body such that before rotation, the X'-system coincides with the X-system. Let OK be the line of intersection of the X_1X_2 and $X_1'X_2'$ planes. OK is called the nodal line. The line of intersection of X_1X_2 and X_3X_3' planes is denoted by OL and the line of intersection $X_1'X_2'$ and X_3X_3' planes is denoted by OM. The angles X_3OX_3', X_2OK and $X_2'OK$ are denoted by θ, ϕ and ψ respectively. These are known as the Eulerian angles. They specify completely the position of the rigid body after rotation. The rotation itself is denoted by $R(\phi\theta\psi)$. It may be noted that in the first rotation by ϕ, the spherical triangle $X_3X_1X_2$ goes to X_3LK, X_3 being kept fixed. In the second rotation by θ, the spherical triangle X_3LK goes to $X_3'MK$, K being kept fixed. In the third rotation by ψ, the spherical triangle $X_3'MK$ goes to $X_3'X_1'X_2'$, X_3' being kept fixed. In order to find the expressions for a_{ij} in terms of ϕ, θ, ψ, one may proceed as follows.

Take a unit length along OX_1. The projection of this unit length on OX_1' gives the cosine of the angle between OX_1 and OX_1' which is equal to a_{11}. Now this unit length has projections $\cos\phi$ along OL and $-\sin\phi$ along OK. A length $\cos\phi$ along OL has projection $\cos\phi\cos\theta$ along OM and this has projection $\cos\phi\cos\theta\cos\psi$ along OX_1'. A length $-\sin\phi$ along OK has projection $-\sin\phi\sin\psi$ along OX$'_1$. Thus $a_{11} = (\cos\phi\cos\theta\cos\psi - \sin\phi\sin\psi)$. Proceeding in this way, expressions for all a_{ij} can be derived in terms of the Eulerian angles. They are given in Table I.

TABLE I

Transformation matrix in terms of Eulerian angles

	X_1	X_2	X_3
X'_1	$\cos\phi\cos\theta\cos\psi - \sin\phi\sin\psi$	$\sin\phi\cos\theta\cos\psi + \cos\phi\sin\psi$	$-\sin\theta\cos\psi$
X'_2	$-\cos\phi\cos\theta\sin\psi - \sin\phi\cos\psi$	$-\sin\phi\cos\theta\sin\psi + \cos\phi\cos\psi$	$\sin\theta\sin\psi$
X'_3	$\cos\phi\sin\theta$	$\sin\phi\sin\theta$	$\cos\theta$

1.5 General Linear Transformations

We shall consider linear transformations with real coefficients which are such that the determinant of the transformation is non-vanishing. We may write

$$x'_i = a_{ij}x_j \quad \text{with} \quad a_{ij} \neq 0. \tag{15}$$

Denoting the value of the determinant $|a_{ij}|$ by Δ and the cofactor of a_{ij} in the determinant by A_{ij}, we can solve the equations (15) for x_1, x_2, x_3 and obtain (16).

$$x_1 = \frac{A_{11}}{\Delta}x'_1 + \frac{A_{21}}{\Delta}x'_2 + \frac{A_{31}}{\Delta}x'_3$$

$$x_2 = \frac{A_{12}}{\Delta}x'_1 + \frac{A_{22}}{\Delta}x'_2 + \frac{A_{32}}{\Delta}x'_3$$

$$x_3 = \frac{A_{13}}{\Delta}x'_1 + \frac{A_{23}}{\Delta}x'_2 + \frac{A_{33}}{\Delta}x'_3. \tag{16}$$

The transformation (15) considered as a transformation of space does not generally keep lengths invariant. It represents a deformation of space. For example, the simple transformation $x'_1 = kx_2$; $x'_2 = x_2$; $x'_3 = x_3$ is a shear in the X_1X_2 plane which transforms a rectangle in that plane into a parallelogram. The transformation (15), however, preserves parallelism in that a pair of straight lines which are initially parallel remain parallel after deformation. Such deformations are called homogeneous deformations. It is easily seen, as in the case of orthogonal transformations, that the successive application of two linear transformations is a linear transformation. The linear orthogonal transformations are only a special kind of linear transformations.

2

1.6 Linear Equations in Several Variables

We note that linear transformations discussed above are only a particular kind of simultaneous linear equations. In the following chapters, we have often to deal with simultaneous linear relations between several variables. The linear dependence of the six components of stress on the six components of strain in the case of elastic behaviour of crystals and the linear dependence of three components of magnetic moment on the six components of stress in the case of piezomagnetic behaviour of certain crystals are examples which make use of simultaneous linear equations. The general scheme of simultaneous linear equations which expresses the variables Y_i; $i = 1$ to m as linear expressions in variables X_i; $i = 1$ to n are written as

$$Y_i = a_{ij} X_j \quad (i = 1 \text{ to } m; j = 1 \text{ to } n).$$

If the variables Z_i; $i = 1$ to l depend linearly on Y_i, which in turn depend linearly on X_i, the dependence of variables Z on variables X is linear. This result is a generalization of successive application of linear transformations. If the relation between Zs and Ys is given by

$$Z_i = b_{ij} Y_j \quad (i = 1 \text{ to } l; j = 1 \text{ to } m)$$

the relation between the Zs and Xs is given by

$$Z_i = c_{ij} X_j \quad (i = 1 \text{ to } l; j = 1 \text{ to } n)$$

where $c_{ij} = a_{ik} b_{kj}$ with $k = 1$ to m. This result may be easily verified.

CHAPTER 2

Tensors

2.1 Introduction

Any physical quantity or physical property, to be recognized and designated as such, requires to be independent of the system of coordinates with reference to which measurements are made to describe it. It follows that the mathematical entities used to represent a physical quantity or a physical property should possess features which are independent of the system of coordinates chosen. Tensor analysis is concerned with the study of such entities.

Let us consider the description of physical space as an example. The simplest coordinate system needed for such a description is the cartesian system. We shall confine ourselves to such systems in what follows. Each point of space is denoted by an ordered triplet of numbers which are its coordinates in that system. The coordinates of the same point are different in different coordinate systems. Of course, all these triplets of numbers—one for each coordinate system—describe *the same point in space*. This is because all the points constituting the physical space are independent of the coordinate system chosen to describe it. The choice of a particular coordinate system is arbitrary and dictated by considerations of convenience.

Consider a physical quantity like temperature which is specified at any point P by just one number, which in fact is the magnitude of the temperature at that point. If the point P is specified by coordinates x_1, x_2, x_3 in the X-system, the temperature distribution is given as a function of position $T(x_1, x_2, x_3)$. In the X'-system, the same point P in the body has coordinates x_1', x_2', x_3' and the temperature distribution in this system is another function $T'(x_1', x_2', x_3')$. Since the temperature at the point P is a physical quantity independent of the coordinate system chosen, we have

$$T'(x_1', x_2', x_3') = T(x_1, x_2, x_3).$$

Thus, for each temperature distribution, there is a set of functions, one for each coordinate system, which are all related to each other in the above manner. They are said to transform invariantly. Such physical quantities are called scalars. Other examples of scalars are electric potential, density, etc.

If x_1, x_2, x_3 are the coordinates of a point of space in a coordinate system called the X-system; and x_1', x_2', x_3' are the coordinates of the same point in another system called the X'-system, we have already seen that the transformation equation is

$$x_i' = a_{ij} x_j. \tag{1}$$

It is evident that components of directed line segments also transform in accordance with the transformation law contained in equation (1). If we consider a physical quantity like the electric field which is specified at any point by three numbers, namely, its components along the coordinate axes, the set of equations (1) can be used for relating the three components in two different coordinate systems, the physical quantity itself, which in this case is the electric field, being a quantity independent of the choice of coordinate system. Thus it is evident that the totality of the sets of ordered triplets of numbers, one set for each coordinate system, which are all related to each other according to the transformation law given in equation (1), serves as a mathematical representation of such quantities. We are familiar with several physical quantities whose specification at each point in space requires 3 numbers taken in order and these are called vectors. Other examples of vectors are velocity, electric moment, force, etc. These are the physical quantities which possess a direction as well as a magnitude.

There are other physical quantities which cannot be specified at a point in space by a single number like the scalars, or by 3 numbers like the vectors. Some require 6 numbers, some 9 numbers, some 27 numbers and so on. We can cite the somewhat familiar example of stress at a point inside an elastic material. For a complete specification of it, we should have 9 numbers but owing to certain additional physical considerations, this number reduces to 6. We can again mention here that a physical quantity like stress cannot in any way depend on the particular coordinate system chosen to describe it. Its six components may take different values in different coordinate systems, but the force acting on a surface element oriented in a definite way remains independent of the coordinate system chosen. We shall later show that the six stress components transform like the products of components of two vectors taken two at a time.

The mathematical entities which possess the transformation properties required by physical quantities as illustrated in the previous examples are called tensors. We shall proceed to give the formal definition of tensors of different ranks and cite some known physical examples in each case. We shall, however, confine to functions of three variables even though the generalization to several variables is straightforward. Our suffixes run from 1 to 3 as usual.

2.2 Definitions

A tensor of rank zero is the totality of functions $A(x_i)$, $A'(x_i')$, $A''(x_i'')$, ..., one for each coordinate system, related to one another by the transformation law

$$A'(x_i') = A(x_i) \qquad (2)$$

where $x_i' = a_{ij} x_j$. $A(x_i)$ denotes a function $A(x_1, x_2, x_3)$ of the three variables. A tensor of rank zero is also called a scalar. In this case, equation (2) simply means that the scalar physical quantity under consideration transforms invariantly when the coordinate system changes from one to another.

A tensor of rank one is the totality of sets of functions $A_i(x)$, $A_i'(x')$, $A_i''(x'')$, ..., one for each coordinate system, related to one another by a transformation of the form

$$A_i'(x') = a_{ij} A_j(x) \qquad (3)$$

where $x_i' = a_{ij} x_j$. $A_i(x)$ denotes a set of three functions $A_1(x)$, $A_2(x)$, $A_3(x)$ in the three variables x_1, x_2, x_3. In what follows, x shall be understood to stand for the three variables x_1, x_2, x_3. $A_1(x), A_2(x), A_3(x)$ are called the components of the tensor. Equation (3) implies that a vector quantity transforms on a change of coordinate system in such a manner that each of its components in the new system can be obtained as a linear combination of its three components in the original system.

A tensor of rank two is the totality of sets of functions $A_{ij}(x)$, $A_{ij}'(x')$, $A_{ij}''(x'')$, ..., one for each coordinate system, related to one another by the transformation law

$$A_{ij}'(x') = a_{ik} a_{jl} A_{kl}(x) \qquad (4)$$

where $x_i' = a_{ij} x_j$. $A_{ij}(x)$ denotes a set of nine functions called its components in each coordinate system. Besides the example of stress already mentioned, strain may be cited as another example of a tensor of rank two with the restriction that the components A_{ij} and A_{ji} equal each other. Thermoelectric power is an example of a tensor of rank two with no such additional restriction. As in the cases of scalars and vectors, equation (4) lays down the manner in which the nine components that constitute a tensor of rank two transform on a change of coordinate system and can conveniently be used to define such a tensor.

We may now extend the considerations set out above formally to a tensor of rank r and regard it as the totality of the sets of functions $A_{ijk...}(x), A_{ijk...}'(x'), A_{ijk...}''(x''), ...$, one for each coordinate system, which are related to one another by a transformation of the form

$$A'_{ijk...}(x') = a_{il} a_{jm} a_{kn...} A_{lmn...}(x)$$

where $x'_i = a_{ij} x_j$. $A_{lmn...}(x)$ denotes a set of 3^r functions, called the components of the tensor in each coordinate system.

2.3 Algebra of Tensors

Even though the theorems that follow are stated for the general rank tensors, proofs are given for tensors of particular rank like 1, 2 or 3, whenever it is felt that the generalization is obvious. We shall simply write A_i to mean the tensor $A_i(x)$ dropping the variable referring to the coordinate system.

The sum (or difference) of two tensors of the same rank, term by term, is again a tensor of the same rank. If A_i and B_i are two tensors which on transformation of coordinates transform to A'_i and B'_i, then $A'_i + B'_i = a_{ij} A_j + a_{ij} B_j = a_{ij}(A_j + B_j)$ which proves the statement. The multiplication of the components of a tensor by a number gives a tensor of the same rank. It follows that any linear combination of tensors of the same rank is again a tensor of the same rank.

The set of quantities consisting of the product of each element of a tensor of rank r with each element of a tensor of rank s is a tensor whose rank is $(r+s)$. This is called the *outer product* of the two tensors. Let A_{ij} and B_{ij} be two tensors of rank two which, on transformation to the X'-system of coordinates, transform to A'_{ij} and B'_{ij}. All possible products of components A_{ij} and B_{ij} are denoted by four different suffixes $A_{ij} B_{kl}$.

$$A'_{ij} B'_{kl} = (a_{im} a_{jn} A_{mn}) (a_{kp} a_{lq} B_{pq})$$

$$= a_{im} a_{jn} a_{kp} a_{lq} A_{mn} B_{pq}. \tag{5}$$

Equation (5) shows that $A_{mn} B_{pq}$ transform as a tensor of rank four. It follows that a tensor of rank r transforms as the outer product of r vectors. This is again the same as the transformation law for the products of coordinates x_i taken r at a time. The manner in which these products are formed is the same as the manner in which the outer product of r vectors is formed. Instead of taking r different vectors, we consider the same triplet (x_1, x_2, x_3) r times and form all possible products of r components, taking one component from each triplet at a time. To give an example, the nine components of a second rank tensor transform as the nine products, $x_1 x_1$, $x_1 x_2$, $x_1 x_3$, $x_2 x_1$, $x_2 x_2$, $x_2 x_3$, $x_3 x_1$, $x_3 x_2$, $x_3 x_3$ formed out of the coordinates x_1, x_2, x_3.

If in a tensor $A_{ijk...}$ of rank r, we equate two suffixes, say, i and j, that is, introduce the same letter i in their place, summation convention requires a summation to be performed on that suffix over all its possible values. This operation of equating two suffixes is called *contraction*. If an operation of contraction is performed on two suffixes of a tensor of rank r, then the resulting set of components is a tensor of rank $(r-2)$. We take $A'_{ijkl} = a_{im} a_{jn} a_{kp} a_{lq} A_{mnpq}$ as an example and equate i and j in it. We have $A'_{iikl} = a_{im} a_{in} a_{kp} a_{lq} A_{mnpq}$ where $a_{im} a_{in} = \delta_{mn}$ and hence $A_{iikl} = a_{kp} a_{lq} A_{mnpq}$. Thus A_{iikl} is a tensor of rank two.

If all components of a tensor vanish in one coordinate system, then they necessarily vanish in all other admissible coordinate systems. This is evident from the fact that the transformation equations are homogeneous.

Terms of the type $A(p, q) B_p$, where it is understood that there is a summation over p, are called *inner products* of sets of functions $A(p, q)$ and B_p. We define an inner product whether the sets of functions form tensors or not.

If we are given that the inner product $A(i, j) B_j$ is a tensor of rank one, and B_j is an arbitrary tensor of rank one, then $A(i, j)$ is a tensor of rank two. We have $A'(i, j) B'_j = a_{ip} A(p, q) B_q$ and $B_q = a_{jq} B'_j$. Therefore $[A'(i, j) - a_{ip} a_{jq} A(p, q)] B'_j = 0$. But B_j and hence B'_j are arbitrary tensors. Consequently, all the coefficients of B'_j must be zero, giving $A'(i, j) = a_{ip} a_{jq} A(p, q)$. This shows that $A(p, q)$ is a tensor of rank two and is represented by symbols A_{pq}. More generally, if we know that a set of 3^r functions is such that their inner product with an arbitrary vector is a tensor of rank $(r-1)$, it follows that the set of 3^r functions constitute a tensor of rank r. There is another form of the above result which is easily established. If a set of nine functions $A(i, j)$ are such that $A(i, j) x_i x_j$ is an invariant, it can be shown in a similar way that the set $A(i, j)$ constitutes a second rank tensor. This result can again be generalized to a set of 3^r functions. These results are different forms of what is known as the *quotient theorem*. They provide a means of determining the tensor nature of a set of functions without having to study their transformation properties in detail. In the following chapters, we shall have occasion to refer to and use the quotient theorem. It may, however, be noted that we have refrained from stating the theorem here in its most general form.

2.4 Symmetry and Skew-symmetry

If when two indices in the components of a tensor are interchanged, it does not alter the value of the components, the tensor is said to be *symmetric* with respect to those indices. Symmetry is preserved under coordinate transformations. This can be shown in the following manner. If A_{ijkl} is symmetric in the indices i and j, $A_{ijkl} = A_{jikl}$.

Hence $(A_{ijkl} - A_{jikl}) = 0$. The difference of two tensors is a tensor and if the components of a tensor vanish in one coordinate system they vanish in every other system. Thus we have $(A_{ijkl} - A_{jikl})' = 0$ and $A'_{ijkl} = A'_{jikl}$.

We say that a tensor is *skew-symmetric* or *antisymmetric* with respect to a pair of indices, if an interchange of these indices merely changes the sign of the components. Skew-symmetry is preserved under coordinate transformations. The proof is straightforward. It is also possible that all the components of a tensor may remain invariant when some of its indices are permuted in all possible ways. In such a case the tensor is said to be totally symmetric with respect to those indices. Total symmetry is also preserved under coordinate transformations. The symmetry, skew-symmetry and total symmetry that the components of a tensor may possess is referred to as the intrinsic symmetry of the tensor.

2.5 Axial Tensors

The components of the cross product of two vectors A_i and B_i are

$$C_1 = (A_2 B_3 - A_3 B_2); \quad C_2 = (A_3 B_1 - A_1 B_3); \quad C_3 = (A_1 B_2 - A_2 B_1).$$

It can be seen that these components do not transform according to the tensor law. Instead we have

$$C'_1 = (A'_2 B'_3 - A'_3 B'_2) = a_{2i} a_{3j}(A_i B_j - A_j B_i)$$

which on writing *in extenso* gives

$$C'_1 = (a_{22} a_{33} - a_{23} a_{32}) (A_2 B_3 - A_3 B_2)$$
$$+ (a_{23} a_{31} - a_{21} a_{33}) (A_3 B_1 - A_1 B_3)$$
$$+ (a_{21} a_{32} - a_{22} a_{31}) (A_1 B_2 - A_2 B_1).$$

The coefficients $(a_{22} a_{33} - a_{23} a_{32})$, etc. are minors of a_{11}, etc. respectively in the determinant $|a_{ij}|$ and the following equations hold:

$$a_{11} = \pm (a_{22} a_{33} - a_{23} a_{32})$$
$$a_{12} = \pm (a_{23} a_{31} - a_{21} a_{33})$$
$$a_{13} = \pm (a_{21} a_{32} - a_{22} a_{31}).$$

The $\pm$ sign is valid according as the determinant of the transformation is $+1$ or -1, i.e. according as the transformation is a rotation or a rotation-reflection. Therefore it follows that $C'_1 = \pm a_{11} C_1 \pm a_{12} C_2 \pm a_{13} C_3$ and in general $C'_i = \pm a_{ij} C_j$ according as the transformation is a rotation or a rotation-reflection. Quantities $C_i(x)$ which transform according to the above law are called *axial vectors* or *axial tensors* to distinguish them from the vectors or tensors defined earlier which are called true vectors or true tensors. Axial vectors or axial tensors are sometimes also referred to as pseudo vectors or pseudo tensors. In general, the totality of sets of functions $A_{ijk...}(x), A'_{ijk...}(x'), A''_{ijk...}(x''), ...$, one for each co-ordinate system, which are related to one another by the transformation of the form

$$A'_{ijk...}(x') = \pm a_{ip}\, a_{jq}\, a_{kr} \ldots A_{pqr...}(x),$$

where the negative sign must be taken for transformations which are rotation-reflections and the positive sign for transformations which are

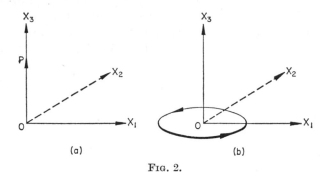

(a)   (b)

FIG. 2.

rotations, is defined as an *axial tensor* or a *pseudo tensor*. The outer product of an even number of axial tensors transforms as a true tensor. The outer product of an odd number of axial tensors is not a true tensor but is an axial tensor and the transformation law therefore acquires an additional product with -1 whenever the transformation is a rotation-reflection.

It is useful to note that a second rank skew-symmetric tensor can be handled as an axial vector, but this is true in three dimensions only. Enantiomorphism is an example of a pseudo scalar. Angular momentum and magnetic moment are examples of a pseudo vector or an axial vector. Optical rotation is an example of a symmetric pseudo tensor or an axial tensor of the second rank.

While it is possible to get a proper pictorial representation of a polar or true vector by showing the same with the help of a simple arrow OP with a specific direction and magnitude, as in Fig. 2(a), it should be noted that in order to similarly represent an axial vector like the magnetic moment, we should use a circle with a sense of rotation as in Fig. 2(b) indicating the nature of the electric current which forms the genesis of the magnetic moment. The difference between the transformation properties of a vector like the magnetic moment and a vector like the electric field may be brought out in the manner shown in Fig. 2, p. 15.

For instance, vector OP has its direction normal to the X_1X_2 plane and will change sign when the transformation of a reflection in the X_1X_2 plane or of an inversion about the origin is performed. On the other hand, the circular current in the X_1X_2 plane of Fig. 2(b) which is equivalent to a magnetic field along the X_3-axis is to be regarded as an axial vector and will transform as the function $x_1 x_2' - x_1' x_2$ where x_1, x_2, x_3 and x_1', x_2', x_3' are the coordinates of two points. Since the coordinates x_1, x_2, x_1' and x_2' do not change sign on reflection in the X_1X_2 plane, the axial vector remains invariant under this transformation unlike the polar vector. Similarly, since the coordinates x_1, x_2, x_1' and x_2' all change sign on inversion, the axial vector again remains invariant under the transformation of inversion unlike the polar vector.

CHAPTER 3

Matrices

3.1 Definitions

A rectangular array of mn numbers arranged in m rows and n columns is called an $m \times n$ matrix. The set of mn numbers may be conveniently denoted by a two-suffix notation such as a_{ij}, $i = 1$ to m and $j = 1$ to n. The matrix itself is written as

$$\left\|\begin{array}{ccccc} a_{11} & a_{12} & a_{13} & \cdots & a_{1n} \\ a_{21} & a_{22} & a_{23} & \cdots & a_{2n} \\ a_{31} & a_{32} & a_{33} & \cdots & a_{3n} \\ \cdots & \cdots & \cdots & \cdots & \cdots \\ a_{m1} & a_{m2} & a_{m3} & \cdots & a_{mn} \end{array}\right\|$$

and may be denoted by A or $\|a_{ij}\|$. If $m = n$ then A is an n-square matrix. A $1 \times n$ matrix is called a row vector and an $n \times 1$ matrix is called a column vector. The numbers a_{ij} are called the elements of the matrix. The scheme of coefficients given in equation (1) of Chapter 1, representing an orthogonal transformation of coordinates, is an example of a 3×3 matrix. In fact, the scheme is called the matrix of the transformation. Similarly the scheme of coefficients in Table I is called the matrix of the transformation $R(\phi\theta\psi)$. We shall say that the matrix $A = \|a_{ij}\|$ equals the matrix $B = \|b_{ij}\|$ if the corresponding elements are equal to each other, i.e. if $a_{ij} = b_{ij}$ for all i and j. The sum of two matrices containing the same number of rows and columns is defined as the matrix obtained by adding corresponding terms.

Scalar multiplication of a matrix $\|a_{ij}\|$ by a number λ is defined as the matrix $\|\lambda a_{ij}\|$. The product of two matrices A and B, denoted as AB, is defined if only the number of columns in A is equal to the number of rows in B. If $A = \|a_{ij}\|$ is an $m \times n$ matrix and $B = \|b_{ij}\|$ is an $n \times p$ matrix, their product $C = \|c_{ij}\|$ is defined by

$$AB = C = \|c_{ij}\| = \|a_{ik}b_{kj}\|$$

where the summation is over k from 1 to n. AB is obviously a matrix with m rows and p columns. The ith row jth column element c_{ij} of the product matrix, written *in extenso* as the sum of n terms $(a_{i1}b_{1j} + a_{i2}b_{2j} + \ldots a_{in}b_{nj})$, is obtained by multiplying each term of the

ith row of the matrix A with the corresponding term in the kth column of matrix B and adding. In particular if A is a 1×3 row vector and B is a 3×1 column vector, their product

$$AB = \| a_1\, a_2\, a_3 \| \begin{Vmatrix} b_1 \\ b_2 \\ b_3 \end{Vmatrix} = (a_1 b_1 + a_2 b_2 + a_3 b_3).$$

This is the familiar scalar product or inner product of two vectors A and B whose components are a_1, a_2, a_3 and b_1, b_2, b_3 respectively.

The simultaneous linear equations $x'_i = a_{ij} x_j$ in three dimensions can be written in the matrix notation as

$$\begin{Vmatrix} x'_1 \\ x'_2 \\ x'_3 \end{Vmatrix} = \begin{Vmatrix} a_{11} & a_{12} & a_{13} \\ a_{21} & a_{22} & a_{23} \\ a_{31} & a_{32} & a_{33} \end{Vmatrix} \begin{Vmatrix} x_1 \\ x_2 \\ x_3 \end{Vmatrix}$$

or simply as $X' = AX$ in the short notation. The manner in which simultaneous linear equations connecting m variables with n other variables in matrix notation is written is similar. In this text, however, we do not always adopt the matrix notation to write down simultaneous linear equations. Depending on considerations of usefulness, we adopt either the matrix notation or the condensed notation using summation convention. At times we even write them down in full expanded form.

The following example serves as a useful exercise in matrix multiplication. The rotation of a rigid body about a fixed point denoted by $R(\phi\theta\psi)$ has been shown in Chapter 1 to be equivalent to successive application of rotations through the Eulerian angles ϕ, θ, ψ in that order. These successive rotations are represented by transformations whose matrices are

$$S(\phi) = \begin{Vmatrix} \cos\phi & \sin\phi & 0 \\ -\sin\phi & \cos\phi & 0 \\ 0 & 0 & 1 \end{Vmatrix}; \quad T(\theta) = \begin{Vmatrix} \cos\theta & 0 & -\sin\theta \\ 0 & 1 & 0 \\ \sin\theta & 0 & \cos\theta \end{Vmatrix};$$

$$S(\psi) = \begin{Vmatrix} \cos\psi & \sin\psi & 0 \\ -\sin\psi & \cos\psi & 0 \\ 0 & 0 & 1 \end{Vmatrix}.$$

It can be verified that the product of the matrices $S(\psi), T(\theta), S(\phi)$ taken in that order gives the matrix representing the rigid body rotation $R(\phi\theta\psi)$ whose elements are given in Table I.

Matrices obey the following fundamental laws of arithmetic. Addition of matrices is commutative, i.e. $A+B = B+A$. This law follows from the fact that the matrix sum is obtained by adding the corresponding elements, which is commutative. Addition of matrices is associative, i.e. $(A+B)+C = A+(B+C)$. This law follows from the fact that the sums of the corresponding elements are associative. Multiplication of matrices is distributive with respect to addition both on the right and on the left.

$$A(B+C) = AB+AC \quad \text{and} \quad (B+C)A = BA+CA.$$

The proof of these results follows from the fact that the elements in the product are homogeneous and linear functions of the elements in either the right-hand or the left-hand factor. Multiplication of matrices is associative. $(AB)C = A(BC)$. This follows from the fact that the ith row jth column element in either product is equal to $a_{il}b_{lm}c_{mj}$. The fifth fundamental law of arithmetic is the commutative law of multiplication. For any two numbers a and b we have $ab = ba$. This law is not in general true for matrices as can be verified from the fact that

$$\left\| \begin{array}{cc} 1 & 0 \\ 0 & -1 \end{array} \right\| \left\| \begin{array}{cc} 0 & 1 \\ 0 & 0 \end{array} \right\| = \left\| \begin{array}{cc} 0 & 1 \\ 0 & 0 \end{array} \right\|$$

whereas

$$\left\| \begin{array}{cc} 0 & 1 \\ 0 & 0 \end{array} \right\| \left\| \begin{array}{cc} 1 & 0 \\ 0 & -1 \end{array} \right\| = \left\| \begin{array}{cc} 0 & -1 \\ 0 & 0 \end{array} \right\|$$

which is obviously different from the previous product.

The transpose of an $m \times n$ matrix A is defined as the $n \times m$ matrix obtained by changing the rows into columns and columns into rows in A. It is denoted by the symbol A^+. The transpose of the product of two matrices is equal to the product of their transposes taken in the reverse order. This may be proved as follows. If we take $AB = \|a_{ik}b_{kj}\|$, then $(AB)^+ = \|a_{jk}b_{ki}\| = \|b_{ki}a_{jk}\| = \|b_{ji}\|\|a_{ji}\| = B^+A^+$.

3.2 Square Matrices

We mentioned that if, in a matrix, the number of rows is equal to the number of columns, it is called a *square matrix* and that an $n \times n$ matrix is called an n-square matrix. An n-square matrix is also referred to as a matrix of dimension n. It is obvious that any two n-square matrices can be added or multiplied. In what follows we deal with only square matrices unless otherwise specified. The *zero matrix* is the matrix every element of which is zero. It may be denoted by the letter O. It is obvious that $A+O = A$ for every A. The *unit matrix* is the square matrix in which the elements in the leading diagonal are unity while all other elements are zero. It is denoted by the letter I.

$$I = \begin{Vmatrix} 1 & 0 & 0 & \ldots & 0 \\ 0 & 1 & 0 & \ldots & 0 \\ 0 & 0 & 1 & \ldots & 0 \\ \ldots & \ldots & \ldots & \ldots & \ldots \\ 0 & 0 & 0 & \ldots & 1 \end{Vmatrix}.$$

It is obvious that $IA = AI = A$ for every A. The *determinant* of a square matrix is the number evaluated from the matrix by the ordinary rules for evaluating a determinant. It is denoted by the symbol $|a_{ij}|$ or $|A|$. The determinant of the product of two square matrices is equal to the product of their determinants. The proof of this theorem is obtained by taking note of the fact that the product of two determinants $|a_{ij}|$ and $|b_{ij}|$ is expressed as the determinant $|a_{ik}b_{kj}|$. A matrix is called a *singular matrix* if its determinant vanishes. A matrix is called *non-singular* if its determinant does not vanish. The *inverse of a square matrix*, denoted by the symbol A^{-1}, is defined by the equation $A^{-1}A = AA^{-1} = I$. It follows that the determinant of A^{-1} is the reciprocal of the determinant of A and that the inverse of a matrix exists only if the matrix is non-singular. If A_{ij} is the determinant of the $(n-1) \times (n-1)$ matrix obtained by deleting the ith row and jth column in $\|a_{ij}\|$, when multiplied by $(-1)^{i+j}$, it is called the *cofactor* of the element a_{ij}. The matrix $\|A_{ij}\|$ is called the *adjoint* of $\|a_{ij}\|$. The adjoint satisfies the relation

$$\|a_{ij}\| \|A_{ij}\| = \begin{Vmatrix} \Delta & 0 & 0 & \ldots & 0 \\ 0 & \Delta & 0 & \ldots & 0 \\ 0 & 0 & \Delta & \ldots & 0 \\ \ldots & \ldots & \ldots & \ldots & \ldots \\ 0 & 0 & 0 & \ldots & \Delta \end{Vmatrix}$$

$$= \Delta \begin{Vmatrix} 1 & 0 & 0 & \ldots & 0 \\ 0 & 1 & 0 & \ldots & 0 \\ 0 & 0 & 1 & \ldots & 0 \\ \ldots & \ldots & \ldots & \ldots & \ldots \\ 0 & 0 & 0 & \ldots & 1 \end{Vmatrix} = \Delta I$$

where Δ is the value of the determinant $|a_{ij}|$. It follows that the inverse of a matrix is the matrix whose elements are its cofactors divided by its determinant.

3.3 Diagonalization of a Matrix

A matrix in which all the terms not in the leading diagonal are zero is called a *diagonal matrix*. The diagonal matrices have the special property that the product of any two of them is commutative.

The equations $\|y_i\| = \|a_{ij}\|\|x_j\|$, or simply $Y = AX$, set up a correspondence between vectors $\|x_i\|$ and $\|y_i\|$. If the space is referred to a new coordinate system related to the old coordinate system by the matrix T, the components of the vectors $\|y_i\|$ and $\|x_i\|$ get transformed. If the new coordinates are denoted by primes, the relation between old coordinates and new coordinates is $X' = TX$; $Y' = TY$. The correspondence between the X' and Y' vectors is expressed in the new coordinate system by writing $Y' = TY = TAX = TAT^{-1}X'$. Thus $Y' = A'X'$ where $A' = TAT^{-1}$. The matrix A' is called the *transform* of A by the non-singular matrix T. It follows that if A' is the transform of A by T, then A is the transform of A' by T^{-1}. A and A' are called *equivalent* matrices because they represent the same correspondence of vectors.

If we wish to transform a matrix A into its diagonal form, we have to find a matrix U such that $UAU^{-1} = \Lambda$ where Λ is a diagonal matrix. It follows that $UA = \Lambda U$. We shall confine to three dimensions for the sake of simplicity. The above matrix equation is in fact a set of equations,

$$u_{ij}a_{jk} = \lambda_i u_{ik} \qquad \text{(No summation on } i.\text{)}$$

It follows that

$$u_{ij}(a_{jk} - \delta_{jk}\lambda_i) = 0 \qquad \text{(No summation on } i.\text{)}$$

If we fix i and give values $1, 2, 3$ to k, we obtain a set of three equations in the elements (u_{i1}, u_{i2}, u_{i3}). If the above set of linear homogeneous equations is to have a non-trivial solution for (u_{i1}, u_{i2}, u_{i3}), then λ_i must be such a value which makes the determinant of the set of equations zero. In other words, λ_i must be a root of the determinantal equation

$$|a_{ij} - \delta_{ij}\lambda| = 0.$$

This is a third degree polynomial equation in λ and is referred to as the characteristic equation of the matrix. It has three roots called the *characteristic values* of the matrix A. To each characteristic value λ_i of the matrix there is at least one solution (u_{i1}, u_{i2}, u_{i3}) of the set of equations associated with the matrix. The solutions are called characteristic vectors of the matrix. If the three roots are distinct, it can be shown that the system of equations yields three linearly independent vectors (u_{i1}, u_{i2}, u_{i3}), $i = 1, 2, 3$, each corresponding to a root λ_i. By the linear independence of vectors is meant that we cannot find a linear combination of the vectors equal to zero. It can be shown that the matrix $\| u_{ij} \|$ formed by the three linearly independent characteristic vectors is non-singular. Thus the diagonal matrix equivalent to A is the matrix whose diagonal elements are the characteristic values $\lambda_1, \lambda_2, \lambda_3$ and the transformation is effected by the non-singular matrix U. We have given here the procedure for the diagonalization of a matrix, the characteristic values of which are distinct. This is only a special case of a more general theorem which states that if an n-square matrix has n linearly independent characteristic vectors, then it may be transformed into a diagonal form. However, we will be more often concerned with the diagonalization of a real symmetric matrix and it can be shown that every such matrix can be diagonalized by an orthogonal matrix. An orthogonal matrix is the matrix of a linear orthogonal transformation, and its elements therefore satisfy the orthogonality relations.

The sum of the leading diagonal elements of a square matrix is called the *spur* or *trace* of the matrix. On expanding the characteristic equation of the matrix, we find that the spur is the first coefficient of the equation. From the elementary theory of equations, we know that it is equal to the sum of the roots of the characteristic equation, i.e. to the sum of the characteristic values of the matrix. Since a matrix and its transform have the same characteristic equation, it follows that all equivalent matrices have the same spur.

3.4 Kronecker Square and Symmetrized Kronecker Square Matrices

We have seen that the scheme of coefficients of a linear transformation is a 3-square matrix. In a similar way, linear transformations in an n-dimensional space are effected by n-square matrices. It is usual to refer to the space in which the matrix is operating as the carrier space of the matrix. Consider the set of equations

$$x_1' = a_{11} x_1 + a_{12} x_2; \quad x_2' = a_{21} x_1 + a_{22} x_2.$$

The matrix $\left\| \begin{matrix} a_{11} & a_{12} \\ a_{21} & a_{22} \end{matrix} \right\|$ operates on the carrier space defined by the coordinates (x_1, x_2). We have from the above

$$(x_2')^2 = a_{11}^2 x_1^2 + a_{11} a_{12} x_1 x_2 + a_{12} a_{11} x_2 x_1 + a_{12}^2 x_2^2$$

$$x_1' x_1' = a_{11} a_{21} x_1^2 + a_{11} a_{22} x_1 x_2 + a_{12} a_{21} x_2 x_1 + a_{12} a_{22} x_2^2$$

$$x_2' x_1' = a_{21} a_{11} x_1^2 + a_{21} a_{12} x_1 x_2 + a_{22} a_{11} x_2 x_1 + a_{22} a_{12} x_2^2$$

$$(x_2')^2 = a_{21}^2 x_1^2 + a_{21} a_{22} x_1 x_2 + a_{22} a_{21} x_2 x_1 + a_{22}^2 x_2^2.$$

These equations may be written in the form

$$
\left\| \begin{array}{c} (x_1')^2 \\ x_1' x_2' \\ x_2' x_1' \\ (x_2')^2 \end{array} \right\|
=
\left\| \begin{array}{cccc} a_{11} a_{11} & a_{11} a_{12} & a_{12} a_{11} & a_{12} a_{12} \\ a_{11} a_{21} & a_{11} a_{22} & a_{12} a_{21} & a_{12} a_{22} \\ a_{21} a_{11} & a_{21} a_{12} & a_{22} a_{11} & a_{22} a_{12} \\ a_{21} a_{21} & a_{21} a_{22} & a_{22} a_{21} & a_{22} a_{22} \end{array} \right\|
\left\| \begin{array}{c} x_1^2 \\ x_1 x_2 \\ x_2 x_1 \\ x_2^2 \end{array} \right\|.
$$

The matrix of transformation will be written as $A \times A$ and is also equal to

$$
\left\| \begin{array}{cc} a_{11} A & a_{12} A \\ a_{21} A & a_{22} A \end{array} \right\|
\quad \text{where } A \text{ stands for the matrix} \quad
\left\| \begin{array}{cc} a_{11} & a_{12} \\ a_{21} & a_{22} \end{array} \right\|
$$

and is called the Kronecker square of the matrix A.

If in the above set of equations we take $x_1 x_2$ to be equal to $x_2 x_1$, we obtain a matrix of three rows and three columns only as

$$
\left\| \begin{array}{c} (x_1')^2 \\ x_1' x_2' \\ (x_2')^2 \end{array} \right\|
=
\left\| \begin{array}{ccc} a_{11} a_{11} & 2 a_{11} a_{12} & a_{12} a_{12} \\ a_{11} a_{21} & a_{11} a_{22} + a_{12} a_{21} & a_{12} a_{22} \\ a_{21} a_{22} & 2 a_{21} a_{22} & a_{22} a_{22} \end{array} \right\|
\left\| \begin{array}{c} x_1^2 \\ x_1 x_2 \\ x^2 \end{array} \right\|.
$$

The transformation matrix may now be symbolically written as $A^{(2)}$ and is called the symmetrized Kronecker square of A. Its carrier space is defined by the set of products $(x_1 x_1, x_1 x_2, x_2 x_2)$. It may be noted that

$$\operatorname{spur} A \times A = (\operatorname{spur} A)^2 = (a_{11} + a_{22})^2$$

$$\operatorname{spur} A^{(2)} = \frac{(\operatorname{spur} A)^2 + (\operatorname{spur} A^2)}{2}$$

$$= \frac{(a_{11} + a_{22})^2 + a_{11}^2 + 2 a_{12} a_{21} + a_{22}^2}{2}.$$

3.5 Kronecker Direct Product of Two Matrices

Consider the sets of equations:

$$x_1' = a_{11}x_1 + a_{12}x_2; \quad x_2' = a_{21}x_1 + a_{22}x_2$$

and

$$y_1' = b_{11}y_1 + b_{12}y_2; \quad y_2' = b_{21}y_1 + b_{22}y_2.$$

The products x_1y_1, x_1y_2, x_2y_1, x_2y_2, which define the carrier space of the product matrix, will then transform as

$$
\begin{Vmatrix} x_1'y_1' \\ x_1'y_2' \\ x_2'y_1' \\ x_2'y_2' \end{Vmatrix}
=
\begin{Vmatrix}
a_{11}b_{11} & a_{11}b_{12} & a_{12}b_{11} & a_{12}b_{12} \\
a_{11}b_{21} & a_{11}b_{22} & a_{12}b_{21} & a_{12}b_{22} \\
a_{21}b_{11} & a_{21}b_{12} & a_{22}b_{11} & a_{22}b_{12} \\
a_{21}b_{21} & a_{21}b_{22} & a_{22}b_{21} & a_{22}b_{22}
\end{Vmatrix}
\begin{Vmatrix} x_1y_1 \\ x_1y_2 \\ x_2y_1 \\ x_2y_2 \end{Vmatrix}.
$$

This transformation matrix may be written as

$$
\begin{Vmatrix} a_{11}B & a_{12}B \\ a_{21}B & a_{22}B \end{Vmatrix}
\quad \text{where } B \text{ stands for the matrix} \quad
\begin{Vmatrix} b_{11} & b_{12} \\ b_{21} & b_{22} \end{Vmatrix}.
$$

The matrix is called the Kronecker direct product matrix and is written as $A \times B$. The matrices A and B in the general case may be of any dimension and also need not operate on the same number of symbols. The relation

$$\operatorname{spur} A \times B = (\operatorname{spur} A) \times (\operatorname{spur} B)$$

easily follows. Kronecker powers and products involving more than two factors may be similarly defined. If $A = a_{pq}$ and $B = b_{pq}$ are two square matrices of degrees m and n respectively, the mn by mn matrix $A \times B$ defined by

$$
A \times B =
\begin{Vmatrix}
a_{11}B & a_{12}B & \ldots & \ldots \\
a_{21}B & a_{22}B & \ldots & \ldots \\
\ldots & \ldots & \ldots & \ldots
\end{Vmatrix}
$$

is called the Kronecker direct product of the two matrices A and B. We may similarly define the product $B \times A$. If x and y are two vectors in the carrier spaces of A and B with components $x_1, x_2, \ldots, x_m$ and $y_1, y_2, \ldots, y_n$, the mn products $x_r y_s$ $(r = 1, 2, \ldots, m, \ s = 1, 2, \ldots, n)$ may be regarded as components of a vector in the carrier space of $A \times B$. If the matrices are all equal, the Kronecker direct product of r factors is of dimension m^r. The symmetrized Kronecker rth power of A is the transformation induced on the distinct products $x_{j1}x_{j2}, \ldots, x_{jr}$ by the transformation $x \to Ax$. Its dimension is

$$\frac{(r+m-1)!}{(m-1)!\, r!}.$$

We will have occasion to consider transformations of physical property tensors under the symmetry transformations appropriate to crystals. By interpreting the tensors as appropriate outer products of three-dimensional vectors we will be able to write down the matrices of the transformations of the tensor components, as Kronecker direct products or powers of the 3-square matrices of the symmetry transformations. The tensor components form the carrier space of the Kronecker product matrices. Such interpretation will enable us to compute the spur of the transformation matrix of the tensor components which is of particular interest to us.

CHAPTER 4

Groups

4.1 Group Postulates

A group is a set of distinct elements $a, b, c, \ldots$ satisfying the postulates given below.

1. A composition rule called "product" is defined for the set such that, for any two elements a and b of the set, a unique element ab is also an element in the set. The two elements may be distinct or the same.
2. The associative law, namely, $a(bc) = (ab)c$, holds for all elements in the set.
3. The set contains an element E called the identity element such that $aE = Ea = a$ for every a in the set.
4. Each element a of the set has an inverse element represented by the symbol a^{-1} belonging to the set and satisfying the relations $aa^{-1} = a^{-1}a = E$.

The composition rule may be simple or may be of a very general kind. For example, it may be ordinary multiplication or addition when the group elements are numbers. It may also stand for any other specified process if the elements that constitute the group are of a more general kind.

It follows that the product of any three or more elements is also an element in the set. If the product consists of the same element repeated p times, the result is written as a^p. If the multiplication is commutative, i.e. if for every pair of elements a and b we have $ab = ba$, the group is said to be commutative or Abelian. If the elements in a group are finite in number, the group is said to be finite and the number of elements in it is called the order of the group. If the elements are infinite in number, the group is said to be an infinite group. A group which consists of a single element a and its powers $a^2, \ldots, a^p = E$ is called a cyclic group of order p, if p is the smallest positive integer for which $a^p = E$. p is then the order of the cyclic group and is also called the order of the element a. It is easily seen that a cyclic group is Abelian for $a^r a^s = a^s a^r$, because each is the product consisting of the same element repeated $r + s$ times.

We shall consider some specific examples. It may be verified that the group postulates are satisfied in the simple set consisting of the four numbers 1, $\sqrt{-1}$, $-\sqrt{-1}$, -1 where the composition rule is ordinary multiplication. They thus form a group of order 4. 1 is the identity element, 1 and -1 are inverses of themselves and $\sqrt{-1}$ and $-\sqrt{-1}$ are inverses of each other in this group. It may further be noted that the group is cyclic because the different elements are powers of the single element $\sqrt{-1}$ or $-\sqrt{-1}$.

The set of all real numbers forms an infinite group with the operation of addition taken as the rule of composition. The number O is the identity element of the group and the inverse of each number is its negative.

The set of all linear orthogonal transformations forms a group under the composition rule of consecutive application of transformations. The identity transformation $x_i' = x_i$ plays the role of the identity element. We have seen that every linear orthogonal transformation possesses an inverse which is also a linear orthogonal transformation. This group is called the full orthogonal group. The full orthogonal group is an infinite group.

The set of all the linear orthogonal transformations whose determinants equal $+1$ is a sub-set of the set of all linear orthogonal transformations. They by themselves form a group under the same composition rule and with the same identity element. It is evident that the inverse of such a transformation is a transformation of the same type, i.e. one with $\Delta = +1$. As we have seen, the transformations with $\Delta = +1$ can be interpreted as rigid body rotations of space. Thus, this set of transformations consists of all rotations of space about all possible axes passing through a fixed point. In this interpretation, it is easily seen that the inverse of the transformation of a rotation about an axis is the transformation of an equal rotation in the reverse sense about the same axis. This group which is an infinite group is called the rotation group.

The set of all transformations of rotations about a fixed axis by themselves form an infinite group under the same composition rule. Again the finite set of p-fold rotation transformations, which are rotations through angles which are integral multiples of $2\pi/p$ where p is a fixed integer, form a cyclic group of order p under the same composition rule.

Among the linear orthogonal transformations, the identity transformation $x_i' = x_i$ and the inverse transformation $x_i' = -x_i$ together form a group of two elements under the same composition rule. This group is denoted by the symbol $\bar{1}$.

The sets of matrices that correspond to the groups of transformations given above form groups under the operation of matrix multiplication. The identity elements and inverses in each case are those matrices which correspond to the identity transformation and inverse transformations. The transformation groups and the corresponding matrix groups are indistinguishable in a sense. We shall discuss this property later on.

4.2 Subgroups

A sub-set of elements in a group forming a group by itself under the same composition rule is defined as a subgroup of the original group. For example, the rotation group is a subgroup of the full orthogonal group. The rotations about a fixed axis form a subgroup within the rotation group. The p-fold rotations about an axis form a subgroup of the group of all rotations about the same axis. The integers form a subgroup of the group of all real numbers with addition as composition rule. In a group, the set of all the distinct powers of an element forms a cyclic group which is a subgroup of the original group.

The subgroups of a finite group have the following important property which we state here without proof. The order of a subgroup is a divisor of the order of the group. This means that if G be a group of order N and H a subgroup of order h, then N is an integral multiple of h.

The order of an element in a group has been defined as the order of the cyclic group generated by the element. Since this cyclic group is a subgroup of the original group, it follows that the order of an element is also a divisor of the order of the group.

4.3 Classes of Conjugate Elements

Let s and t be any two elements of a group. $t^{-1}st$ which may be denoted by u will also be an element of the group. u is called the transform of s by the element t. It is easily seen that s is the transform of u by the element t^{-1}. Two such elements s and u which may be transformed into one another by one element or other of the group are called conjugate elements. If u happens to be the same as s, then $t^{-1}st = s$ or $st = ts$. In such a case, s and t commute with each other. The complete set of distinct elements which are transforms of s with all the elements of a group G constitute a conjugate class of elements of G. The number of such elements in any class is defined as the order of the class. If s is the transform of a with t_1 and of b with t_2, then b is the transform of a with $t_1 t_2^{-1}$. Thus if s is conjugate to a and b, it follows that a and b are conjugate to one another. Hence the elements of a conjugate class are conjugate to one another. Another property of the elements in a conjugate class is that all the elements in a conjugate class have the same order. For, if $u = t^{-1}st$, then $u^2 = t^{-1}st$,

$t^{-1}st = t^{-1}s^2 t, ..., u^n = t^{-1}s^n t$ and $u^n = E$, when $s^n = E$ and vice versa. In every group, the identity element forms a class by itself. We can decompose a group into classes of conjugate elements. In a group of orthogonal matrices, it is evident that the elements of a conjugate class are equivalent matrices.

It can be proved that the order of a conjugate class in a group is a divisor of the order of the group. We shall, however, assume the theorem without proof.

4.4 Isomorphous Groups

If G_1 and G_2 are two groups of the same order, not necessarily with the same composition rule, and if each element G_1 can be made to correspond uniquely to an element of G_2 in such a way that the product of two elements of G_1 corresponds to the product of the corresponding two elements of G_2, then G_1 and G_2 are said to be simply isomorphous or isomorphous. Two groups which are isomorphous are thus indistinguishable for all practical purposes. Every mathematical property of one group is also possessed by the other group.

The matrix groups we have mentioned which correspond to the various transformation groups are thus isomorphous with the transformation groups. This fact enables us to handle the groups of linear orthogonal transformations with which we are mainly concerned in terms of the isomorphous matrix groups.

If G_1 and G_2 are two groups of different order and if to each element of G_1 there corresponds one or more elements of G_2, and also the product of any two elements of G_1 corresponds to the product of any two corresponding elements of G_2, the two groups G_1, G_2 are then said to be homomorphous and their relationship is called general isomorphism.

4.5 Direct Product Groups

If G_1 and G_2 are two groups with the same composition rule and if the elements of G_1 commute with the elements of G_2, there being no common element between G_1 and G_2 except the identity element, the totality of the elements t, where $t = s_1 s_2$ forms a group G which is called the direct product of G_1 and G_2. s_1 is an element of G_1 and s_2 is an element of G_2. The direct product G may be symbolically written as $G_1 \times G_2$. The above definition may be extended to the direct product of any number of groups. For example, the full orthogonal group can be obtained as a direct product of the rotation group with the group $\bar{1}$. This is possible because identity and inversion commute with all the elements of the rotation group.

In fact from every finite group of pure rotations, we can obtain a mixed group containing rotations and rotation-inversions by taking the direct product of the pure rotation group and the group $\bar{1}$. In such a mixed group, there will be as many rotation-inversions as there are pure rotations and its order is twice the order of the pure rotation group from which it is obtained.

4.6 Permutation Groups

Permutation groups are of some importance and will be considered here. Let the integers 1 to 6 be regarded as symbols. These 6 symbols when written in the form $P = (143)\,(25)\,(6)$ imply that in the operation P each number in a bracket is to be replaced by the succeeding number in it, and the last number in the bracket is to be replaced by the first in that bracket. Thus the operation P changes the symbols 1, 2, 3, 4, 5 and 6 respectively into 4, 5, 1, 3, 2 and 6. Such an operation which involves a re-arrangement of a set of chosen symbols is called a permutation. The unaltered symbols like 6 in P are sometimes omitted in writing the permutations. It follows from the definition that a permutation is not altered by changing the symbols in the bracket without affecting the cyclic order. The arrangement of the cycles in a permutation is also arbitrary. Thus P may be written as $(25)\,(431)\,(6)$. If permutation consists of only one cycle, it is called a *cyclic permutation*. If P and Q are two permutations, the product permutation PQ is defined as that which gives the same result as may be obtained by first performing the re-arrangement as per the permutation P and then as per Q. If Q stands for $(123)\,(46)\,(5)$, the product PQ, where P stands for the permutation already chosen, may be written as

$$(143)\,(25)\,(6) \times (123)\,(46)\,(5) = (164)\,(253).$$

Denoting $(164)\,(253)$ by S, the multiplication may easily be verified by taking any arbitrary arrangement of the six symbols 1 to 6 and operating upon it with the permutation S. The result will be identical with that obtained by operating first with P and then with Q which is the product permutation PQ. The process of writing down the product permutation PQ will also be clear from the above example. In the permutation P, 1 is followed by 4 and in the permutation Q, 4 is followed by 6. Therefore, 1 is to be followed by 6 in the product permutation S and similarly for 6 and the other symbols. The multiplication of permutations is not commutative. In the above example, whereas $PQ = (164)\,(252)$, $QP = (152)\,(346)$. If P, Q and R are three permutations on n symbols and if P changes the symbol α to β, Q changes

β to γ and R changes γ to δ, it is easily seen that both the operations $(PQ)R$ and $P(QR)$ change α to δ. This is true for all the n symbols. Thus $(PQ)R = P(QR)$ which establishes the associative law for the multiplication of permutations. A set of permutations on n symbols, which forms a group under the combination rule explained above, is called a permutation group of degree n. The set of all possible permutations of n symbols forms a group of order n! This may also be referred to as the symmetric group of degree n. It may easily be verified that the elements E, $(123)(456)$, $(321)(654)$, $(14)(26)(35)$, $(15)(24)(36)$, $(16)(25)(34)$, form a permutation group. If it is intended to write E explicitly, it is to be written as $(1)(2)(3)(4)(5)(6)$. It may be noted that the permutation $(321)(654)$ is the inverse of the permutation $(123)(456)$. The inverse permutation is always obtained by writing down in the reverse order the symbols in each bracket of the original permutation.

If we take the digits $1, 2, 3$ as our symbols and construct a group out of them taking all possible permutations, we obtain the symmetric group of order 3! and it consists of the following six elements divided into three conjugate classes. As is to be expected, the identity element is a class by itself.

$$(1)(2)(3) \qquad \text{Class 1 } (E)$$

$$\left.\begin{array}{l} (12)(3) \\ (13)(2) \\ (23)(1) \end{array}\right\} \qquad \text{Class 2 } (C_1)$$

$$\left.\begin{array}{l} (123) \\ (132) \end{array}\right\} \qquad \text{Class 3 } (C_2)$$

We shall use the word *interchange* to denote an operation in which two symbols are interchanged, the others remaining unaffected. A cyclic permutation $(123\ldots n)$ is equivalent to the product $(12)(13)\ldots(1n)$. Any permutation is a product of cyclic permutations and is therefore expressible as a product of interchanges. The expression of a given permutation as a product of interchanges is not unique. It may be shown that the number of interchanges in various forms of the product is always odd or even according as it is odd or even in any one alternative. Permutations can thus be divided into two types, namely, odd and even, according as they can be expressed as products of an odd or an even number of interchanges. In the example cited earlier, the permutations (123) and (132) can be expressed as products of interchanges like $(12)(13)$ and $(13)(12)$. They may also be written as

(12)(23)(13)(12) and (13)(23)(12)(13) and so on. Similarly permutations of the type (12)(3) may be written as (12) or (13)(12)(23), etc. Thus the permutations coming under the class C_1 are odd and those coming under the classes E and C_2 are even.

4.7 Matrix Representations of Groups

If G is a group consisting of elements $S_0, S_1, \ldots$, etc. and H a group of matrices $M_0, M_1, \ldots$, etc. such that each element S_i corresponds to a matrix M_i and also the product of two S's corresponds to the product of the two corresponding matrices, the group of matrices is said to define a representation Γ of the group G. The same matrix may correspond to several elements of the group but to each element of the group G must correspond only one matrix in H.

If for two non-singular matrix representations $\Gamma_1(M_0 M_1 \ldots)$ and $\Gamma_2(N_0 N_1 \ldots)$ of a group G, it is possible to find a fixed matrix T such that $N_r = T^{-1} M_r T$ for all r, the two representations Γ_1 and Γ_2 are said to be equivalent. Similarly, if S is a non-singular matrix, the set of matrices SMS^{-1} define another representation of the group G equivalent to Γ_1. The representations of a group can thus be divided into classes of equivalent representations. In fact, by representation we mean generally a class of equivalent representations.

If a representation Γ of a group G is such that the matrices of one of its equivalent representations take the form

$$
\left\|
\begin{array}{ccccc}
A_i & & & & \\
& B_i & & & 0 \\
& & C_i & & \\
0 & & & \cdots & \\
& & & \cdots & \\
& & & & D_i
\end{array}
\right\|
$$

where $A_i, B_i, C_i, \ldots, D_i$ are square matrices, not necessarily of the same dimension, it is said to be a completely reducible representation. Such a situation arises when the variables $x_1, x_2, \ldots$, etc., upon which the matrices may be assumed to operate (the carrier space of the matrices) can be combined into different linear combinations $y_1, y_2, \ldots$, etc. which may be divided into sets such that the y's belonging to a set combine among themselves only. The fixed matrix T referred to before will then be the matrix of transformation of the x's into y's for, if

$y = Tx$ and $x' = Mx$, we have $y' = Tx' = TMx = TMT^{-1}y$. It is evident that the matrices $A_i, B_i, C_i, \ldots, D_i$ separately define representations of G and the reducible representation is a direct sum of these irreducible representations in a sense that is obvious. When a representation is not reducible, it is called an irreducible representation of the group. In the simple case, where H consists of the identity matrix of dimension one, that is unity itself, the representation is called the identity or total symmetric representation. There are an infinite number of representations of a given group, but they can all be shown to be equivalent to representations which are direct sums of a few irreducible representations in each case. We shall, however, assume this theorem without proof.

The character of an element R of a group, denoted by the symbol $\chi(R)$, in a matrix representation is the spur of the matrix corresponding to it. Since equivalent matrices have the same spur, group elements have the same characters in equivalent representations. The character of an element R of a group in a reducible representation is evidently the sum of the characters of the irreducible representations which add up to form it. We note that an irreducible representation may be contained more than once in a reducible representation. The number n_i of times an irreducible representation Γ_i is contained in a reducible representation Γ of a group G of order N is given by the formula

$$n_i = \frac{1}{N} \sum_\rho h_\rho \chi_\rho(R) \chi_i(R)$$

where h_ρ is the number of elements in the ρth class.

$\chi_\rho(R)$ is the character of the element R in the representation Γ and $\chi_i(R)$ is the character of the same element R in the irreducible representation Γ_i, where the element R belongs to the ρth class. The formula is of considerable importance for us. Its derivation is not within the scope of the present treatise. Reference may be made to works which deal with the theory of groups.[†]

4.8 Kronecker Direct Product Representations

It is easily verified that if a set of matrices define a representation of a group, the set consisting of the Kronecker squares of the corresponding matrices also defines a representation of the group.

It may be noted from Section 3.4 that the character of an element in the Kronecker square representation is equal to the square of the character in the original representation. From the same section of

† Bhagavantam, S and Venkatarayudu, T., "Theory of Groups and Its Application to Physical Problems", 3rd Ed. Andhra University, Waltair (1962).

Chapter 3, one can see how the character of an element in the symmetrized Kronecker square representation may also be obtained. The Kronecker rth power representation and the symmetrized rth power representation can be analogously defined.

In general, if the sets of matrices A_i and B_i separately form representations Γ_1 and Γ_2 of a group G whose elements are denoted by g_i, the Kronecker direct product matrices $A_i \times B_i$ also form a representation Γ_3 of G. If $\chi_1(g_i)$, $\chi_2(g_i)$ and $\chi_3(g_i)$ are characters in the representations Γ_1, Γ_2 and Γ_3 respectively, we have

$$\chi_3(g_i) = \chi_1(g_i) \cdot \chi_2(g_i).$$

CHAPTER 5

Crystallographic Groups

5.1 Displacement of a Rigid Body

If a point of a rigid body is held fixed, it is free to rotate about that point. If another point of the body is also kept fixed, the body is free to rotate about the line joining the two fixed points. The fixing of a third point of the body, not collinear with the other two, fixes the position of the body. Hence the position of a body in space is uniquely determined, if the positions of any three non-collinear points in it are known. The most general displacement of a rigid body is therefore one in which any three non-collinear points A, B, C of the body are displaced to say A', B', C'. It may be proved that this displacement can be effected by a translation of the body as a whole followed by a rotation about a suitable axis.

In the above displacement, the translation is not necessarily in the direction of the rotation axis, but it can be effected by a rotation of the body about a suitable parallel axis followed by a translation in the direction of the rotation axis itself. The latter operation is called a screw. A general displacement of a rigid body is thus a screw.

5.2 Symmetry Operations

For a rigid body, the displacements that have the special property of bringing the body into superposition (congruence) with itself are called symmetry operations. In the case of a finite body, because of the condition of congruence, no displacement which involves a bodily translation either by itself or in combination with other movements can be a symmetry operation. The rigid body displacements that do not involve bodily translations are pure rotations. It is easily seen that the set of all rotations that bring a finite body into superposition with itself forms a group under the composition rule of consecutive application.

Let us consider all those transformations which preserve the distance between any two points. If we exclude translations, all such transformations are linear orthogonal transformations as shown in Chapter 1. Pure rotations form a sub-set of such transformations. The conventional definition of symmetry operations of a finite rigid body is not confined to pure rotations. They are defined as those linear orthogonal transformations which bring the body into superposition with itself. Linear orthogonal transformations which are not pure rotations have the determinant of their transformation matrix equal to -1. We have shown that such a transformation can always be interpreted as the result of a pure rotation followed by an inversion. For this reason, such transformations are called rotation-inversions. The inversion transformation denoted by i can itself be interpreted as the result of a rotation about an axis through $180°$ followed by a transformation in which all the points are taken into their mirror images in a plane perpendicular to the rotation axis. If we interpret i as the product of a rotation about the X_1-axis through $180°$, followed by a reflection in the X_2X_3-plane, this is expressed in matrix notation by the equation:

$$\begin{Vmatrix} -1 & 0 & 0 \\ 0 & -1 & 0 \\ 0 & 0 & -1 \end{Vmatrix} = \begin{Vmatrix} -1 & 0 & 0 \\ 0 & 1 & 0 \\ 0 & 0 & 1 \end{Vmatrix} \begin{Vmatrix} 1 & 0 & 0 \\ 0 & -1 & 0 \\ 0 & 0 & -1 \end{Vmatrix}.$$

The transformation of reflection in a plane can be interpreted as rotation through $0°$ about an axis perpendicular to the plane followed by a reflection in it and thus can be classified as a rotation-reflection. We shall henceforward call the transformations other than rotations as rotation-reflections in general, which include pure inversion and pure reflections and rotation-reflections. From the definition of a symmetry operation, it follows that a complete set of symmetry operations, namely, rotations and rotation-reflections, of any particular body will form a group under the composition rule of consecutive application of operations. Since we have already noted that from amongst the symmetry operations of a body the rotations by themselves form a group, it means that the pure rotation group of the body is a subgroup of the group of all symmetry operations it possesses.

We shall give some useful results in combining various symmetry operations and develop a notation to designate various symmetry operations. The combination of two rotations is obviously a rotation. The combination of reflections in two planes is a rotation about the line of intersection of the two reflection planes, the angle of rotation being twice the angle between the reflection planes. To show this, we notice that the result of two successive reflections which necessarily have the determinants of their transformation matrices equal to -1 is a transformation whose matrix has its determinant equal to $+1$ and is hence a rotation. In Fig. 3, OA, OB are traces of the mirror planes inclined at an angle α, on a plane perpendicular to the mirrors, in this case the plane of the paper. A point P is reflected to Q in the plane OB and the image point Q is reflected in OA to R. If $\angle POB = \angle BOQ = \beta$, it is evident that $\angle AOR = \angle AOQ = (\alpha+\beta)$ and that $\angle POQ = 2\beta$, which shows that P is taken to R by a single rotation through $\angle PQR = 2\alpha$ about the line of intersection of the two mirror planes, which in Fig. 3 is the vertical axis through O.

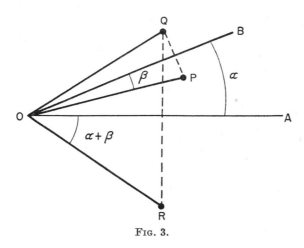

FIG. 3.

Combinations of rotations and reflections are of two kinds. In the first, the plane of reflection contains the axis of rotation and this combination is equivalent to a reflection in a plane intersecting the original plane of reflection in the axis of rotation and making an angle equal to half the rotation. In the second, the plane of reflection is inclined to the axis of rotation, and this combination is equivalent to a rotation-reflection, a rotation about a different axis followed by a reflection in a plane perpendicular to that axis.

When the smallest angle of rotation which brings the body to superposition with itself is $2\pi/p$ where p is an integer, then the corresponding axis is called a p-fold axis of rotation and the symmetry operation is usually designated by the symbol C_p. A plane of reflection is designated by the symbol σ. The plane of reflection may sometimes contain the symmetry axis of the body in which case the subscript v is used to describe it. The plane of reflection may sometimes be perpendicular to the symmetry axis and in this case the subscript h is used to describe it. When a body contains reflection planes of more than one type, they are described by different superscripts as σ_v, σ_v', etc. When it contains several symmetry elements of the same type, the number p of such symmetry elements is indicated by a coefficient as in pC_2, $p\sigma_v$, etc. Other elements such as rotation-reflections are described by the symbol S_p which stands for an operation in which a rotation of $2\pi/p$

about an axis is followed by reflection in a plane normal to the rotation axis. The special element of a centre of inversion which is an S_2 is designated by the symbol i. The symbols C_2, C_2', C_2'' are used for digonal rotations about the coordinate axes X_1, X_2, X_3 respectively. Similarly the symbols $\sigma_h, \sigma_v', \sigma_v''$ are used for reflections in the coordinate planes X_2X_3, X_3X_1 and X_1X_2 respectively. Identity operation, which is the same as rotation through 0 or 2π about any axis, is a symmetry operation for all bodies and is designated by the symbol E. This element takes the place of the identity element in the group.

5.3 Point Groups

As an illustration of a group of symmetry operations, we enumerate the symmetry appropriate to an isosceles triangle. This figure can be brought to superposition with itself by a rotation of 2π about any axis (E), by a rotation of π about an axis in the plane of the triangle and bisecting the vertical angle of the triangle (C_2), by a reflection in the plane of the triangle (σ_v) and by a reflection in a plane perpendicular to the plane of the triangle and containing the C_2 axis (σ_v'). These symmetry elements constitute a point group of order 4. The group is Abelian because all the elements taken in pairs are commutative. Also the result of combining any two of the three elements C_2, σ_v, and σ_v' is the third one. It may be noted that every element is its own inverse in this group.

We shall next take the example of a regular tetrahedron and deal with its symmetry operations in some detail. A tetrahedron can be brought to superposition with itself by a rotation of 360° about any axis through its centre (E), by a rotation of 120° either way about the four tetrahedral axes formed by joining the centre to each one of the vertices ($8C_3$), by a rotation of 180° either way about the three mutually perpendicular lines obtained by joining the middle points of opposite edges of the tetrahedron ($3C_2$), by reflection in any one of the six planes formed by the centre with each one of the six edges (6σ) and by a rotation through 90° either way about the three mutually perpendicular lines cited above followed by reflections in planes passing through the centre and perpendicular to the rotation axis in each case ($6S_4$). The coefficients like 8 in $8C_3$, 3 in $3C_2$, etc. denote the number of symmetry operations of the particular type. It may be noted that in the case of C_3, the two rotations in opposite directions about the same axis are counted as distinct elements whereas in the case of C_2 they are counted as one element. This is a consequence of the fact that in the latter case, any given point of the body moves into the same position for both types of rotation which thus become indistinguishable from each other.

In the former case, the point moves into different positions. The symmetry operations will be written as E, $8C_3$, $3C_2$, 6σ, $6S_4$. They constitute a point group of order 24 and thus become the group elements. That these elements satisfy all the group requirements may easily be verified. By numbering the corners of the tetrahedron as $1, 2, 3, 4$ we can build a permutation group of degree 4 or order 24 which is isomorphous with the above group. Reference to Fig. 4 will help identification of the group elements and the building of this permutation group. Both the groups and the correspondence between them is shown below.

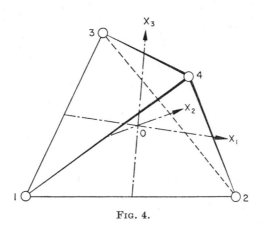

FIG. 4.

E	(1) (2) (3) (4)
$8C_3$	(1) (234); (1) (243); (2) (134); (2) (143);
	(3) (124); (3) (142); (4) (123); (4) (132)
$3C_2$	(12) (34); (13) (24); (14) (23)
6σ	(12) (3) (4); (13) (2) (4); (14) (2) (3);
	(24) (1) (3); (34) (1) (2); (23) (1) (4)
$6S_4$	(1234); (1432); (1342); (1243);
	(1423); (1324)

The case of the geometrical figure of a regular hexagon is also instructive as it exhibits several of the typical symmetry operations appropriate to a finite body. The symmetry operations are identity (E), a rotation of 60° either way about the symmetry axis normal to the hexagonal plane ($2C_6$), a rotation of 120° either way about the same axis ($2C_3$), a rotation of 180° either way about the same axis (C_2), a rotation of 180° either way about the three lines joining the opposite vertices of the hexagon ($3C_2'$), a rotation of 180° either way about the three lines joining the middle points of opposite edges ($3C_2''$), a centre

3

of inversion at the centre of the hexagon (i), a rotation of $60°$ either way followed by a reflection in the plane of the hexagon $(2S_6)$, a rotation of $120°$ either way followed by a reflection in the same plane $(2S_3)$, a reflection in the plane of the hexagon (σ_h), a reflection in any one of the three planes perpendicular to the plane of the hexagon and passing through opposite vertices $(3\sigma_v')$, a reflection in any one of the three planes perpendicular to the plane of hexagon and passing through the middle points of opposite edges $(3\sigma_v'')$. These operations constitute a point group of order 24.

This group furnishes a good example of a direct product group. It may be seen that the group which consists of $E, 2C_6, 2C_3, C_2, 3C_2', 3C_2'', i, 2S_3,$ $2S_6, \sigma_h, 3\sigma_v', 3\sigma_v''$ is the direct product of the groups G_1 and G_2 where G_1 consists of the elements $E, 2C_6, 2C_3, C_2, 3C_2', 3C_2''$ and G_2 of E and i.

We may note that a sphere is symmetrical with respect to the entire set of rotations and rotation-reflections. This entire set is no other than the set of linear orthogonal transformations which constitute a group called the full orthogonal group. The entire set of pure rotations, namely, those orthogonal transformations which have their determinant equal to $+1$, form a subgroup of the full orthogonal group and it is called the *rotation group*.

The symmetry group of any other finite geometrical body or structure evidently forms a subgroup of the full orthogonal group. The full orthogonal group and all its subgroups leave at least one point in space invariant. For this reason they are known as point groups.

5.4 Translational Symmetry of Crystal Lattices

Crystals are built by locating a group of atoms at every lattice point of a three-dimensional infinite lattice. Such a lattice is called a space lattice. A set of points obtained by starting from any one of them and by performing all possible translations which are integral multiples of three non-coplanar primitive translations T_1, T_2, T_3 is said to constitute a space lattice. It can be shown that there are only 14 different kinds of space lattices called the Bravais lattices. Obviously, space lattices are self-coincident under any translation of the type $lT_1 + mT_2 + nT_3$ where l, m, n are integers, and all such translations are symmetry operations for the lattice. Thus the set of all such translations forms an infinite group. The symmetry group of a crystal therefore contains a translation group as a subgroup. Besides the translational symmetry, a lattice possesses directional symmetry as well. By the directional symmetry of a lattice, we understand the set of all rotations and rotation-reflections that carry the lattice into superposition with itself. This set of symmetry operations of a lattice forms a group called the point group of the lattice. It may be noted that every lattice possesses inversion about any of its lattice points as a symmetry operation.

It has been pointed out that a crystal is built by locating identical groups of atoms at every point of a lattice. The group of atoms possesses its own point group symmetry. If the point group of the group of atoms possesses symmetry elements not contained in the point group of the lattice, the structure obtained—that is the crystal—cannot acquire these additional elements of symmetry. In fact, the crystal will possess only these elements of symmetry which are common to the lattice and the group of atoms which forms the motif for the structure. Moreover, certain restrictions are imposed on the possible directional symmetry of a crystal due to its lattice structure. In the next section, it is shown that the only rotation axes of symmetry that an infinite three-dimensional lattice can possess are 1-, 2-, 3-, 4- and 6-fold. This restriction, therefore, applies to crystals. The possible point groups of symmetry subject to this restriction may be shown to be only 32 in all. It follows that the possible directional symmetry of any crystal must fall into one of these 32 point groups.

5.5 Rotational Symmetry of Crystal Lattices

We shall take directions along the basic lattice vectors as coordinate axes and the lengths of these vectors as unit lengths.

In this coordinate system, any lattice point has integers as its coordinates. A rotation, if it is a symmetry operation of the lattice, carries the lattice into itself. Therefore the matrix of the transformation equations under the symmetry operation, when referred to the lattice vector system, consists of integers only and consequently its spur is also an integer. The same lattice can be referred to an orthogonal cartesian system of coordinates in which the matrix of a rotation operation has its spur equal to $(1 + 2\cos\theta)$ where θ is the angle of rotation. The two different coordinate systems, namely, the lattice vector system and the orthogonal cartesian system are related by a linear transformation, and therefore the matrices of the same operation in the two different coordinate systems are equivalent and have the same spur. It follows that the spur of the rotation operation in the cartesian system must be an integer. Hence the only possible values of θ are those for which $1 + 2\cos\theta$ is an integer, and since $|\cos\theta| \leqslant 1$, we have $\cos\theta = 0$, $\pm\frac{1}{2}$ or ± 1. Therefore, $\theta = 2\pi/p$ where p is 1, 2, 3, 4 or 6. The possible axes of rotational symmetry in an infinite three-dimensional lattice are thus seen to be 1-, 2-, 3-, 4- and 6-fold only. This is referred to as the crystallographic restriction on the period of rotation of symmetry axes.

5.6 Eleven Crystallographic Rotational Point Groups

In order to obtain the crystallographically significant point groups, we shall first enumerate all the crystallographically possible groups of rotation. We shall arrive at the result that there are only 11 possible crystallographic rotational point groups. The derivation given below follows closely Coxeter.†

Any finite group G of rotations may be regarded as generated by its various axes of symmetry intersecting at a point. Consider a sphere with its centre as the point of intersection of the symmetry axes. Each of the axes pierces the surface of the sphere at two diametrically opposite points called its poles. The poles of a p-fold axis are called p-fold poles. The system of symmetry axes is self-coincident under the various symmetry operations of the group. Any other rotation of G transforms a p-fold axis into another p-fold axis called its "equivalent". At the same time the poles of the axis are carried into "equivalent" poles. Now consider the entire set of poles of various "periods" distributed over the surface of the sphere. It falls into sub-sets of equivalent poles such that all the poles in the same sub-set have the same period, but two poles of the same period need not fall into the same sub-set. They belong to the same sub-set if only there is a rotation of G carrying one into the other. For example, the two poles of the same p-fold axis need not belong to the same sub-set unless there is a 2-fold axis in the group, perpendicular to the p-fold axis.

A little reflection will show that each such sub-set of p-fold poles contains exactly (N/p) poles, where N is the order of the group G. This is so because a point on the sphere arbitrarily near to a p-fold pole is carried into p vertices of a p-sided regular polygon described around the pole and into N equivalent points over the surface of the sphere by the N rotations of the group. Thus the N equivalent points are distributed on the vertices of (N/p) regular p-sided polygons which are themselves equivalent, that is, carried into each other by the operations of the group. It follows that the number of equivalent p-fold poles in a sub-set is N/p.

Now the group G has $N-1$ rotations other than the identity element and each p-fold axis in the group contributes $p-1$ of these rotations. To each p-fold axis there correspond two p-fold poles. Therefore to each p-fold pole correspond $(p-1)/2$ rotations other than identity and to each set of equivalent p-fold poles correspond $\dfrac{N}{p}\dfrac{(p-1)}{2}$ such elements of the group. All the elements of the group other than the identity are

† Coxeter, H. S. M., "Introduction to Geometry". Wiley, New York (1961).

thus distributed among the sets of equivalent poles and hence

$$(N-1) = \tfrac{1}{2} N \sum \frac{(p-1)}{p}$$

where the summation is over the sets of equivalent poles. After rearranging, the above equation may be expressed as

$$2 - \frac{2}{N} = \sum \left(1 - \frac{1}{p}\right).$$

If $N = 1$, so that G consists of the identity alone; there are no poles and the sum on the right-hand side has no terms. In all other cases, $N \geqslant 2$ and, therefore, $1 \leqslant 2 - (2/N) \leqslant 2$. It follows that the number of sets of poles can only be 2 or 3; for, the single term $1 - (1/p)$ would be less than 1, and the sum of 4 or more terms would be $\geqslant 4(1 - \tfrac{1}{2}) = 2$.

If there are two sets of poles, we have

$$2 - \frac{2}{N} = 1 - \frac{1}{p_1} + 1 - \frac{1}{p_2},$$

that is

$$\frac{N}{p_1} + \frac{N}{p_2} = 2.$$

Two positive integers can have their sum equal to 2 only if each equals 1; thus $p_1 = p_2 = N$. Each of the two sets of poles consists of one N-fold pole and we have the cyclic group C_N with a pole at each end of its single axis. We can denote this case by writing

$$p_1 = p ; \quad p_2 = N ; \quad N = \frac{p}{2}. \tag{1}$$

In the only other alternative where there can be three sets of poles, we have

$$2 - \frac{2}{N} = 1 - \frac{1}{p_1} + 1 - \frac{1}{p_2} + 1 - \frac{1}{p_3},$$

whence

$$\frac{1}{p_1} + \frac{1}{p_2} + \frac{1}{p_3} = 1 + \frac{2}{N}.$$

Since this is greater than $\tfrac{1}{3} + \tfrac{1}{3} + \tfrac{1}{3} = 1$, the three periods p_i cannot all be 3 or more. Hence at least one of them has to be 2, say $p_3 = 2$, and we have

$$\frac{1}{p_1} + \frac{1}{p_2} = \frac{1}{2} + \frac{2}{N},$$

whence

$$(p_1 - 2)(p_2 - 2) = 4\left(1 - \frac{p_1 p_2}{N}\right) < 4,$$

so that the only possibilities (taking $p_1 \leqslant p_2$ for definiteness) are

$$p_1 = 2; \quad p_2 = p; \quad N = 2p \tag{2}$$

$$p_1 = 3; \quad p_2 = 3; \quad N = 12 \tag{3}$$

$$p_1 = 3; \quad p_2 = 4; \quad N = 24 \tag{4}$$

$$p_1 = 3; \quad p_2 = 5; \quad N = 60. \tag{5}$$

Groups arising from (1), (2), (3), (4) and (5) are respectively called the cyclic, the dihedral, the tetrahedral, the octahedral and the icosahedral groups and are denoted by the symbols C_p, D_p, T, O and I respectively. Thus it is established that the only finite groups of rotations in three dimensions are the cyclic groups C_p ($p = 1, 2, ...$), the dihedral groups D_p ($p = 2, 3, ...$), the tetrahedral group T, the octahedral group O and the icosahedral group I.

We apply to each of the above five cases the crystallographic restriction that p should be 1, 2, 3, 4 or 6 only and note that the following rotation groups alone are permissible from a crystallographic point of view:

C_1 C_2 C_3 C_4 C_6	Cyclic groups
D_2 D_3 D_4 D_6	Dihedral groups
T	Tetrahedral group
O	Octahedral group.

As the icosahedral group contains a 5-fold axis, it is not compatible with the crystallographic restriction. Of these, the cyclic groups are generated by a single p-fold axis and consist of the symmetry operations which can be readily derived. They are

C_1	E
C_2	$E\ C_2$
C_3	$E\ 2C_3$
C_4	$E\ 2C_4\ C_2$
C_6	$E\ 2C_6\ 2C_3\ C_2.$

It follows from (2) that the dihedral groups D_p ($p = 2, 3, 4, 6$) are of the order $2p$ and consist of a p-fold axis which gives rise to a subgroup C_p of order p. The rest of the elements are C_2s. From the fact that there is only one set of equivalent p-fold poles it follows that the two poles at the opposite ends of the p-fold axis are equivalent. This is possible if only there is a 2-fold axis perpendicular to the p-fold axis and that the 2-fold axes which give rise to the C_2s are in a plane perpendicular to the p-fold axis. From the principle that the system of axes that gives rise to the group must be self-coincident under the operations of the group, it follows that there must be p 2-fold axes symmetrically distributed in the plane perpendicular to the p-fold axis. We have from (2) that there is one set of p-fold poles and two sets of 2-fold poles. When p is odd, it is evident that the p-fold rotations cannot make the poles at the ends of a 2-fold axis at right-angles to the p-fold axis equivalent; and it follows that the 2-fold axes are equivalent and the poles fall into two sets. When p is even the two poles at the ends of a 2-fold axis at right-angles to the p-fold axis are equivalent because a suitable integral multiple of p-fold rotations is now a rotation through 180°. As there are two sets of 2-fold poles it follows that there are two sets of equivalent 2-fold axes. It is easily seen that equivalent 2-fold axes are alternately disposed in the plane perpendicular to the p-fold axis. From these considerations, it can be shown that the dihedral groups D_p $(p = 2, 3, 4, 6)$ consist of the symmetry operations given below:

$$D_2 \qquad E\ C_2\ C_2'\ C_2''$$

$$D_3 \qquad E\ 2C_3\ 3C_2$$

$$D_4 \qquad E\ 2C_4\ C_2\ 2C_2'\ 2C_2''$$

$$D_6 \qquad E\ 2C_6\ 2C_3\ C_2\ 3C_2'\ 3C_2''.$$

Superscript primes are used to indicate their grouping into different categories.

It follows from (3) that the tetrahedral group T consists of two sets of equivalent 3-fold poles and one set of 2-fold poles and its order is 12. If there is only one 3-fold axis, the 2-fold axis must be perpendicular to it, in which case we cannot have two sets of equivalent 3-fold poles and we get again the group D_3. There is therefore more than one 3-fold axis. Two 3-fold axes, however they are oriented to each other, imply at least four 3-fold axes because the rotations about one of them take the other into three equivalent positions. Also a 3-fold axis and a 2-fold axis, however they are oriented, imply at least three 2-fold axes because the rotations about the 3-fold axis take the 2-fold axis into three equivalent positions. Thus there are at least four 3-fold axes and three 2-fold axes and they together make up the total number of elements of the group T. Therefore, it follows that these are all the axes possible. The four 3-fold axes are equivalent and the eight rotations arising therefrom fall into a class. Also the three 2-fold axes are equivalent and the three rotations arising therefrom fall into a class.

The elements consisting of the group T can thus be seen to be

$$T \qquad E \; 8C_3 \; 3C_2.$$

Regarding the group O, equation (4) shows that there is one set of equivalent 4-fold poles, one set of 3-fold poles and one set of 2-fold poles, and that the order of the group is 24. Similar arguments as the above show that there are at least three equivalent 4-fold axes and four

TABLE II

Rotational point groups

No.	Class symbol		Elements of symmetry
	International	Schönflies	
1	1	C_1	E
2	2	C_2	$E \; C_2$
3	3	C_3	$E \; 2C_3$
4	4	C_4	$E \; 2C_4 \; C_2$
5	6	C_6	$E \; 2C_6 \; 2C_3 \; C_2$
6	222	D_2	$E \; C_2 \; C_2' \; C_2''$
7	32	D_3	$E \; 2C_3 \; 3C_2$
8	422	D_4	$E \; 2C_4 \; C_2 \; 2C_2' \; 2C_2''$
9	622	D_6	$E \; 2C_6 \; 2C_3 \; C_2 \; 3C_2' \; 3C_2''$
10	23	T	$E \; 8C_3 \; 3C_2$
11	432	O	$E \; 8C_3 \; 3C_2 \; 6C_2 \; 6C_4$

equivalent 3-fold axes. Each of the 4-fold axes implies a 2-fold axis and it follows that there are three 2-fold axes so distributed that the four 3-fold axes are equivalent with respect to them. Thus the group O contains the group T as a subgroup. The fact that there is only one set of 4-fold poles and one set of 3-fold poles implies that there are 2-fold axes perpendicular to them and also that there are no other sets of 3-fold and 4-fold axes. It also implies that the 4-fold rotations fall into one class and the 3-fold rotations fall into another class. The axes enumerated thus far account for 18 elements of the group and the remaining six elements are 2-fold rotations. The six 2-fold rotations must be due to six 2-fold axes such that they are all equivalent to one another and their poles are all in an equivalent set. They all fall into one class. The symmetry operations that constitute the group O are therefore seen to be

$$O \qquad E \; 8C_3 \; 3C_2 \; 6C_2 \; 6C_4.$$

Thus, the eleven crystallographic rotational point groups along with the symmetry elements of each group are given together in Table II.

5.7 Thirty-two Crystallographic Conventional Point Groups

It has already been pointed out that all symmetry operations which do not involve translations can be regarded either as simple rotations or rotation-reflections. That all space lattices explicitly possess a centre of inversion as a symmetry operation is evident. A centre of inversion should therefore be recognized as a crystallographically possible symmetry operation. If we form the direct product of each one of the pure rotation groups with the group $\bar{1}$ which consists of elements E and i, we obtain the eleven mixed groups listed below against the pure rotation groups from which they are formed.

$$C_1 \quad C_2 \quad C_3 \quad C_4 \quad C_6 \quad D_2 \quad D_3 \quad D_4 \quad D_6 \quad T \quad O \tag{6}$$

$$C_i \quad C_{2h} \quad C_{3i} \quad C_{4h} \quad C_{6h} \quad D_{2h} \quad D_{3d} \quad D_{4h} \quad D_{6h} \quad T_h \quad O_h \tag{7}$$

The order of each direct product group thus obtained is twice the order of the corresponding pure rotation group and the elements are easily written out by combining E and i with each of the elements of the rotation group in turn.

From the fact that all the pure rotations of a mixed group must in themselves form a subgroup and the fact that i must explicitly occur in the point group of a lattice, it follows that all the possible point groups of space lattices should be among those given in (7). We have already stated that a crystal is a structure built up from a space lattice by locating identical groups of atoms at all the lattice points. The structure possesses the point group symmetry common to the point group of the group of atoms placed at the lattice points and the lattice itself. We should now note that the set of elements common to two groups forms a group which is a subgroup of both the parent groups. It therefore follows that the possible point groups of crystals are among those given in (7) and all their distinct subgroups. The pure rotation groups given in (6) are eleven such subgroups. Besides these, there are ten more subgroups which are mixed groups that do not possess i explicitly. These can be obtained by examination and they are

$$C_s \quad C_{2v} \quad S_4 \quad C_{4v} \quad D_{2d} \quad C_{3v} \quad C_{3h} \quad D_{3h} \quad C_{6v} \quad T_d. \tag{8}$$

The possible crystallographic point groups are thus 32 in number and given in (6), (7) and (8).

All crystals which possess the same point group symmetry are said to form one crystal class. As has been shown in the foregoing paragraphs, there are 32 possible point groups and consequently there are 32 crystal classes which correspond to them. We have also noted that the possible point groups of space lattices are among the 11 groups given in (7). It can be shown that all space lattices will be characterized by one of the 7 point groups namely, C_i, C_{2h}, D_{2h}, D_{4h}, D_{3d}, D_{6h} and O_h. These 7 groups are called the holohedral groups and it is easily seen that the 32 point groups are subgroups of these 7 holohedral groups. Thus the 32 classes are divided into 7 crystal systems. They are the triclinic (C_i), monoclinic (C_{2h}), orthorhombic (D_{2h}), tetragonal (D_{4h}), rhombohedral (D_{3d}), hexagonal (D_{6h}) and cubic (O_h) systems respectively.

The crystal systems, the crystal classes that fall under each system and the elements of symmetry in each class are given in Table III. The point groups described in detail in Section 5.3 may be recognized under symbols C_{2v}, T_d and D_{6h} respectively in Table III.

5.8 Ninety Crystallographic Magnetic Point Groups

Conventional symmetry operations, namely rotations and rotation-reflections, enable us to build the 32 crystallographic point groups. However, in order to explain the magnetic properties of crystals, the need for an extension of the concept of symmetry operations has been realized in the works of Landau,[†] Shubnikov[‡] and Tavger and

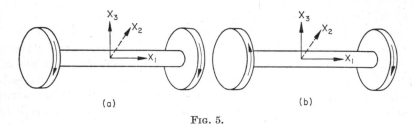

(a)   (b)

Fig. 5.

Zaitsev[§]. In addition to the spatial arrangement of atoms in a point group, the orientation of the atomic magnetic moments (spins) becomes important. It may turn out that the usual spatial symmetry operation of a rotation or a rotation-reflection, while bringing the group into coincidence with itself in regard to its geometrical structure, will reverse the orientation of spins. For instance, in Fig. 5(a) if the arrows indicating internal spins are ignored, X_2X_3 is a reflection plane and X_3 is a 2-fold rotation axis. If spins are present and cannot be ignored, while X_2X_3 is still a reflection plane, X_3 is no longer a 2-fold rotation axis. Similarly, in Fig. 5(b) if the arrows indicating internal spins are ignored, X_2X_3 is a reflection plane and X_3 is a 2-fold rotation axis. In fact there is no difference between the structures of Fig. 5(a) and of Fig. 5(b) if the spins are ignored. On the other hand, if the spins as

† Landau, L. D. and Lifshitz, E. M., "Electrodynamics of Continuous Media". Pergamon Press, Oxford (1960).

‡ Shubnikov, A. N., "Symmetry and Antisymmetry of Finite Figures", Izd. Acad. Sci. USSR (1951).

§ Tavger, B. A. and Zaitsev, V. M., *Soviet Phys. JETP* **3**, 430 (1956).

shown in Fig. 5(b) cannot be ignored, X_3 is still a 2-fold rotation axis but X_2X_3 is no longer a reflection plane. In such a case, a further

TABLE III

Conventional point groups

Crystal system	No.	Class symbol		Elements of symmetry
		International	Schönflies	
Triclinic	1	1	C_1	E
	2	$\bar{1}$	$-C_i$	$E\ i$
Monoclinic	3	m	$-C_s$	$E\ \sigma_h$
	4	2	C_2	$E\ C_2$
	5	$2/m$	C_{2h}	$E\ C_2\ i\ \sigma_h$
Orthorhombic	6	$2mm$	C_{2v}	$E\ C_2\ \sigma_v'\ \sigma_v''$
	7	222	D_2	$E\ C_2\ C_2'\ C_2''$
	8	mmm	D_{2h}	$E\ C_2\ C_2'\ C_2''\ i\ \sigma_h\ \sigma_v'\ \sigma_v''$
Tetragonal	9	4	C_4	$E\ 2C_4\ C_2$
	10	$\bar{4}$	S_4	$E\ 2S_4\ C_2$
	11	$4/m$	C_{4h}	$E\ 2C_4\ C_2\ i\ 2S_4\ \sigma_h$
	12	$4mm$	C_{4v}	$E\ 2C_4\ C_2\ 2\sigma_v'\ 2\sigma_v''$
	13	$\bar{4}2m$	D_{2d}	$E\ C_2\ C_2'\ C_2''\ \sigma_v'\ 2S_4\ \sigma_v''$
	14	422	D_4	$E\ 2C_4\ C_2\ 2C_2'\ 2C_2''$
	15	$4/mmm$	D_{4h}	$E\ 2C_4\ C_2\ 2C_2'\ 2C_2''\ i\ 2S_4\ \sigma_h\ 2\sigma_v'\ 2\sigma$
Rhombohedral	16	3	C_3	$E\ 2C_3$
	17	$\bar{3}$	$-C_{3i}$	$E\ 2C_3\ i\ 2S_6$
	18	$3m$	C_{3v}	$E\ 2C_3\ 3\sigma_v$
	19	32	D_3	$E\ 2C_3\ 3C_2$
	20	$\bar{3}m$	D_{3d}	$E\ 2C_3\ 3C_2\ i\ 2S_6\ 3\sigma_v$
Hexagonal	21	$\bar{6}$	C_{3h}	$E\ 2C_3\ \sigma_h\ 2S_3$
	22	6	C_6	$E\ 2C_6\ 2C_3\ C_2$
	23	$6/m$	C_{6h}	$E\ 2C_6\ 2C_3\ C_2\ i\ 2S_3\ 2S_6\ \sigma_h$
	24	$\bar{6}m2$	D_{3h}	$E\ 2C_3\ 3C_2\ \sigma_h\ 2S_3\ 3\sigma_v$
	25	$6mm$	C_{6v}	$E\ 2C_6\ 2C_3\ C_2\ 3\sigma_v'\ 3\sigma_v''$
	26	622	D_6	$E\ 2C_6\ 2C_3\ C_2\ 3C_2'\ 3C_2''$
	27	$6/mmm$	D_{6h}	$E\ 2C_6\ 2C_3\ C_2\ 3C_2'\ 3C_2''\ i\ 2S_3\ 2S_6\ \sigma_h\ 3\sigma_v'\ 3\sigma_v$
Cubic	28	23	T	$E\ 8C_3\ 3C_2$
	29	$m3$	T_h	$E\ 8C_3\ 3C_2\ i\ 8S_6\ 3\sigma$
	30	$\bar{4}3m$	T_d	$E\ 8C_3\ 3C_2\ 6\sigma\ 6S_4$
	31	432	O	$E\ 8C_3\ 3C_2\ 6C_2\ 6C_4$
	32	$m3m$	O_h	$E\ 8C_3\ 3C_2\ 6C_2\ 6C_4\ i\ 8S_6\ 3\sigma\ 6\sigma\ 6S_4$

reversal of the spins of all atoms should evidently follow the rotation or rotation-reflection as the case may be in order to bring about coincidence of structure in the full sense of the term. The operation of such a reversal of the spins will be denoted by the symbol $\mathscr{R}$. A combined operation consisting of an ordinary symmetry operation followed by $\mathscr{R}$ may significantly be defined and recognized as a new type of symmetry operation which may be called a complementary operation. This designation, namely a complementary operation, is taken from the work of Zheludev[†].

The recognition of new complementary symmetry operations as explained above in the context of magnetic structures results in an additional number of 90 possible crystallographic point groups. These new groups may be called the magnetic point groups which are crystallographically significant. They may be derived in a number of ways and the one which is adopted here may be described as follows. Let us take a crystallographic conventional point group and denote its elements by $E, R_1, R_2, \ldots$ and the product of any two elements R_1 and R_2 by $R_1 . R_2$. A complementary symmetry operation which consists of the application of an ordinary symmetry operation R_i followed by the reversal of all atomic magnetic moments is denoted by $\underline{R_i}$ and sometimes referred to as the complement of R_i for convenience. The product rules which involve the complementary symmetry operations are easily seen to be as follows: If $R_1 . R_2 = R_3$, then $\underline{R_1} . R_2 = \underline{R_3}$ and $\underline{R_1} . R_2 = R_1 . \underline{R_2} = \underline{R_3}$. We shall now examine the possibility of replacing some of the symmetry elements in the point group under consideration by their complementary operations such that the resulting set of operations forms a group under the product rules defined. Usual product rules still apply to the ordinary symmetry elements. The new group thus obtained may be called a variant of the original group.

From a given point group, we may obtain more than one variant by exhausting all possibilities of replacement as outlined above. In this process, one finds that there are only 58 distinct variants that can be obtained from the 32 ordinary groups. The total number of magnetic groups is thus 90 and these are shown in Table IV. The elements for each of the 32 ordinary groups are described in full adopting the usual notation. The variants derived from each group are shown under that group using $+$ and $-$ symbols only. $+$ in the place of any element has to be understood as the element itself and $-$ in the place of any element has to be understood to mean that the original element is to be replaced by its complement. International symbols with appropriate modifications are given for all the 90 classes in the column under class symbol.

Shubnikov first derived the 90 magnetic groups listed in Table IV in a slightly different manner by assuming that the constituents may be

---

† Zheludev, I.`S., *Soviet Phys. Crystallography* **5**, 328 (1960).

TABLE IV

Magnetic point groups

No.	Class symbol	Elements of symmetry
1	1	E
2	$\bar{1}$	$E\ i$
3	$\underline{\bar{1}}$	$+\ -$
4	m	$E\ \sigma_h$
5	$\underline{m}$	$+\ -$
6	2	$E\ C_2$
7	$\underline{2}$	$+\ -$
8	$2/m$	$E\ C_2\ i\ \sigma_h$
9	$\underline{2}/m$	$+\ -\ -\ +$
10	$2/m$	$+\ +\ -\ -$
11	$2/\underline{m}$	$+\ -\ +\ -$
12	$2mm$	$E\ C_2\ \sigma_v'\ \sigma_v''$
13	$\underline{2mm}$	$+\ -\ +\ -$
14	$2\underline{mm}$	$+\ +\ -\ -$
15	222	$E\ C_2\ C_2'\ C_2''$
16	$\underline{222}$	$+\ -\ -\ +$
17	mmm	$E\ C_2\ C_2'\ C_2''\ i\ \sigma_h\ \sigma_v'\ \sigma_v''$
18	$\underline{m}mm$	$+\ +\ -\ -\ -\ -\ +\ +$
19	$\underline{mmm}$	$+\ +\ +\ +\ -\ -\ -\ -$
20	$\underline{mm}m$	$+\ +\ -\ -\ +\ +\ -\ -$
21	4	$E\ 2C_4\ C_2$
22	$\underline{4}$	$+\ -\ +$
23	$\bar{4}$	$E\ 2S_4\ C_2$
24	$\underline{\bar{4}}$	$+\ -\ +$
25	$4/m$	$E\ 2C_4\ C_2\ i\ 2S_4\ \sigma_h$
26	$\underline{4}/m$	$+\ -\ +\ -\ +\ -$
27	$4/\underline{m}$	$+\ +\ +\ -\ -\ -$
28	$\underline{4}/\underline{m}$	$+\ -\ +\ +\ -\ +$
29	$4mm$	$E\ 2C_4\ C_2\ 2\sigma_v'\ 2\sigma_v''$
30	$\underline{4mm}$	$+\ +\ +\ -\ -$
31	$4\underline{mm}$	$+\ -\ +\ +\ -$
32	$\bar{4}2m$	$E\ C_2\ C_2'\ C_2''\ \sigma_v'\ 2S_4\ \sigma_v''$
33	$\underline{\bar{4}}2\underline{m}$	$+\ +\ +\ +\ -\ -\ -$

TABLE IV (*contd.*)

No.	Class symbol	Elements of symmetry
34	$\overline{4}2m$	+ + − − + − +
35	$\overline{4}2m$	+ + − − − + −
36	422	$E\ 2C_4\ C_2\ 2C_2'\ 2C_2''$
37	$\underline{422}$	+ + + − −
38	$\underline{422}$	+ − + + −
39	$4/mmm$	$E\ 2C_4\ C_2\ 2C_2'\ 2C_2''\ i\ 2S_4\ \sigma_h\ 2\sigma_v'\ 2\sigma_v''$
40	$\underline{4/mmm}$	+ − + − + − + − + −
41	$4/\underline{mmm}$	+ + + − − − − − + +
42	$4/\underline{mmm}$	+ + + − − + + + − −
43	$4/\underline{mmm}$	+ + + + + − − − − −
44	$4/\underline{mmm}$	+ − + + − + − + + −
45	3	$E\ 2C_3$
46	$\overline{3}$	$E\ 2C_3\ i\ 2S_6$
47	$\underline{\overline{3}}$	+ + − −
48	$3m$	$E\ 2C_3\ 3\sigma_v$
49	$\underline{3m}$	+ + −
50	32	$E\ 2C_3\ 3C_2$
51	$\underline{32}$	+ + −
52	$\overline{3}m$	$E\ 2C_3\ 3C_2\ i\ 2S_6\ 3\sigma_v$
53	$\overline{3}m$	+ + − + + −
54	$\overline{3}\underline{m}$	+ + − − − +
55	$\overline{3}\underline{m}$	+ + + − − −
56	$\overline{6}$	$E\ 2C_3\ \sigma_h\ 2S_3$
57	$\underline{\overline{6}}$	+ + − −
58	6	$E\ 2C_6\ 2C_3\ C_2$
59	$\underline{6}$	+ − + −
60	$6/m$	$E\ 2C_6\ 2C_3\ C_2\ i\ 2S_3\ 2S_6\ \sigma_h$
61	$\underline{6/m}$	+ + + + − − − −
62	$\underline{6/m}$	+ − + − − + − +
63	$\underline{6/m}$	+ − + − + − + −
64	$\overline{6}m2$	$E\ 2C_3\ 3C_2\ \sigma_h\ 2S_3\ 3\sigma_v$
65	$\overline{6}m2$	+ + − + + −
66	$\overline{6}\underline{m2}$	+ + − − − +
67	$\overline{6}\underline{m2}$	+ + + − − −
68	$6mm$	$E\ 2C_6\ 2C_3\ C_2\ 3\sigma_v'\ 3\sigma_v''$

TABLE IV (*contd.*)

No.	Class symbol	Elements of symmetry
69	$6mm$	+ + + + − −
70	$6mm$	+ − + − − +
71	622	$E\ 2C_6\ 2C_3\ C_2\ 3C_2'\ 3C_2''$
72	$6\underline{2}2$	+ + + + − −
73	$\underline{6}22$	+ − + − + −
74	$6/mmm$	$E\ 2C_6\ 2C_3\ C_2\ 3C_2'\ 3C_2''\ i\ 2S_3\ 2S_6\ \sigma_h\ 3\sigma_v'\ 3\sigma_v$
75	$6/mm\underline{m}$	+ + + + − − − − − − − + +
76	$6/m\underline{mm}$	+ + + + − − + + + + − −
77	$6/\underline{m}mm$	+ + + + + + − − − − − −
78	$\underline{6}/\underline{mm}m$	+ − + − − + − + − + + −
79	$\underline{6}/\underline{m}m\underline{m}$	+ − + − + − + − + − + −
80	23	$E\ 8C_3\ 3C_2$
81	$m3$	$E\ 8C_3\ 3C_2\ i\ 8S_6\ 3\sigma$
82	$m\underline{3}$	+ + + − − −
83	$\overline{4}3m$	$E\ 8C_3\ 3C_2\ 6\sigma\ 6S_4$
84	$\overline{4}3\underline{m}$	+ + + − −
85	432	$E\ 8C_3\ 3C_2\ 6C_2\ 6C_4$
86	$43\underline{2}$	+ + + − −
87	$m3m$	$E\ 8C_3\ 3C_2\ 6C_2\ 6C_4\ i\ 8S_6\ 3\sigma\ 6\sigma\ 6S_4$
88	$m3\underline{m}$	+ + + + + − − − − −
89	$m\underline{3m}$	+ + + − − − + + + − −
90	$m\underline{3}m$	+ + + − − − − − + +

regarded as coloured black or white and that an operation of inter-changing black and white colours is to be accepted as a possible symmetry operation in addition to the usual spatial symmetry operations. The colour change is analogous to the reversal of magnetic moments mentioned above. The reversal of magnetic moments is often interpreted as the reversal of current directions which in turn may be looked upon as equivalent to time reversal. The conventional symmetry group of a crystal characterizes the symmetry of the time-averaged charge distribution in the equilibrium state of the crystal and this is what is revealed in the X-ray analysis. In a crystal, there may also be present a non-vanishing time-averaged current distribution, which, however, must be such that the net outward flux over an elementary cell is always zero. Such currents give rise to a magnetic moment distribution in the crystal. If the net magnetic moment in a unit cell is not zero, the crystal becomes ferromagnetic. On the other hand, when such currents are present but give rise to individual magnetic moments so distributed as to make the net magnetic moment in a unit cell equal to zero, then the crystal becomes antiferromagnetic. It must be mentioned here that the unit cell we are referring to is not necessarily the same as the one normally understood in the chemical sense. A unit cell in the magnetic sense has sometimes been called the magneto-crystalline unit cell in order to distinguish it from the chemical unit

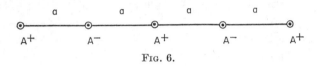

Fɪɢ. 6.

cell or the crystallochemical unit cell. For instance, if we have a chain of atoms A^+, A^-, etc. at equal distances a along a line as shown in Fig. 6, A^+ being chemically identical with A^- but differing from it in regard only to its spin orientation being parallel or antiparallel to a given direction, one can easily see that while the chemical unit cell is of length a, the magnetocrystalline unit cell is of length $2a$. In fact, the magnetocrystalline unit cell is either equal to or larger than the chemical unit cell, by an integral factor. The above arrangement will be antiferromagnetic. If all the A^-'s are replaced by A^+'s, the resulting structure will be ferromagnetic.

The symmetry of the current distribution in a crystal is thus equivalent to the symmetry of the arrangement of the magnetic moments of the individual atoms in the crystal. A reversal of time would mean a reversal in the direction of the currents in the crystal which would in turn imply a reversal of magnetic moment distribution. Time reversal or reversal of magnetic moments is to be considered as a new symmetry element of the current distribution or magnetic moment distribution and we have already designated it by the symbol $\mathscr{R}$. The 90 magnetic groups derived above do not contain $\mathscr{R}$ explicitly. One can easily see that if after the recognition of the new operator $\mathscr{R}$, we try to build all possible point groups, they fall into three categories. They are (i) those groups which include the operation $\mathscr{R}$ explicitly, (ii) those groups which do not include the operation $\mathscr{R}$ either explicitly or in conjunction with a conventional symmetry operation, and (iii) those groups which do not include $\mathscr{R}$ explicitly but contain at least one complementary operation. These three categories of groups are sometimes called the Shubnikov generalizations of the 32 conventional point groups.

It is evident that we have not shown separately the groups of category (i) in our derivation and in Table IV. These are simply obtained by adding to each of the conventional point groups, the complements of all the conventional operations in the group. In such an extension, the operation $\mathscr{R}$ corresponds to the identity E and to each symmetry operation corresponds its complement. The extension may be formally carried out by taking the direct product of the conventional point group with the group of two elements $E, \mathscr{R}$. That the two elements $E, \mathscr{R}$ form a group is evident. Each group thus obtained has twice as many elements as the conventional group from which it is derived. Since it contains the operation $\mathscr{R}$ explicitly, such a group cannot be the symmetry group of a magnetic structure. It is therefore concluded that such a group can be used to build only a paramagnetic or a diamagnetic crystal. For such crystals the time-averaged current distribution is everywhere zero. Under the colour symmetry interpretation of Shubnikov, the groups of category (i) represent configurations, the constituents of which are simultaneously black as well as white. They are in fact called the grey groups.

The groups of category (ii) consist of spatial point symmetry operations alone and they are not distinct from the conventional crystallographic point groups. Obtaining these 32 conventional point groups and listing them in Table IV within the possible point groups of magnetic structures only means that it is permissible to orient atomic magnetic moments in a crystal, such that the orientation of all magnetic moments also remains invariant under all the spatial point symmetry operations of the crystal. In other words, it is possible to orient atomic magnetic moments in a crystal such that there is no deterioration of spatial symmetry even if invariance of magnetic moment orientation under a symmetry operation is demanded. These may be regarded as single coloured groups and since the single colour can be any colour, they are also called the colourless groups.

The groups of category (iii) are the 58 variants we obtained above. These are called the double coloured or mixed groups. The procedure to obtain the magnetic variants from the conventional groups may also be laid down in the following manner. Select a point group G and choose any subgroup H, the order of which is half that of G. Multiply by $\mathscr{R}$ the elements of G which are not in H. Then the elements in H and the complementary elements obtained comprise a variant. The procedure we have adopted is not different in principle to the one given above. It may be mentioned that replacement of ordinary elements by complementary elements and obtaining the variant by inspection is not particularly difficult. Another point which may also be mentioned here is that the magnetic variants of a point group are isomorphous with the one-dimensional representations of the point group. This is evident from the very structure of the variants as they are presented in Table IV.

5.9 Magnetic Space Groups

Since we are here interested in the macroscopic properties of crystals, for most purposes it is not necessary to know the complete symmetry group of either the charge distribution in the crystal (conventional space group of the crystal) or the magnetic moment distribution (magnetic space group of the crystal).

We have seen that the properties of crystals that do not possess a magnetic structure are related to their macroscopic symmetry which is classified under the conventional 32 classes. While dealing with the magnetic properties of ferromagnetic or antiferromagnetic crystals, we have to note that they are related to their macroscopic symmetry as classified under the 90 magnetic classes. Even though we are here not directly interested in the magnetic space groups, some understanding of the magnetic structures is gained by learning the principles which constitute the basis for their derivation. The magnetic space groups are sometimes referred to as Shubnikov groups and they may again be classified under three categories. They are (i) those groups which include the operation $\mathscr{R}$ explicitly. Each such group can be obtained by taking the direct product of each of the conventional space groups with the group $E, \mathscr{R}$. They are 230 in number and are called the grey groups; (ii) those groups which do not include $\mathscr{R}$ either explicitly or in conjunction with a conventional symmetry operation but consist of spatial symmetry transformations, namely rotations, rotation-reflections and translations. These may be called single colour groups or colourless groups. They are 230 in number and are indistinguishable from the conventional space groups; (iii) those groups which do not include $\mathscr{R}$ explicitly but which contain complementary symmetry operations. These groups may be called mixed groups. They are 1191 in number.

Evidently, the derivation of Shubnikov groups of categories (i) and (ii) is trivial. Derivation of the 1191 Shubnikov groups of category (iii) which are the mixed groups needs some consideration. The derivation is in principle not different from the one adopted by which the 58 mixed point groups have been derived. It consists in replacing a certain chosen half of the elements of a conventional space group by the corresponding complementary elements such that the resulting set forms a group and picking out all the distinct groups from among those thus obtained.

For details of derivation, the reader may refer to the work of Belov, Neronova and Smirnova†. As an illustration, we shall here take up the

† Belov, N. V., Neronova, N. N. and Smirnova, T. S., *Soviet Phys. Cryst.* **2**, 311 (1957).

derivation of the Shubnikov groups pertaining to what may be called the one-dimensional strip decorations. The conventional one-dimensional strip decorations are obtained by placing a two-dimensional motif on a one-dimensional lattice. We further assign a positive ($+$) sign or a negative ($-$) sign to the motif and define a Shubnikov group as a group of symmetry and complementary symmetry operations, including translations, which leave the strip invariant. The feature of invariance is applied to the pattern both in regard to its geometry and in regard to the associated signs. The assigning of $+$ or $-$ sign to the motif is equivalent to considering the geometrically identical motif in two colours, say black and white. Thus the Shubnikov groups represent the bi-coloured strip decorations.

A set of points, all of which can be reached by starting from any one of them and by performing a basic or primitive translation T or an integral multiple thereof, the translation being always confined to one direction, constitute a one-dimensional lattice. The lattice is taken as extending to infinity and a primitive translation or an integral multiple thereof brings the lattice into superposition with itself and therefore it is a symmetry operation of the lattice. Let us take the X_1-axis along the lattice and stipulate that the lattice has a 2-fold axis of symmetry about the X_1-axis. The reason for this stipulation will be evident as we proceed. The lattice is easily seen to possess the following symmetry elements:

$$E \ C_2 \ C_2' \ C_2'' \ i \ \sigma_h \ \sigma_v' \ \sigma_v''.$$

Strip decorations are generated by placing a two-dimensional motif at each of the lattice points. We shall take it that the motif has extension in X_1 and X_2 directions only but not in the X_3 direction. In such a case the symmetry elements C_2, C_2', i, σ_v'' cannot be distinguished from σ_v', σ_h, C_2'', E respectively. The group of symmetry operations then reduces to one of order 4 and consists of the following elements:

$$E \ \sigma_v' \ i \ \sigma_h.$$

We may drop the prime in σ_v' hereafter without any difficulty. We can locate at every lattice point, a two-dimensional motif possessing all the above symmetry operations and obtain a pattern whose symmetry is the same as that given above. On the other hand, by locating a motif whose symmetry operations constitute a subgroup of the above group we will be obtaining patterns of that lower degree of symmetry. The subgroups of the above group are E; Ei; $E\sigma_v$; $E\sigma_h$ and each one of these four can be used as the symmetry group of the motif for the pattern besides the main group $E \ \sigma_v \ i \ \sigma_h$ itself.

If we further consider an infinite lattice, the possibility of having new symmetry elements such as screw axes of rotation and glide planes of reflection has to be taken into account. The direction of glide should lie in the plane of reflection and the direction of a screw should lie along the axis of rotation. In the symmetry groups relating to one-dimensional patterns, the translation is along one direction only and therefore glide planes of the σ_v class alone are possible. Such a plane will be analytically represented as $X_1 \rightarrow X_1 + \tau$ and $X_2 \rightarrow -X_2$, where the least value of τ is $T_1/2$, because the glide performed twice should result in a full unit of translation bringing every lattice point to its immediate neighbour. Since the glide σ_v^g should be equal to the product $i\sigma_h$, i and σ_h cannot both be situated at the origin. As a consequence of this, a general description of the symmetry elements appropriate to an infinite flat strip will be

$$
\begin{array}{lll}
E & X_1 \rightarrow \ X_1 & X_2 \rightarrow \ X_2 \\
i & X_1 \rightarrow -X_1 + b & X_2 \rightarrow -X_2 \\
\sigma_h & X_1 \rightarrow -X_1 + a & X_2 \rightarrow \ X_2 \\
\sigma_v & X_1 \rightarrow \ X_1 + a + b & X_2 \rightarrow -X_2
\end{array}
$$

where a and b are parameters. It may be noted that $2a$ or $2b$ is equivalent to identity, and thus there is no distinction between a and $-a$ or b and $-b$. Each one of the symbols E, i, σ_h, σ_v really stands for a class of symmetry elements for an infinite lattice. For example, the plane σ_h cuts the X_1-axis at the point $a/2$, 0 and all other elements of this class pass through corresponding points. If i is chosen as the origin itself, b becomes zero and we will be left with a single parameter a alone. As every operation done twice should give rise to either the identity element E or a full unit of translation T_1, the parameter a can take the values 0 or $T_1/2$. It is obvious that a space group will contain a glide plane only when $a = T_1/2$. Otherwise, σ_v becomes a simple reflection plane. The distinct symmetry patterns may then be described by the space groups $E\,\sigma_v\,i\,\sigma_h$ and $E\,\sigma_v^g\,i\,\sigma_h$. We can also have symmetry patterns having subgroups of either of the above space groups. Each of the groups E; Ei; $E\sigma_h$; $E\sigma_v$; $E\sigma_v^g$ is a subgroup of either one or both of the above two space groups. Thus, when the lattice is an infinite one, two more symmetry patterns, namely $E\,\sigma_v^g\,i\,\sigma_h$ and $E\,\sigma_v^g$ are possible in addition to the five that are present in the case of a finite lattice. The superscript g indicates that the symmetry element is a glide plane of reflection. We have thus been enabled to build 7 space groups in the case under consideration, whereas there are only 5 point groups. These 7 alternatives are the well-known infinitely repeated strip decorations of the flat type and are diagrammatically represented in Fig. 7. The lattice is unique and one-dimensional .

All possible Shubnikov groups may be obtained from the above 7 one-dimensional space groups by replacing some of the symmetry operations including those which involve a translation, by the

E

$E\,i$

$E\,\sigma_v$

$E\,\sigma_h$

$E\,\sigma_v\,i\,\sigma_h$

$E\,\sigma_v$

$E\,\sigma_v^g\,i\,\sigma_h$

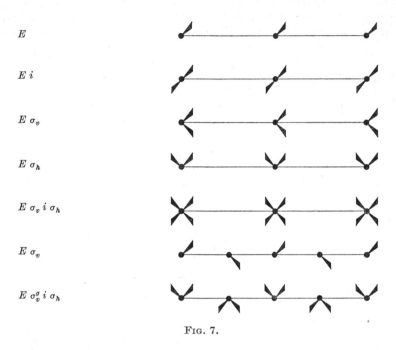

FIG. 7.

corresponding complementary operations and picking out the distinct groups from among those thus obtained. This procedure is here carried out in the following three steps.

(a) Derive all possible magnetic point groups from the 5 distinct conventional point groups, namely, E; $E\,i$; $E\,\sigma_v$; $E\,\sigma_h$; $E\,\sigma_v\,i\,\sigma_h$. From these, we obtain the same 5 as single colour groups and 6 mixed point groups, namely, $E\,\underline{i}$; $E\,\underline{\sigma_v}$; $E\,\underline{\sigma_h}$; $E\,\underline{\sigma_v}\,i\,\underline{\sigma_h}$; $E\,\sigma_v\,\underline{i}\,\underline{\sigma_h}$; $E\,\underline{\sigma_v}\,\underline{i}\,\sigma_h$. We thus have 11 magnetic point groups.

(b) Derive all possible mixed translation groups. This amounts to finding as the first step the magnetic variants of the one-dimensional lattice. We obtain only one variant in the one-dimensional case. It is described by the complementary operation $\tfrac{1}{2}T_1$ denoted by the symbol $\mathscr{R}^g$. We shall refer to such a lattice as the magnetic lattice. The operation is like a glide or screw in the sense that the motif is moved to the position $\tfrac{1}{2}T_1$ and then its parity changed from $+$ to $-$ and vice versa,

or from black to white and vice versa, or spins reversed, depending on
the nature of the structure we are considering.

(c) The 7 grey space groups and the 7 single colour space groups are
readily obtained from the 7 conventional space groups. They are given
in the first 14 rows of Fig. 8. The mixed space groups are obtained in
two steps. The first step is to place the 6 motifs with mixed point group
symmetry on the ordinary lattice. The space groups thus obtained are
given in the next 6 rows in Fig. 8. By introducing glide operations

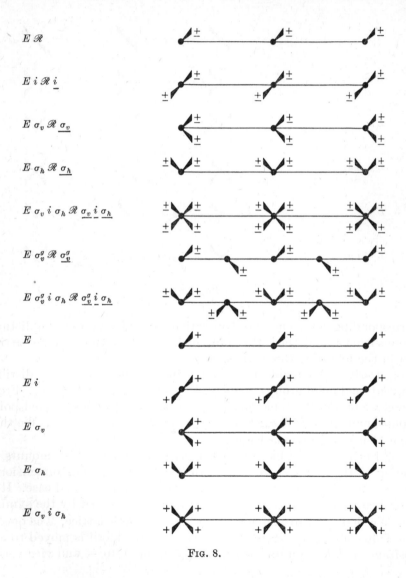

Fig. 8.

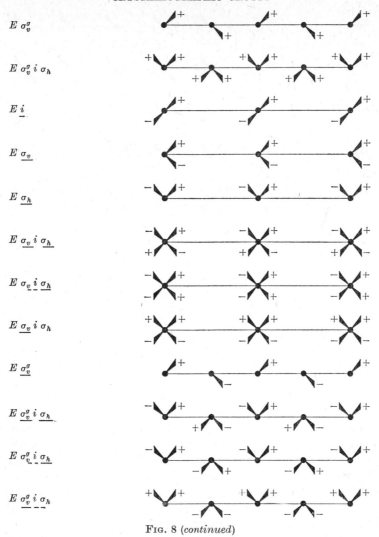

FIG. 8 (*continued*)

σ_v^g and $\underline{\sigma_v^g}$ in place of σ_v and $\underline{\sigma_v}$ wherever it is possible in the 6 mixed space groups mentioned above, we obtain 4 more distinct space groups. They are given in the next 4 rows in Fig. 8. The second step is to place the 5 motifs with single colour point group symmetry and the 6 motifs with mixed point group symmetry on the magnetic lattice and eliminate repetitions. In this step we obtain 7 more distinct mixed space groups. They are given in the last 7 rows in Fig. 8. It is readily seen that introduction of glide operations σ_v^g and $\underline{\sigma_v^g}$ in these groups is taken care of by the operation $\mathscr{R}^g$ itself. These 7 mixed groups may

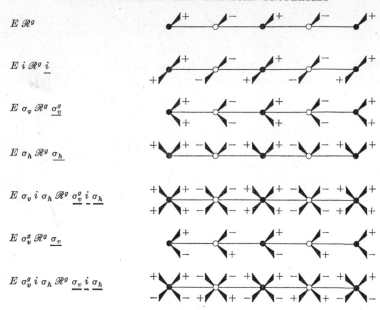

$$E \, \mathscr{R}^g$$

$$E \, i \, \mathscr{R}^g \, \underline{i}$$

$$E \, \sigma_v \, \mathscr{R}^g \, \underline{\sigma_v^g}$$

$$E \, \sigma_h \, \mathscr{R}^g \, \underline{\sigma_h}$$

$$E \, \sigma_v \, i \, \sigma_h \, \mathscr{R}^g \, \underline{\sigma_v^g} \, \underline{i} \, \underline{\sigma_h}$$

$$E \, \sigma_v^g \, \mathscr{R}^g \, \underline{\sigma_v}$$

$$E \, \sigma_v^g \, i \, \sigma_h \, \mathscr{R}^g \, \underline{\sigma_v} \, \underline{i} \, \underline{\sigma_h}$$

Fig. 8 (*concluded*).

directly be obtained by introducing the operation $\mathscr{R}^g$ into the 7 single colour space groups.

Thus, in all there are 31 distinct one-dimensional Shubnikov space groups obtained with a two-dimensional motif. In Fig. 8, alternate white and black dots signify a magnetic lattice. Evidently each space group is an infinite group and each element in a group as given in Fig. 8 stands for the whole set of symmetry elements obtained by multiplying it with all possible translations of the lattice. Against each group is given a sketch of a strip decoration with a simple motif. The + and − signs associated with a motif can also be interpreted as a relief of the motif in the X_3-direction. The + sign can be interpreted as the projection of the motif in the positive X_3-direction and the − sign as its projection in the negative X_3-direction by an equal amount. In such an interpretation, the Shubnikov groups considered are not distinct from the ordinary space groups obtained and described earlier by the author by using a three-dimensional motif on a one-dimensional lattice.†

In fact, the 7 conventional space groups representing the strip decorations, which are the space groups obtained by using a two-

† Bhagavantam, S. and Venkatarayudu, T., "Theory of Groups and Its Application to Physical Problems", 3rd Ed. Andhra University, Waltair (1962).

dimensional motif on a one-dimensional lattice can also be interpreted as the Shubnikov generalizations of the groups obtained by using a one-dimensional motif on a one-dimensional lattice. There are only 2 conventional space groups in such a case, namely those designated by E and $E\,i$. Figure 9 gives these 7 groups in a notation that brings out

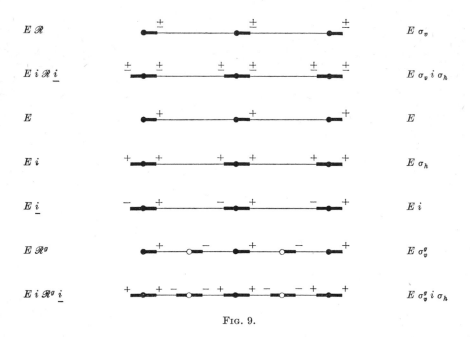

FIG. 9.

this interpretation. The symbols used are self-explanatory. The sixth and the seventh groups in Fig. 9, namely, $E\,\mathscr{R}^g$ and $E\,i\,\mathscr{R}^g\,i$ are obtained by using the groups E and $E\,i$ on the magnetic lattice. This fact is shown in the figures corresponding to these groups by alternate black and white dots. The $\pm$ sign can be interpreted as giving an extension along X_2 in the $+$ or $-$ direction respectively to the linear motif. Such an extension will result in the motif becoming two-dimensional. This makes the strips in Fig. 9 look like those in Fig. 7.

In a manner similar to the one-dimensional case just considered, it can be shown that the 80 space groups obtained by using a motif in three dimensions on two-dimensional lattices are isomorphous with the Shubnikov generalizations of the 17 space groups obtained by using a two-dimensional motif on two-dimensional lattices. Similarly, the 1651 Shubnikov generalizations of the 230 conventional space groups can be interpreted as having been obtained by using a motif in four dimensions on three-dimensional lattices. These inter-relationships are given below in a tabular form.

		Lattices	Point groups	Space groups
Linear strips	Conventional	1	5	7
	Magnetic	2	11	24
Surface decorations	Conventional	5	10	17
	Magnetic	10	21	63
Crystal structures	Conventional	14	32	230
	Magnetic	36	90	1421

CHAPTER 6

Symmetry and Physical Properties

6.1 Physical Property as a Relation between Two Physical Quantities

A study of the physical properties of matter and the effect thereon of various parameters that characterize the state of matter in respect of which measurements are made is of great importance from several points of view. If the study refers to a single crystal, the symmetry of the crystal has a marked and distinctive effect on the physical property under consideration. In the approach presented here, issues relating to a wide variety of physical properties in respect of all the crystal classes are brought under a single formalism.

Most physical properties can be associated with and therefore formally defined by a relation between two measurable quantities. These quantities which will be called physical quantities may be simple ones or complicated ones. For instance, if we choose mass and volume as the two physical quantities, a specific relation exists between these two quantities in respect of matter in a given state and the physical property of density can be associated with such a relation. A formal definition of density is obtained by stating that it is the mass per unit volume. It may be noted that both mass and volume are scalars (tensors of rank zero) and their magnitudes do not depend on the directions within the crystal, along which measurements are made. Their ratio, which we have called the density, is thus a physical property which does not depend on the direction in which it is measured. All crystals, irrespective of their symmetry, are *isotropic* in regard to density.

On the other hand, if we choose the electric moment induced in a crystal by an external electric field furnished by incident electromagnetic radiation and the external electric field itself as the two physical quantities, again a specific relation exists between these two quantities in respect of matter the state of which is characterized by certain parameters of temperature, pressure, etc. The physical property which we may designate as the electric polarizability can be associated with that relation. Electric polarizability leads to the definition of refractive index in a simple manner. A formal definition of electric polarizability may be obtained by stating that it is the electric moment induced per unit volume by unit external electric field. It may be noted that both the moment induced and the external electric field are vectors (first rank tensors), their magnitudes depending on the direction of measurement. Thus, the physical property of electric polarizability or of the related optical refraction which we have associated with the relation between these two quantities will also depend on the direction of measurement within the crystal. Some crystals, depending on their symmetry, are *anisotropic* in regard to refraction. The symmetry of the appropriate crystal class determines the type and extent of anisotropy exhibited by a given crystal.

We may go a step further along the line of increasing complexity and choose as our two physical quantities the mechanical stress to which a crystal is subjected and the deformation or strain that will result therefrom in the crystal. Both these quantities are second rank symmetric tensors and a specific relation exists between them. A well-known physical property, namely elasticity, is associated with this relation. Some of the laws of elasticity and basic definitions are easily obtained from this relation in the same manner as in the simpler cases cited earlier. Here again, the symmetry of the class to which a particular crystal belongs determines the type and extent of anisotropy exhibited by a given crystal in regard to elasticity.

To give an example from a different class of properties, we may choose electric current density J_i and electric field intensity E_i as our physical quantities. The fundamental relation between J_i and E_i in a conducting crystal is the generalized Ohm's law

$$J_i = \sigma_{ik} E_k$$

where σ_{ik} is the electrical conductivity. Thus the physical property of electrical conductivity σ_{ik} of a crystal relates the physical quantities, electric current density and electric field intensity.

6.2 Physical Quantities regarded as Tensors

We may now go back to the general statement already made that a physical property can be associated with the relation between two measurable physical quantities. Each such measurable physical quantity may be regarded as a tensor of an appropriate type and rank. In Tables V and VI are given a few examples: physical properties like enantiomorphism, elasticity and piezoelectricity are shown also as examples of measurable physical quantities and are associated with tensors. It will be seen that they may conveniently be regarded as such if we wish to study a physical property arising for instance from the relation between another measurable quantity like temperature on the one hand and elasticity or piezoelectricity on the other.

Thus it appears that most of the physical properties can be associated with the interaction of two physical quantities represented by tensors of appropriate rank. To a first order approximation, all such relations will take the general form,

$$B_{ijk...} = a_{ijk...lmn...} A_{lmn...} \qquad (1)$$

where $A_{lmn...}$ and $B_{ijk...}$ represent physical quantities and $a_{ijk...lmn...}$

TABLE V

Physical quantities as tensors

Examples	Associated tensor	Rank	Description
Volume	Scalar	0	Denoted by a simple number like ρ
Mass	Scalar	0	
Temperature	Scalar	0	
Electric field	Vector	1	Denoted by components like E_i; $i = 1, 2, 3$
Electric current density	Vector	1	
Heat current density	Vector	1	
Electric moment	Vector	1	
Stress	Second rank tensor	2	Denoted by components like σ_{ij}; $i, j = 1, 2, 3$
Strain	Second rank tensor	2	
Piezoelectricity	Third rank tensor	3	Denoted by components like d_{ijk}; $i, j, k = 1, 2, 3$
Elasticity	Fourth rank tensor	4	Denoted by components like c_{ijkl}; $i, j, k, l = 1, 2, 3$

TABLE VI

Physical quantities as pseudo tensors

Examples	Associated tensor	Rank	Description
Enantiomorphism	Pseudo scalar	0	Denoted by a simple number like δ
Magnetic field	Axial vector	1	Denoted by components like H_i; $i = 1, 2, 3$
Magnetic moment	Axial vector	1	
Angular momentum	Axial vector	1	
Gyration tensor	Second rank axial tensor	2	Denoted by components like g_{ij}; $i, j = 1, 2, 3$

represents the physical property connecting the two physical quantities. The above equation being a tensor equation should be such that all terms on both sides must be tensors of the same rank. Thus, if the influence tensor $A_{lmn...}$ is of rank p and the effect tensor $B_{ijk...}$ is of rank q, the physical property $a_{ijk...lmn...}$ must be a tensor of rank $(p+q)$. That $a_{ijk...lmn}$ is a tensor of rank $(p+q)$ follows from the quotient law. This formalism enables every physical quantity and every physical property to be classified as a tensor of particular kind and rank. Such a classification is helpful, particularly in the investigation of how the various physical properties are effected by the symmetry of the crystalline media in which they are observed. In the following pages, we will show that a given symmetry has the same effect on different physical properties represented by the same tensor irrespective of their physical nature. In a crystal belonging to a particular class, all physical properties represented by a tensor of the same kind and rank possess the same scheme of non-vanishing coefficients. Once the effect of various crystal class symmetries on the tensors of different ranks and types is worked out, all that is necessary to determine the effect of symmetry on a particular physical property is to determine the kind and rank of the tensor by which it is represented. The usefulness and convenience of such a broad classification and general treatment are thus apparent. For example, physical properties like thermal conductivity, electrical conductivity, electrical susceptibility and so on, irrespective of their diverse physical natures, all of them being associated with an interaction between two vector quantities, are represented by the same kind of second rank tensor and possess identical schemes of non-vanishing coefficients in various crystals. Throughout the text, as and when we take up various physical properties, we shall try to exploit the power of these general principles as far as possible.

6.3 Magnetic Properties Regarded as Tensors

Physical properties which arise from the interaction of two physical quantities, either or both of which involve magnetic vectors like the magnetic field, magnetic induction or the magnetic moment, are represented by tensors of a different kind. These may be referred to as the magnetic tensors. The distinctive feature of magnetic tensors consists in their transformation properties under complementary symmetry operations.

A magnetic vector such as the magnetic field H_i transforms as an axial vector under a conventional symmetry operation. The transformation equations may be written as $H'_i = \pm a_{ij} H_j$, where $\pm$ is taken according as the operation is a pure rotation or a rotation-reflection.

A complementary symmetry operation, as explained in section 5.8, is equivalent to an ordinary operation followed by a current reversal operation $\mathscr{R}$. To understand the effect of $\mathscr{R}$ on H_i, we consider its effect on a physical system equivalent to the magnetic field. The magnetic field can be considered as generated by an electric current and a reversal of current reverses the field. Therefore, we have to conclude that the effect of a complementary operation on H_i is given by the equation

$$H_i' = -(\pm a_{ij})H_j \tag{2}$$

with the same convention for $\pm$.

We can generalize the notion introduced in equation (2) and define magnetic tensors by the transformation equations (3). If $P_{ijk...}$ is a polar tensor and is also magnetic, we have

$$P_{ijk...}' = a_{il}\,a_{jm}\,a_{kn}\ldots P_{lmn...} \tag{3a}$$

if the operation is a conventional symmetry operation given by $x_i' = a_{ij}x_j$. If the operation is a complementary operation, we have (3b) instead of (3a).

$$P_{ijk...}' = -a_{il}\,a_{jm}\,a_{kn}\ldots P_{lmn...} \tag{3b}$$

If $Q_{ijk...}$ is an axial tensor and is also magnetic, we have

$$Q_{ijk...}' = \pm a_{il}\,a_{jm}\,a_{kn}\ldots Q_{lmn...} \tag{3c}$$

if the operation is a conventional one. The $\pm$ is taken according as the operation is a pure rotation or a rotation-reflection. If the operation is a complementary operation, we have (3d) instead of (3c), with the same convention regarding $\pm$ sign.

$$Q_{ijk...}' = -(\pm a_{il}\,a_{jm}\,a_{kn}\ldots)Q_{lmn...}. \tag{3d}$$

The magnetic nature of a tensor representing a magnetic property is decided by the constitutive equations similar to (1) that define it. For example, magneto-electric polarizability is a property observed in certain crystals in their antiferromagnetic state. It describes the production of magnetic moment I_i in a crystal due to the application of electric field E_i and the constitutive equations that define the property are given in (4).

$$I_i = \lambda_{ij}E_j. \tag{4}$$

I_i is an axial vector which is also magnetic and E_i is a polar vector and it follows from (4) that the physical property λ_{ij} is an axial tensor of second rank which is also magnetic. Piezomagnetism which relates the two physical quantities magnetic moment and stress is another example of a physical property which is represented by a magnetic tensor. Further clarification regarding the properties of magnetic tensors is given in Chapter 15, where specific examples of magnetic properties are dealt with. Reference may be made to a recent exhaustive survey article by Birss† for a detailed treatment of magnetic tensors.

6.4 Intrinsic Symmetry of Physical Properties

We have seen that the kind and rank of a tensor representing a physical property is determined by the kind and rank of the tensors that represent the physical quantities that are related by the physical property. However, in the case of certain physical properties an intrinsic symmetry may exist. The existence of any intrinsic symmetry in a physical property formally manifests as symmetry of the tensor representing it, with respect to certain permutations of its indices. For example, we may take the physical property of elasticity which is the result of the interaction of two second rank symmetric tensors, namely stress and strain. Elasticity is thus represented by a fourth rank tensor denoted by c_{iklm}. We will show later that, if we denote the places of the indices $iklm$ by $1, 2, 3, 4$ in order, the tensor c_{iklm} is symmetric with respect to the group of permutations:

$$E,\ (12),\ (34),\ (13)(24),\ (12)(34),\ (14)(23),\ (1423),\ (1324).$$

This symmetry is something inherent to the property of elasticity and persists irrespective of the symmetry of the crystal under consideration. To choose another example, the physical property of electrical conductivity represented by a second rank tensor σ_{ik} is symmetric with respect to interchange of the two suffixes. The group of permutations of indices with respect to which the tensor is symmetric can formally be given as the group consisting of two elements E, (12).

The considerations that are responsible for such an intrinsic symmetry of physical properties are mainly thermodynamical. In the case of equilibrium properties, i.e. properties described with reference to changes which are thermodynamically reversible, the intrinsic symmetry is derived by the method of thermodynamic potentials. The intrinsic symmetry of transport properties, i.e. those which can be measured in a system not in thermodynamic equilibrium, but in a steady state, is a result of Onsager's principle. We shall take up these considerations in detail at the appropriate place later. Sometimes, the definition of the physical property itself may be to some extent responsible for its intrinsic symmetry. For example, in the case of elasticity, the symmetry due to the permutations (12) and (34) is due to the fact that the

† Birss, R. R., *Rep. Progr. Phys.* **26**, 307 (1963).

interacting physical quantities, namely stress and strain (which are second rank tensors), are themselves symmetric with respect to an interchange of their indices. In its turn, the symmetry of strain is due to its very definition and the symmetry of stress is due to certain mechanical principles assumed.

6.5 Second and Higher Order Effects

The relations between the various physical quantities need not necessarily be linear. Situations in which the relation cannot be considered as linear are not uncommon. In such cases the physical quantity which is taken as the dependent variable (effect) is expressed as a power series in the physical quantity which is taken as the independent variable (influence). The coefficient of the first degree term in such an expansion gives the linear or first order effect as it might be called. The coefficient of the second degree term may be called the second order effect and coefficient of the third degree term the third order effect and so on. The physical situation demands the relation to be a tensor relation and all the terms in the series expansion to be tensors of the same rank. It follows that the consecutive coefficients in the series expansion are tensors whose rank differs by the rank of the independent variable. For example, the electric displacement D cannot be taken as linear function of the field E at higher field strengths. Therefore a functional dependence of the following form is postulated.

$$D_i = K_{ij} E_j + K_{ijk} E_j E_k + K_{ijkl} E_j E_k E_l + \ldots \qquad (5)$$

The ranks of the various coefficients are evident from the notation adopted. They are called first order, second order, third order, etc. effects respectively. For small fields, only the first order terms are of significance and K_{ij} is the field-independent dielectric constant. To bring out the physical significance of the higher order terms, we differentiate (5) with respect to the field.

$$\frac{dD_i}{dE_j} = K_{ij} + K_{ijk} E_k + K_{ijkl} E_k E_l + \ldots \qquad (6)$$

dD_i/dE_j may be designated as the dielectric permittivity which depends on the field. Thus, relation (6) treats the physical property of dielectric permittivity itself as a physical quantity depending on another physical quantity E. In a similar manner, several physical properties, which ultimately could be interpreted as second or higher order effects relating the basic physical quantities, are treated as first order effects relating what may be called derived physical quantities which are, in fact,

4

physical properties. In relation (6) the coefficient K_{ijk} describes the first order effect of E on the dielectric permittivity, even though it is, in fact, a second order effect according to relation (5).

In a power series expansion like equation (5) the coefficients are first, second, third, etc. derivatives of the dependent variable with respect to the independent variable. We have seen that the first order coefficients, i.e. coefficients of the linear part of the relations, are second order partial derivatives of a suitable thermodynamic potential defined in terms of the independent physical quantity. It follows that the second order coefficients are the third order partial derivatives of the same thermodynamic potential. In the case of elasticity, it is in fact more satisfactory to consider the second order effects as described by the third order coefficients in the thermodynamic potential, namely the strain energy function, and derive the non-linear stress–strain relation from it. For this reason the second order effects in elasticity are called third order effects and the corresponding coefficients third order elastic coefficients.

6.6 Effect of Symmetry on Physical Properties—Neumann's Principle

The effect of symmetry of a crystal on its physical properties can be studied by accepting Neumann's principle as the basis. Neumann's principle states that *the symmetry elements of any physical property of a crystal must include all the symmetry elements of the point group of the crystal*. This implies that any given physical property may possess a higher symmetry than that possessed by the crystal. What is mandatory is that it cannot be of a lower symmetry than that of the crystal. An alternative way of stating the same principle is that *every physical property of a crystal must possess at least the symmetry of the point group of the crystal*. A third way of stating Neumann's principle would be that *any kind of symmetry which is possessed by the crystallographic form of a material is possessed by the material in respect of every physical property*. This principle, laid down a long time ago, with an uncommon and far-reaching insight, requires to be qualified in the present context, when the magnetic crystal classes have gained recognition. Some physical properties like piezomagnetism were thought to be forbidden effects, relying on arguments which considered the conventional point group symmetries of 32 classes only. In recent times, they have been shown to be possible after recognizing the magnetic symmetry classes, and their existence has received experimental confirmation. In this context we have to understand that, in the statement of Neumann's principle, the term "point group of a crystal" means the appropriate point group, one of the 32 conventional point groups, or one of the 90 magnetic point groups, depending on the nature of the physical property under consideration.

In the case of a physical property for which an intrinsic symmetry exists, the physical property will not only acquire the symmetry of the point group of the crystal in which it is observed as dictated by Neumann's principle, but also continue to possess its intrinsic symmetry. For example, properties such as optical refraction and elasticity are inherently centrosymmetric. Such a physical property, when it is manifest in a crystal, will not only acquire the symmetry of the point group of the crystal, but also continue to be centrosymmetric. This situation sometimes results in the physical property exhibiting a higher symmetry than that possessed by the point group of the crystal.

The imposition of the condition that a physical property tensor observed in a crystal possessing a particular point group symmetry will acquire the symmetry of the crystal results in the emergence of certain relations between the various components of the physical property tensor. As pointed out above, this is in addition to the relations among the tensor components already existing as a result of the intrinsic symmetry of the physical property. This means that the number of independent components of a physical property tensor is reduced when it is subjected to the point group symmetry of a crystal. The consequence of this, from a physical point of view, is that the number of independent measurements required to be made to determine the physical property under consideration is reduced and depends on the point group symmetry of the crystal on which measurements are made. The actual set of components (or their independent linear combinations) that survive depends on the relative orientation of the crystal with respect to the coordinate system chosen to describe the physical property. However, well-accepted conventions regarding the choice of coordinate system in each case, conditioned by the aspects of interest of the physical property under consideration, have developed and there is no room for confusion due to such arbitrariness in the choice of coordinates. For instance, in the cubic, tetragonal and orthorhombic systems, the crystallographic axes are themselves chosen as the coordinate axes. In the hexagonal, rhombohedral and monoclinic systems, the principal axis of symmetry in each case is always chosen as one of the coordinate axes, often this being designated as the X_3. In the triclinic system, the choice is, however, arbitrary.

6.7 Effect of Symmetry on Physical Properties—Methods

The classical method of studying the effect of symmetry on the physical properties of a crystal, originally due to Neumann, is the following. The symmetry operations constituting the point group of the crystal are successively applied on the set of equations representing the property, and each time it is demanded that the equations should remain invariant. Certain conditions governing the relations between the various constants emerge, and arising out of these conditions, some of them vanish leaving a given number of non-vanishing and mutually independent constants for a given physical property for a crystal of certain symmetry. We shall first take up a simple example to illustrate this method and then proceed to give other methods which are more commonly in use. In the next section we shall take up some particular examples of physical properties and investigate the effect of symmetry appropriate to one crystal class in each case.

We will take the case of optical or electric polarization. This arises from a vector–vector combination, the equations representing the property being written as

$$P_1 = \alpha_{11} E_1 + \alpha_{12} E_2 + \alpha_{13} E_3$$

$$P_2 = \alpha_{21} E_1 + \alpha_{22} E_2 + \alpha_{23} E_3$$

$$P_3 = \alpha_{31} E_1 + \alpha_{32} E_2 + \alpha_{33} E_3.$$

P_1, P_2, P_3 are the components of the electric moment induced by an external electric field E whose components along the same axes are E_1, E_2, E_3.

With the condition $\alpha_{ij} = \alpha_{ji}$, etc., imposed by the intrinsic symmetry of the property, the number of constants reduces to 6. Considering an orthorhombic crystal as an example, we have the following 8 elements as the symmetry operations which must be satisfied by the physical property:

$$E \; C_2 \; C_2' \; C_2'' \; i \; \sigma_h \; \sigma_v' \; \sigma_v''.$$

E and i stand for identity and centre of inversion respectively. C_2, C_2', C_2'' are 2-fold rotations about X_1, X_2, X_3, respectively. $\sigma_h, \sigma_v', \sigma_v''$ are planes of reflection perpendicular to the same axes. Applying each of these elements to each of the above equations, and demanding that they remain invariant, it will be seen that some coefficients vanish.

For the element C_2, we have the transformation $x_1 \to x_1$; $x_2 \to -x_2$ and $x_3 \to -x_3$. It follows that $P_1 \to P_1$; $P_2 \to -P_2$ and $P_3 \to -P_3$ and $E_1 \to E_1$; $E_2 \to -E_2$ and $E_3 \to -E_3$. We replace the transformed components of P_i and E_i in the above set of equations and demand invariance. We obtain the result that this is possible only if $\alpha_{12} = \alpha_{13} = 0$. Similarly for the element C_2', $x_1 \to -x_1$; $x_2 \to x_2$ and $x_3 \to -x_3$ and α_{23} vanishes.

Consequently only the three coefficients α_{11}, α_{22} and α_{33} remain. In this particular case the operation i when performed yields no new results since the property itself possesses the element i. It will be seen that the rest of the operations will also result in the above conditions being repeated. In fact, for a given point group, only the generating elements amongst all the symmetry elements need be considered. In the above set, they are C_2, C'_2 and i. Thus we obtain that the scheme of coefficients of the optical polarization tensor appropriate to the orthorhombic class taken is given by

$$
\begin{matrix}
\alpha_{11} & 0 & 0 \\
\\
0 & \alpha_{22} & 0 \\
\\
0 & 0 & \alpha_{33}.
\end{matrix}
$$

Three independent parameters are therefore needed for describing the optical refraction of an orthorhombic crystal.

The power of the general method of treatment may to some extent be brought out here. We conclude that *for all physical properties of the vector–vector type with the intrinsic symmetry $\alpha_{ij} = \alpha_{ji}$, we need only 3 independent constants for a full description of such properties in an orthorhombic crystal.* This result has been obtained from considerations of symmetry and has no reference to the particular physical property. It follows that since all physical properties belong to one or other of the possible combinations mentioned above, the effect of symmetry on groups of properties belonging to specific types can be obtained straightaway.

The various methods used to study the effect of a given point group symmetry on a tensor are all theoretically equivalent. They differ to some extent in practical utility. Preference for one or the other is generally ascribed by the user's background. It must be stated that all the methods in essence amount to applying the coordinate transformations corresponding to the symmetry operations of the group to the tensor components and demanding invariance. To give an illustration, let us choose a second rank tensor α_{ij} subjected to point group C_2. If we effect a coordinate transformation $x'_i = a_{ij} x_j$, the tensor components transform according to equations: $\alpha'_{ij} = a_{li} a_{mj} \alpha_{lm}$. If we choose the diad axis parallel to the X_3-axis, the transformation C_2 takes the form

$$
\begin{Vmatrix} x'_1 \\ x'_2 \\ x'_3 \end{Vmatrix}
=
\begin{Vmatrix} -1 & 0 & 0 \\ 0 & -1 & 0 \\ 0 & 0 & 1 \end{Vmatrix}
\begin{Vmatrix} x_1 \\ x_2 \\ x_3 \end{Vmatrix}.
$$

We can easily determine which α_{ij}s are equal to zero under this transformation taking each tensor component in turn. For example,

$$\alpha'_{31} = a_{13}\,a_{11}\,\alpha_{11} + a_{13}\,a_{21}\,\alpha_{12} + a_{13}\,a_{31}\,\alpha_{13} + \ldots + a_{33}\,a_{11}\,\alpha_{31} + \ldots$$

in which only a_{11}, a_{22}, a_{33} are not zero for the operation C_2. Therefore $\alpha'_{31} = a_{33}\,a_{11}\,\alpha_{31} = -\alpha_{31}$. But C_2 is a symmetry operation according to the assumption and therefore $\alpha_{31} = -\alpha_{31}$. This means that the only possible value for α_{31} is zero. Proceeding in a similar way, we find that the second rank tensor when subjected to the point group symmetry C_2 has the form

$$\begin{array}{ccc} \alpha_{11} & \alpha_{12} & 0 \\ \alpha_{21} & \alpha_{22} & 0 \\ 0 & 0 & \alpha_{33}. \end{array}$$

In general, this procedure of application of a symmetry transformation leads to linear equations (as many as there are tensor components) between the transformed components (dashed) and the original components (undashed). On exhausting all the symmetry transformations appropriate to a group (in fact application of generating elements will be enough) and imposing the condition of invariance will result in certain components vanishing and some relations between the rest of the components emerging.

Fumi[†] has devised a method, which is called the "direct inspection method", by which this procedure is very much simplified. In fact, this method completely eliminates the algebraic calculations. He uses the correspondence between cartesian orthogonal tensor components and coordinate products. In the usual frames, the method can be applied to obtain directly the independent tensor components only for triclinic, monoclinic, orthorhombic, tetragonal and cubic symmetries in which the conventional coordinates do not transform into linear combinations of themselves under the symmetry operations. Symmetries C_3, S_6 and C_{3h} can be treated directly only by using somewhat peculiar frames. However, the method enables us to derive the independent components in the usual frames for all trigonal and hexagonal groups also from the corresponding components for symmetry C_3.

We shall illustrate this method here by taking the elasticity tensor c_{ijkl} subjected to the symmetry D_4. c_{ijkl} is subject to a symmetry of interchange of indices which may be given as

$$ijkl = jikl = ijlk = jilk = klij = lkji = klji = klij.$$

We shall follow the convention that we shall not list the equivalents obtained by interchanging letters in each pair ij and kl separately. The

† Fumi, F. G., *Acta cryst.* **5**, 44 (1952).

elastic constants can then be written as c_{pq} and they transform like the following products.

$$x_1 x_1 x_1 x_1, \quad x_2 x_2 x_2 x_2, \quad x_3 x_3 x_3 x_3,$$

$$x_2 x_3 x_2 x_3, \quad x_1 x_3 x_1 x_3, \quad x_1 x_2 x_1 x_2,$$

$$x_1 x_1 x_2 x_2, \quad x_1 x_1 x_3 x_3, \quad x_1 x_1 x_2 x_3,$$

$$x_1 x_1 x_1 x_3, \quad x_1 x_1 x_1 x_2, \quad x_2 x_2 x_3 x_3,$$

$$x_2 x_2 x_2 x_3, \quad x_2 x_2 x_1 x_3, \quad x_2 x_2 x_1 x_2,$$

$$x_3 x_3 x_2 x_3, \quad x_3 x_3 x_1 x_3, \quad x_3 x_3 x_1 x_2,$$

$$x_2 x_3 x_1 x_3, \quad x_2 x_3 x_1 x_2, \quad x_1 x_3 x_1 x_2.$$

The correspondence between the components of the tensor c_{ijkl} and the above products is readily seen. The operation C_2 about the X_3-axis induces the transformation

$$x_1 \to -x_1, \quad x_2 \to -x_2, \quad x_3 \to x_3.$$

Under this transformation, for example, $x_1 x_1 x_1 x_3$ becomes $-x_1 x_1 x_1 x_3$. However, since C_2 about the X_3-axis is a symmetry operation, the tensor components have to remain invariant so that we have

$$x_1 x_1 x_1 x_3 = 0.$$

Similarly, any product which contains x_3 to an odd power is zero. The 2-fold rotations about X_1- and X_2-axes similarly eliminate products with odd powers in x_1 or x_2. Thus, only the following remain after applying the three 2-fold axes:

$$x_1 x_1 x_1 x_1, \quad x_2 x_2 x_2 x_2, \quad x_3 x_3 x_3 x_3,$$

$$x_2 x_3 x_2 x_3, \quad x_1 x_3 x_1 x_3, \quad x_1 x_2 x_1 x_2,$$

$$x_1 x_1 x_2 x_2, \quad x_1 x_1 x_3 x_3, \quad x_2 x_2 x_3 x_3.$$

Next consider C_4 about the X_3-axis which is given by the transformation

$$x_1 \to x_2; \quad x_2 \to -x_1; \quad x_3 \to x_3.$$

This yields

$$x_1 x_1 x_1 x_1 = x_2 x_2 x_2 x_2; \quad x_2 x_3 x_2 x_3 = x_1 x_3 x_1 x_3; \quad x_1 x_1 x_3 x_3 = x_2 x_2 x_3 x_3$$

which are three relations among nine non-zero components, so that there are only six independent components. We need not proceed further because we have applied all the generating elements of the group. There is another way of knowing where to stop. A group theoretical method given in the next Chapter gives us in a very simple way the number of non-vanishing independent tensor components subjected to a point group symmetry. This method tells us that the number is six in the present case, and therefore we need not proceed further. In the two-suffix notation suggested above, the scheme of coefficients obtained is:

$$
\begin{matrix}
c_{11} & c_{12} & c_{13} & 0 & 0 & 0 \\
c_{12} & c_{11} & c_{13} & 0 & 0 & 0 \\
c_{13} & c_{13} & c_{33} & 0 & 0 & 0 \\
0 & 0 & 0 & c_{44} & 0 & 0 \\
0 & 0 & 0 & 0 & c_{44} & 0 \\
0 & 0 & 0 & 0 & 0 & c_{66}.
\end{matrix}
$$

Reference may be made to the original papers of Fumi[†] for details regarding the method, particularly for the techniques of handling trigonal and hexagonal groups.

6.8 Effect of Symmetry on Physical Properties—Examples

We shall now deal with some particular physical properties for illustrating the applications of Neumann's principle and to serve as examples in investigating the effect of symmetry. The case of second order elasticity, which is a second rank symmetric tensor (stress)–second rank symmetric tensor (strain) combination is a useful example. We have the system of equations, in the usual notation, as

(Stress)   (Strain)

$$\tau_1 = c_{11}\,\varepsilon_1 + c_{12}\,\varepsilon_2 + c_{13}\,\varepsilon_3 + c_{14}\,\varepsilon_4 + c_{15}\,\varepsilon_5 + c_{16}\,\varepsilon_6$$

$$\tau_2 = c_{21}\,\varepsilon_1 + c_{22}\,\varepsilon_2 + c_{23}\,\varepsilon_3 + c_{24}\,\varepsilon_4 + c_{25}\,\varepsilon_5 + c_{26}\,\varepsilon_6$$

$$\tau_3 = c_{31}\,\varepsilon_1 + c_{32}\,\varepsilon_2 + c_{33}\,\varepsilon_3 + c_{34}\,\varepsilon_4 + c_{35}\,\varepsilon_5 + c_{36}\,\varepsilon_6$$

$$\tau_4 = c_{41}\,\varepsilon_1 + c_{42}\,\varepsilon_2 + c_{43}\,\varepsilon_3 + c_{44}\,\varepsilon_4 + c_{45}\,\varepsilon_5 + c_{46}\,\varepsilon_6$$

$$\tau_5 = c_{51}\,\varepsilon_1 + c_{52}\,\varepsilon_2 + c_{53}\,\varepsilon_3 + c_{54}\,\varepsilon_4 + c_{55}\,\varepsilon_5 + c_{56}\,\varepsilon_6$$

$$\tau_6 = c_{61}\,\varepsilon_1 + c_{62}\,\varepsilon_2 + c_{63}\,\varepsilon_3 + c_{64}\,\varepsilon_4 + c_{65}\,\varepsilon_5 + c_{66}\,\varepsilon_6.$$

The notation employed is a simplified one in that the number of suffixes that are attached to the c's has been reduced from four to two. Such a notation, referred to as the two-suffix notation, will be explained more fully in Chapter 11. This does not, however, affect the arguments in any way. The intrinsic symmetry $c_{ik} = c_{ki}$ reduces the maximum number of elastic constants possible to 21. Operating with the three generating elements, we will find that 12 of them again vanish. For

[†] Fumi, F. G., *Phys. Rev.* **83**, 1274 (1951); **86**, 561 (1952).

C_2; c_{15}, c_{16}, c_{25}, c_{26}, c_{35}, c_{36}, c_{45} and c_{46} vanish, while for C_2'; c_{14}, c_{24}, c_{34} and c_{56} vanish. As in the previous case, the element i has no effect in view of the inherent symmetry of the property. Consequently, for an orthorhombic crystal, there are 9 independent constants in respect of elasticity. This again is a general result obtained mathematically and has no special reference to the individual property. We can repeat the work for a crystal of any desired symmetry. It is the application of this method which first led to the knowledge of the existence of 3 independent elastic constants for a cubic crystal. Till then, it was thought that only 2 independent elastic constants were needed for describing the behaviour of a cubic crystal.

To choose a physical property which requires the recognition of the 90 magnetic crystal classes, let us take piezomagnetism. Piezomagnetism may be defined by the equations:

$$I_i = Q_{ijk}\tau_{jk}$$

where I_i is the magnetic moment vector and τ_{jk} is the stress tensor. Q_{ijk} defines the piezomagnetic tensor. Adopting the notation in which we denote $\tau_{11}, \tau_{22}, \tau_{33}, \tau_{23} = \tau_{32}, \tau_{13} = \tau_{31}, \tau_{12} = \tau_{21}$, by $\tau_1, \tau_2, \tau_3, \tau_4, \tau_5, \tau_6$ respectively, the above equations may be written *in extenso* as:

$$I_1 = Q_{11}\tau_1 + Q_{12}\tau_2 + Q_{13}\tau_3 + Q_{14}\tau_4 + Q_{15}\tau_5 + Q_{16}\tau_6$$

$$I_2 = Q_{21}\tau_1 + Q_{22}\tau_2 + Q_{23}\tau_3 + Q_{24}\tau_4 + Q_{25}\tau_5 + Q_{26}\tau_6$$

$$I_3 = Q_{31}\tau_1 + Q_{32}\tau_2 + Q_{33}\tau_3 + Q_{34}\tau_4 + Q_{35}\tau_5 + Q_{36}\tau_6.$$

This property has been experimentally demonstrated in CoF_2 and MnF_2, two examples of antiferromagnetic crystals which belong to the magnetic class $4/mmm$, whose symmetry elements, as may be seen from Table IV, are $\bar{E}$, $2\underline{C_4}$, C_2, $2C_2'$, $2C_2''$, i, $2\underline{S_4}$, σ_h, $2\sigma_v'$ and $2\sigma_v''$. In order to understand the full significance of this result, let us first consider the crystal class with symmetry $4mmm$ (D_{4h}). The elements of this class contain C_4 and C_2' amongst others. These two along with an inversion may, in fact, be regarded as the generating elements for this group. The application of C_4, which we may regard as being parallel to the X_3-axis according to the usual convention, may easily be seen to induce the following transformation in the axes:

$$C_4: \quad 1 \to 2; \quad 2 \to -1; \quad 3 \to 3.$$

From this we can conclude that 11 of the 18 Q's, namely Q_{11}, Q_{22}, Q_{12}, Q_{21}, Q_{13}, Q_{23}, Q_{16}, Q_{26}, Q_{34}, Q_{35} and Q_{36}, vanish and further that the relations $Q_{14} = -Q_{25}$, $Q_{15} = Q_{24}$, $Q_{31} = Q_{32}$ should hold good with Q_{33}

also not vanishing. C_2' is a 2-fold axis in the $X_1 X_2$-plane and we may choose it so as to induce the following transformation in the axes:

$$C_2': \quad 1 \to 2; \quad 2 \to 1; \quad 3 \to -3.$$

From this we can conclude that the additional relations $Q_{15} = -Q_{24}$, $Q_{31} = -Q_{32}$ and $Q_{33} = 0$ should hold good. Inversion introduces no new relationships. Thus, for this group all but Q_{14} and Q_{25} of the piezomagnetic tensor components vanish and $Q_{14} = -Q_{25}$, i.e. only one independent constant survives.

On the other hand, the group $\underline{4}/mm\underline{m}$ appropriate to CoF_2 and MnF_2 is a magnetic variant of $4/mmm$ and has symmetry elements enumerated above. Remembering that the application of a complementary symmetry operation on a physical property tensor which is magnetic is effected by a multiplication of all the elements of the transformation matrix of the physical property tensor corresponding to the ordinary symmetry operation by -1, we can proceed exactly in a manner similar to the previous example. We find for similar reasons as before that all Q_{ij} vanish except Q_{14}, Q_{25} and Q_{36}. Moreover, the presence of a complementary operation of $\underline{C_4}$ results in Q_{14} becoming equal to Q_{25} and not $-Q_{25}$, i.e. piezomagnetism tensor possesses 2 independent non-vanishing coefficients in crystals belonging to the class $\underline{4}/mm\underline{m}$. These results may also be obtained directly from the Tables given later in Section 15.5. Thus if the magnetic symmetry is not taken into account, crystals which fall in the same class (according to the classical notions of symmetry) would have shown different behaviour with respect to the property of piezomagnetism. These two cases furnish clear and unequivocal experimental evidence in favour of the need to recognize magnetic symmetry and magnetic point groups.

6.9 Physical Properties which Cannot Be Represented by Tensors

Sometimes, such as when there are hysteresis effects, the physical behaviour of a material becomes complicated. Under those conditions, the previous history of the specimen that is being studied becomes important. The relation between the physical quantities which pertains to the chosen physical property is no longer unique and this fact prevents such a property from being represented by a tensor.

A simple example of a system exhibiting hysteresis is the behaviour of a ferromagnetic material under the influence of an external magnetic field. The magnetic moment exhibited by the material depends on its previous history and the relationship between the influence and the effect, the magnetic field and the magnetic induction in the present example, is not unique. Although under such circumstances it becomes difficult to uniquely define a physical property of the material, certain parameters partially characterizing the influence–effect relationship can be specified. A set of such parameters either relate to specific situations like the saturation point, the point at which the influence becomes zero and so on or relate to quantities like the area of the hysteresis loop, the slope of the steep portion of the hysteresis curve and so on. These parameters, however, vary with direction in the crystal conforming to the symmetry of the crystal. They are not amenable to the general treatment which forms the subject matter of this treatise.

There is still another category of properties which cannot be brought under the formalism we are developing, i.e. as unique influence–effect relationships. They are properties like hardness, ductility, etc. These properties are defined by prescribing some test to be performed on the material. The quantitative values assigned to materials by the test only serve to rank them with respect to the property on a scale. As an example, we may mention Mohs' hardness scale. The scale ranging from 1 to 10 is based on ten particular minerals each of which will scratch all those of lower number but conversely is not scratched by them. The list of minerals starts with talc which is assigned the value 1 and ends with diamond which is assigned the value 10. There are other kinds of tests prescribed to measure hardness which result in a different assignment of numerical values. Similarly, there are different criteria to measure ductility. There is one feature common to all such properties. They are all defined by tests which permanently alter the test specimen in some manner. Properties of this kind are not defined in a precise sense, but conform in a general way to the anisotropy of the crystal on which they are measured. Obviously, they are not amenable to the treatment we are following in this book.

CHAPTER 7

Group Theoretical Method

7.1 Introduction

The group theoretical method described in the present Chapter is mainly used for obtaining the number of non-vanishing independent components a physical property tensor possesses when subjected to a given point group symmetry. The method was originally developed by the author† with particular reference to photoelasticity. It was later extended to other physical properties. In this method, each symmetry group in respect of a given physical property is treated separately. Juretschke‡ has used group theory to derive the surviving schemes of tensor components as well. However, the main power of the group theoretical method lies in giving the number of independent components by an almost mechanical application of a simple formula. This procedure has the merit of rarely going wrong. Experience has shown that this can serve as a useful check on the results obtained by longer methods. Also, a knowledge of the number of non-vanishing independent components of a physical property is itself quite useful in considering the physical properties of crystals, particularly those possessing higher symmetries.

Jahn§ has suggested a way of avoiding the character calculations by reducing the polar or axial tensor representation of the full rotation group through formulae for the symmetrical products of representations. He comes to the group of interest through correlation tables.

7.2 Procedure Based on Group Theory

Let us consider a physical property represented by a tensor of appropriate rank and kind subjected to the point group symmetry of a crystal. The matrices of the symmetry operations of the crystal form an orthogonal three-dimensional matrix representation of the appropriate point group. Each of the components of the physical property tensor is transformed into linear combinations of all the components, under the symmetry transformations of the crystal.

† Bhagavantam, S., *Proc. Indian Acad. Sci.* **16**, 359 (1942).
‡ Juretschke, H. J., Lecture Notes, Polytechnic Institute of Brooklyn (1951).
§ Jahn, H. A. *Acta cryst.* **2**, 30 (1949).

The matrices of the transformation of the tensor components also form a many-dimensional matrix representation of the same group. For the sake of convenience, we shall refer to such a representation as the tensor representation, or as the representation formed by the tensor. The tensor components may be regarded as components of a vector of many dimensions. The many-dimensional representation is reducible and the reduction can be effected by a non-singular linear transformation of the tensor components. This means that the transformed tensor components, i.e. linear combinations of the tensor components in the original coordinate system, fall into small sets of one, two or three such that the components that belong to a set combine among themselves only in all the transformations of the tensor corresponding to the symmetry operations of the crystal.

If the tensor components are to describe a physical property of a crystal, they must preserve the same numerical value or remain invariant under all symmetry transformations of the crystal. This condition applies to their linear combinations as well. Therefore, only those linear combinations of the tensor components which remain invariant under all the symmetry transformations of the crystal can have non-vanishing numerical values. All the other linear combinations must vanish identically. This is the only way to ensure that they retain the same value under all the symmetry transformations, no matter how they transform among themselves.

If a tensor component or a linear combination of them is invariant under all the symmetry transformations, it means that the matrix of its transformation is just the number unity which can be considered as a matrix of dimension one. Each such invariant linear combination thus generates the total symmetric representation. It follows that the number of non-vanishing components of a tensor subject to the point group symmetry of a crystal is equal to the number of times the total symmetric irreducible representation occurs in the reducible representation formed by the transformation matrices of the tensor components corresponding to the symmetry transformations of the point group.

This number is computed by using formula (1). This formula has already been given in Section 4.7.

$$n_i = \frac{1}{N} \sum_\rho h_\rho \chi_\rho(R) \chi_i(R). \tag{1}$$

In the above formula, n_i is the number of times the irreducible representation Γ_i occurs in a representation Γ of a group G of order N. G is the point group of the crystal and Γ is the tensor representation under consideration. h_ρ is the order of the ρth class and R is the symmetry element belonging to that class. $\chi_i(R)$ is the character of the element R belonging to the ρth class in the representation Γ_i. It has been shown that all elements in the same class have the same character. Γ_i in the present problem is the total symmetric irreducible representation and therefore $\chi_i(R)$ is simply equal to 1 for all R.

We can thus find n_i if we know $\chi_\rho(R)$. Evaluation of $\chi_\rho(R)$ is straightforward in simple cases. The transformations of tensors under the symmetry transformations appropriate to the point group are written down and the character for each R is calculated. In fact, the transformation properties of tensors of various ranks and intrinsic symmetries under a rotation or a rotation-reflection through an arbitrary angle ϕ can be worked out and general expressions for the characters can be written down. From these general expressions, the characters of particular symmetry transformations are evaluated on substituting appropriate values for ϕ. For example, under a transformation R consisting of a rotation about the X_3-axis through ϕ or a rotation-reflection through ϕ, the components of a vector, a symmetric tensor and a general tensor transform according to equations (2), (3) and (4) respectively. The upper and lower signs, where an alternative occurs, refer respectively to a pure rotation and a rotation-reflection.

$$p_1' = p_1 \cos\phi + p_2 \sin\phi$$
$$p_2' = -p_1 \sin\phi + p_2 \cos\phi$$
$$p_3' = \pm p_3. \tag{2}$$

$$a_{11}' = a_{11}\cos^2\phi + a_{22}\sin^2\phi + 2a_{12}\sin\phi\cos\phi$$
$$a_{22}' = a_{11}\sin^2\phi + a_{22}\cos^2\phi - 2a_{12}\sin\phi\cos\phi$$
$$a_{33}' = a_{33}$$
$$a_{23}' = \pm a_{23}\cos\phi \mp a_{31}\sin\phi$$
$$a_{31}' = \pm a_{23}\sin\phi \pm a_{31}\cos\phi$$
$$a_{12}' = -a_{11}\sin\phi\cos\phi + a_{32}\sin\phi\cos\phi + a_{12}(\cos^2\phi - \sin^2\phi). \tag{3}$$

$$b_{11}' = b_{11}\cos^2\phi + b_{22}\sin^2\phi + (b_{12}+b_{21})\sin\phi\cos\phi$$
$$b_{22}' = b_{11}\sin^2\phi + b_{22}\cos^2\phi - (b_{12}+b_{21})\sin\phi\cos\phi$$
$$b_{33}' = b_{33}$$
$$b_{23}' = \mp b_{13}\sin\phi \pm b_{23}\cos\phi$$
$$b_{32}' = \mp b_{31}\sin\phi \pm b_{32}\cos\phi$$
$$b_{31}' = \pm b_{31}\cos\phi \pm b_{32}\sin\phi$$
$$b_{13}' = \pm b_{13}\cos\phi \pm b_{23}\sin\phi$$
$$b_{12}' = -b_{11}\sin\phi\cos\phi + b_{22}\sin\phi\cos\phi + b_{12}\cos^2\phi - b_{21}\sin^2\phi$$
$$b_{21}' = -b_{11}\sin\phi\cos\phi + b_{22}\sin\phi\cos\phi - b_{12}\sin^2\phi + b_{21}\cos^2\phi. \tag{4}$$

The characters of the three transformation matrices of (2), (3) and (4) are easily seen to be respectively

$$(2 \cos \phi \pm 1); \quad (4 \cos^2 \phi \pm 2 \cos \phi); \quad (4 \cos^2 \phi \pm 4 \cos \phi + 1)$$

with the same understanding as before about alternative signs when they occur. Similarly, the transformation matrix and the respective character for tensors of higher order representing any physical property can be deduced.

To obtain the characters in axial tensor representations, we have to multiply all the transformation coefficients in equations (2), (3) and (4) by -1 when the transformation is a rotation-reflection. Thus, in axial vector representation, an operation R has the character $(\pm 2 \cos \phi + 1)$ with the same understanding about the alternative signs. The characters in axial tensor representations of higher rank are derived in the same manner.

The representation formed by higher rank tensors can be interpreted as a Kronecker product or power of simpler representations and the characters can be computed using formulae given in Chapter 3. For example, the character for a polar tensor having 9 components is the square of the character for the polar vector of 3 components. This interpretation finds great use in evaluating expressions for characters in representations formed by tensors of higher ranks. A physical property tensor as pointed out describes a relation between two physical quantity tensors. Such a relation, according to equation (1) of Chapter 6, can be written as

$$A_{ijk\ldots} = a_{ijk\ldots lmn\ldots} B_{lmn\ldots}$$

where, if the physical quantity tensors $A_{ijk\ldots}$ and $B_{lmn\ldots}$ are of ranks p and q, respectively, the physical property tensor $a_{ijk\ldots lmn\ldots}$ is of rank $(p+q)$. The tensor $a_{ijk\ldots lmn\ldots}$ acquires the intrinsic symmetry of the tensor $A_{ijk\ldots}$ with respect to suffixes $ijk\ldots$ and the intrinsic symmetry of the tensor $B_{lmn\ldots}$ with respect to suffixes $lmn\ldots$. It may possess some more intrinsic symmetry depending on the physical property it represents. In case the tensor $a_{ijk\ldots lmn\ldots}$ does not possess any extra intrinsic symmetry besides that acquired from $A_{ijk\ldots}$ and $B_{lmn\ldots}$, the representation formed by it is the same as the Kronecker product of the two representations of the same group formed by $A_{ijk\ldots}$ and $B_{lmn\ldots}$. The characters in the product representation are shown to be equal to the product of the characters in the factor representations. Thus if we happen to know the characters in the representations formed by $A_{ijk\ldots}$ and $B_{lmn\ldots}$ we can find the characters in the representation formed by $a_{ijk\ldots lmn\ldots}$. This rule is again very helpful in evaluating the characters in representations formed by tensors of high rank from a knowledge of characters in representations formed by tensors of lower rank.

In case the physical property tensor has some more intrinsic symmetry than that acquired from the physical quantity tensors, the straight-forward though laborious method would be to write down the trans-formations and compute the characters. A formula given later in this Chapter enables one to calculate $\chi_\rho(R)$ taking the intrinsic symmetry into account.

When the tensor is representing a magnetic property observed in a crystal of a given magnetic point group symmetry, the character $\chi_\rho(R)$ is found in the following way. Magnetic field is an axial vector and under an ordinary symmetry operation, the character of an operation is found in the manner given above. Under a complementary operation, the magnetic field, which can be viewed as the result of an electric current, will get reversed. Therefore, the transformation of a magnetic tensor appropriate to a complementary operation would be obtained by multiplying all the coefficients of the transformation of the tensor due to the corresponding ordinary operation throughout by -1. That is, the transformation matrix of a magnetic tensor due to a complemen-tary operation is obtained from its transformation matrix due to the corresponding ordinary operation by multiplying its elements by -1. It follows that the character of a complementary symmetry operation in the representation formed by a magnetic field is $-(\pm 2\cos\phi + 1)$, the alternative sign having the same interpretation as before.

The representations formed by magnetic property tensors of higher ranks are interpreted as direct products of vector representations of suitable kind, some of which are vectors which transform like the magnetic field. This interpretation evidently depends on the property under consideration. Using the result that the character of a symmetry operation (ordinary or complementary) in a direct product representa-tion is the product of characters in the factor representations, the character $\chi_\rho(R)$ in the representation under consideration is obtained. We may choose the property of piezomagnetism again for illustration. This is defined by relations

$$I_i = Q_{ijk}\tau_{jk}$$

where I_i is the magnetic moment vector, τ_{jk} is the stress tensor and Q_{ijk} is the piezomagnetism tensor. I_i is an axial vector and transforms like H_i. τ_{jk} is a second rank symmetric tensor. The character of an ordinary operation R in the representation formed by Q_{ijk} is $(1 \pm 2\cos\phi)(4\cos^2\phi \pm 2\cos\phi)$ with the same convention as hitherto for signs and the character of a complementary operation $\underline{R}$ is

$-(1 \pm 2\cos\phi)(4\cos^2\phi \pm 2\cos\phi)$. It is readily seen that these results are obtained by forming the products of the individual characters.

A general result is apparent. For physical properties which involve an even Kronecker power of the magnetic vector, the transformation of the property tensor for a complementary operation is identical with that for the corresponding ordinary operation. It follows that such a property cannot distinguish the magnetic classes from the classical ones, and we need consider only the classical 32 classes even though the crystal has a magnetic structure. A simple example is furnished by the property of magnetostriction which relates strain to the square of the magnetic field. Since the magnetic field occurs in an even power, we need consider only the 32 conventional crystal classes while studying the property of magnetostriction.

As in the case of ordinary properties, in magnetic properties as well, when special relations exist between various components, that is, when there is intrinsic symmetry in the tensor, the character has ordinarily to be deduced by writing down the full transformation matrix itself. These characters have been worked out and are given in Tables VII(a) and VII(b). The expressions are presented in such a form that they bring out the rule relating to product transformations.

Let us consider some specific examples to illustrate the method. In Chapter 6 we dealt with the case of optical polarization in an orthorhombic crystal and arrived at the result by the direct method that such a crystal needs 3 independent coefficients in respect of this property. We shall now take up the same property and the same orthorhombic crystal and apply the group theoretical method. The optical polarization is a second rank symmetric tensor for which

$$\chi_\rho(R) = 4\cos^2\phi \pm 2\cos\phi.$$

This may be evaluated as $6, 2, 2, 2, 6, 2, 2, 2$, respectively, for each of the symmetry operations. It may be noted that $h_\rho = 1$ in this case for all "classes". In regard to such a crystal, we therefore have

$$n_i = \tfrac{1}{8}(6+2+2+2+6+2+2+2) = 3.$$

This means, as before, that 3 independent coefficients are needed for describing the optical refraction of an orthorhombic crystal.

Taking the example of second order elasticity and the orthorhombic crystal again, we have

$$\chi_\rho(R) = 16\cos^4\phi \pm 8\cos^3\phi - 4\cos^2\phi + 1.$$

TABLE VII(a)

Classification of physical properties

No.	Physical property represents relation between	Character $\chi_\rho(R)$ ($c = \cos\phi$)	Maximum no. of constants	Physical property
1	Scalar and scalar	1	1	Density
2	Scalar and vector	$2c \pm 1$	3	Pyroelectricity; production of charges by hydrostatic pressure
3	Scalar and symmetric tensor same as vector and vector ($c_{ik} = c_{ki}$)	$4c^2 \pm 2c$	6	Thermal expansion; optical, dielectric and (dia- and para-) magnetic polarization; thermal and electrical conductivities
4	Scalar and unsymmetric tensor same as vector and vector	$(2c \pm 1)^2$	9	—
5	Vector and symmetric tensor	$(2c \pm 1)(4c^2 \pm 2c)$	18	Piezoelectricity; electro-optical Kerr effect
6	Vector and unsymmetric tensor	$(2c \pm 1)(2c \pm 1)^2$	27	—
7	Symmetric tensor and symmetric tensor ($c_{ik} = c_{ki}$)	$16c^4 \pm 8c^3 - 4c^2 + 1$	21	Elasticity
8	Symmetric tensor and symmetric tensor	$(4c^2 \pm 2c)^2$	36	Photoelasticity; effect of pressure on electrical conductivity
9	Symmetric tensor and unsymmetric tensor	$(4c^2 \pm 2c)(2c \pm 1)^2$	54	—
10	Unsymmetric tensor and unsymmetric tensor	$(2c \pm 1)^2 (2c \pm 1)^2$	81	—
11	Vector and square of symmetric tensor ($c_{ik} = c_{ki}$)	$(2c \pm 1)(16c^4 \pm 8c^3 - 4c^2 + 1)$	63	Piezoelectric coefficients
12	Symmetric tensor and square of symmetric tensor ($c_{ikl} = c_{kli} = c_{lik}$, etc.)	$64c^6 \pm 32c^5 - 48c^4 \mp 8c^3 + 16c^2$	56	Elastic coefficients
13	Symmetric tensor and square of symmetric tensor ($c_{ik} = c_{ki}$)	$(4c^2 \pm 2c)(16c^4 \pm 8c^3 - 4c^2 + 1)$	126	Photoelastic coefficients

TABLE VII(b)

Classification of physical properties

No.	Physical property represents relation between	Character $\chi_\rho(R)$ ($c = \cos\phi$)	Maximum no. of constants	Physical property
1	Vector and vector ($\rho_{ik}^\circ = \rho_{ki}^\circ$)	$4c^2 \pm 2c$	6	Electrical resistivity, thermal conductivity
2	Second rank antisymmetric tensor and axial vector same as axial vector and axial vector ($\rho_{ikl} = -\rho_{kil}$)	$4c^2 \pm 4c + 1$	9	Hall effect, Leduc–Righi effect
3	Second rank general tensor and axial vector	$(4c^2 + 4c + 1)(1 \pm 2c)$	27	Nernst effect, Ettingshausen effect
4	Second rank symmetric tensor and second rank symmetric tensor	$(4c^2 \pm 2c)(4c^2 \pm 2c)$	36	Magnetoresistance, magneto-thermal conductivity, piezo-resistance
5	Second rank general tensor and second rank symmetric tensor	$(4c^2 \pm 4c + 1)(4c^2 \pm 2c)$	54	Magnetothermoelectric power, Piezo–Hall effect
6	Axial vector and totally symmetric third rank tensor ($\rho_{iklm} = -\rho_{kilm}$ for all permutations of lmn)	$(1 \pm 2c)(\pm 8c^3 + 4c^2 \mp 2c)$	30	Second order Hall effect, second order Leduc–Righi effect
7	Second rank symmetric tensor and a totally symmetric fourth rank tensor ($\rho_{iklmn} = \rho_{kitmnp}$ for all permutations of $lmnp$)	$(4c^2 \pm 2c) \times (16c^4 \pm 8c^3 - 8c^2 \mp 2c + 1)$	90	Second order magnetoresistance, second order magnetothermal conductivity
8	Second rank general tensor and a totally symmetric third rank tensor (ρ_{iktmn} remains the same for all permutations of lmn)	$(4c^2 \pm 4c + 1) \times (\pm 8c^3 + 4c^2 \mp 2c)$	90	Second order Nernst effect, second order Ettingshausen effect
9	Second rank general tensor and a totally symmetric fourth rank tensor (ρ_{iktmnp} remains the same for all permutations of $lmnp$)	$(4c^2 \pm 4c + 1) \times (16c^4 \pm 8c^3 - 8c^2 \mp 2c + 1)$	135	Second order magnetothermo-electric power
10	Second rank symmetric tensor and a fourth rank tensor of the type No. 4	$(4c^2 \pm 2c) \times (16c^4 \pm 16c^3 + 4c^2)$	216	Piezomagnetoresistance

TABLE VII(c)

Classification of physical properties

No.	Physical property represents relation between	Character ($c = \cos\phi$)		Maximum no. of constants	Physical property
		$\chi_\rho(R)$	$\chi_\rho(\underline{R})$		
1	Magnetic axial vector and scalar	$(1 \pm 2c)$	$-(1 \pm 2c)$	3	Pyromagnetism
2	Magnetic axial vector and polar vector	$(1 \pm 2c)\,(\pm 1 + 2c)$	$-(1 \pm 2c)\,(\pm 1 + 2c)$	9	Magnetoelectric polarizability
3	Magnetic axial vector and polar second rank symmetric tensor	$(1 \pm 2c)\,(4c^2 \pm 2c)$	$-(1 \pm 2c)\,(4c^2 \pm 2c)$	18	Piezomagnetism

After evaluating the same as $21, 5, 5, 5, 21, 5, 5, 5$, respectively, for each of the symmetry operations,

$$n_i = \tfrac{1}{8}(21 + 5 + 5 + 5 + 21 + 5 + 5 + 5) = 9.$$

Consequently, for an orthorhombic crystal, we conclude that there are 9 independent constants in respect of elasticity. This agrees with the result deduced directly.

Physical properties like enantiomorphism and optical activity which are represented respectively by a pseudo scalar and an axial tensor can be dealt with by the same method, taking proper account of their special transformation properties.

7.3 Results in Respect of all Crystal Classes

In Table VIII(a), the numbers of independent constants that are needed for each of the 32 classes in a group of physical properties arising out of different combinations are given. Numbers 1 to 13 at the head of each column in this Table correspond with the same numbers in front of each row in Table VII(a) and this correspondence enables the particular physical property to be identified. For instance, the numbers in the column headed by 7 pertain to elasticity and so on. Columns 11, 12 and 13 pertain to higher order piezoelectricity, elasticity and photo-elasticity, respectively. Table VIII(b) gives results in respect of a group of galvanomagnetic properties and is related to Table VII(b) in the same manner as Tables VIII(a) and VII(a) are related.

Particular attention may be drawn to the numbers under column 8 of Table VIII(a). These are applicable to physical properties, an example of which is photoelasticity. When the results in respect of this property were originally obtained by Pockels, mistakes were made in 10 out of the 32 classes. These are C_3, C_{3i}, C_4, S_4, C_{4h}, C_{3h}, C_6, C_{6h}, T and T_h. T and T_h belong to the cubic system and will be dealt with more fully in Chapter 16.

Two additional columns for enantiomorphism and optical activity are added to Table VIII(a). Although these are of the axial type as has already been pointed out, they are included in this Table so as not to mix them up with the galvanomagnetic properties listed separately in Table VIII(b). The results in respect of magnetic properties in magnetic structures are listed in Table IX.

At this stage we may note that certain general results are apparent. Physical properties represented by polar tensors of odd rank and by axial tensors of even rank vanish or are forbidden in all crystal classes exhibiting a centre of inversion. The pyroelectric effect is one such property as it is represented by a polar tensor of rank one. This, as well as all other similar physical properties, can exist only in 10 of the 32 classes as may be seen from column 2 of Table VIII(a).

To give another illustration, we may refer to relation (3) of Chapter 6. Since refractive index is the square root of dielectric permittivity, it depends on the field E exactly in the same manner as the latter. It can be concluded that centrosymmetric crystals cannot exhibit the optical effects represented by the coefficients of odd powers in the series

TABLE VIII(a)

Number of coefficients in each of the 32 crystal classes

Class symbol	1	2	3	4	5	6	7	8	9	10	11	12	13	En.	Op.	A.
1	1	3	6	9	18	27	21	36	54	81	63	56	126	1		6
$\bar{1}$	1	0	6	9	0	0	21	36	54	81	0	56	126	0		0
m	1	2	4	5	10	14	13	20	28	41	34	32	68	0		2
2	1	1	4	5	8	13	13	20	28	41	29	32	68	1		4
$2/m$	1	0	4	5	0	0	13	20	28	41	0	32	68	0		0
$2mm$	1	1	3	3	5	7	9	12	15	21	17	20	39	0		1
222	1	0	3	3	3	6	9	12	15	21	12	20	39	1		3
mmm	1	0	3	3	0	0	9	12	15	21	0	20	39	0		0
4	1	1	2	3	4	7	7	10	14	21	15	16	34	1		2
$\bar{4}$	1	0	2	3	4	6	7	10	14	21	14	16	34	0		2
$4/m$	1	0	2	3	0	0	7	10	14	21	0	16	34	0		0
$4mm$	1	1	2	2	3	4	6	7	8	11	10	12	22	0		0
$\bar{4}2m$	1	0	2	2	2	3	6	7	8	11	7	12	22	0		1
422	1	0	2	2	1	3	6	7	8	11	5	12	22	1		2
$4/mmm$	1	0	2	2	0	0	6	7	8	11	0	12	22	0		0
3	1	1	2	3	6	9	7	12	18	27	21	20	42	1		2
$\bar{3}$	1	0	2	3	0	0	7	12	18	27	0	20	42	0		0
$3m$	1	1	2	2	4	5	6	8	10	14	13	14	26	0		0
32	1	0	2	2	2	4	6	8	10	14	8	14	26	1		2
$\bar{3}m$	1	0	2	2	0	0	6	8	10	14	0	14	26	0		0
$\bar{6}$	1	0	2	3	2	2	5	8	12	19	10	12	24	0		0
6	1	1	2	3	4	7	5	8	12	19	11	12	24	1		2
$6/m$	1	0	2	3	0	0	5	8	12	19	0	12	24	0		0
$\bar{6}m2$	1	0	2	2	1	1	5	6	7	10	5	10	17	0		0
$6mm$	1	1	2	2	3	4	5	6	7	10	8	10	17	0		0
622	1	0	2	2	1	3	5	6	7	10	3	10	17	1		2
$6/mmm$	1	0	2	2	0	0	5	6	7	10	0	10	17	0		0
23	1	0	1	1	1	2	3	4	5	7	4	8	13	1		1
$m3$	1	0	1	1	0	0	3	4	5	7	0	8	13	0		0
$\bar{4}3m$	1	0	1	1	1	1	3	3	3	4	3	6	9	0		0
432	1	0	1	1	0	1	3	3	3	4	1	6	9	1		1
$m3m$	1	0	1	1	0	0	3	3	3	4	0	6	9	0		0

TABLE VIII(b)

Number of coefficients in each of the 32 crystal classes

Class symbol	Property No.									
	1	2	3	4	5	6	7	8	9	10
$1, \bar{1}$	6	9	27	36	54	30	90	90	135	216
$m, 2, 2/m$	4	5	13	20	28	16	48	44	69	112
$2mm, 222, mmm$	3	3	6	12	15	9	27	21	36	60
$4, \bar{4}, 4/m$	2	3	7	10	14	8	24	22	35	56
$4mm, \bar{4}2m, 422, 4/mmm$	2	2	3	7	8	5	15	10	19	32
$3, \bar{3}$	2	3	9	12	18	10	30	30	45	72
$3m, 32, \bar{3}m$	2	2	4	8	10	6	18	14	24	40
$\bar{6}, 6, 6/m$	2	3	7	8	12	6	16	16	23	40
$\bar{6}m2, 6mm, 622, 6/mmm$	2	2	3	6	7	4	11	7	13	24
$23, m3$	1	1	2	4	5	3	9	7	12	20
$\bar{4}3m, 432, m3m$	1	1	1	3	3	2	6	4	7	12

TABLE VIII(c)

Number of coefficients in each of the 90 magnetic crystal classes

No.	Class symbol	No. of independent constants		
		Pyro-magnetism	Magneto-electric polarizability	Piezo-magnetism
1	1	3	9	18
2	$\bar{1}$	3	0	18
3	$\underline{\bar{1}}$	0	9	0
4	m	1	4	8
5	$\underline{m}$	2	5	10
6	2	1	5	8
7	$\underline{2}$	2	4	10
8	$2/m$	1	0	8
9	$2/m$	0	4	0
10	$2/\underline{m}$	0	5	0
11	$\underline{2/m}$	2	0	10
12	$2mm$	0	2	3
13	$\underline{2mm}$	1	2	5
14	$\underline{2mm}$	1	3	5
15	222	0	3	3

TABLE VIII(c) (*continued*)

No.	Class symbol	No. of independent constants		
		Pyro-magnetism	Magneto-electric polarizability	Piezo-magnetism
16	222	1	2	5
17	mmm	0	0	3
18	mmm	0	2	0
19	mmm	0	3	0
20	mmm	1	0	5
21	4	1	3	4
22	4	0	2	4
23	$\bar{4}$	1	2	4
24	$\bar{4}$	0	3	4
25	4/m	1	0	4
26	4/m	0	2	0
27	4/m	0	3	0
28	4/m	0	0	4
29	4mm	0	1	1
30	4mm	1	2	3
31	4mm	0	1	2
32	$\bar{4}2m$	0	1	1
33	$\bar{4}2m$	0	2	2
34	$\bar{4}2m$	0	1	2
35	$\bar{4}2m$	1	1	3
36	422	0	2	1
37	422	1	1	3
38	422	0	1	2
39	4/mmm	0	0	1
40	4/mmm	0	1	0
41	4/mmm	0	1	0
42	4/mmm	1	0	3
43	4/mmm	0	2	0
44	4/mmm	0	0	2
45	3	1	3	6
46	$\bar{3}$	1	0	6

TABLE VIII(c) (*continued.*)

No.	Class symbol	No. of independent constants		
		Pyro-magnetism	Magneto-electric polarizability	Piezo-magnetism
47	$\bar{3}$	0	3	0
48	$3m$	0	1	2
49	$3\underline{m}$	1	2	4
50	32	0	2	2
51	$3\underline{2}$	1	1	4
52	$\bar{3}m$	0	0	2
53	$\bar{3}\underline{m}$	1	0	4
54	$\underline{\bar{3}}m$	0	1	0
55	$\underline{\bar{3}m}$	0	2	0
56	$\bar{6}$	1	0	4
57	$\underline{\bar{6}}$	0	3	2
58	6	1	3	4
59	$\underline{6}$	0	0	2
60	$6/m$	1	0	4
61	$6/\underline{m}$	0	3	0
62	$\underline{6}/m$	0	0	0
63	$\underline{6/m}$	0	0	2
64	$\bar{6}m2$	0	0	1
65	$\bar{6}\underline{m}2$	1	0	3
66	$\underline{\bar{6}m}2$	0	1	1
67	$\underline{\bar{6}m2}$	0	2	1
68	$6mm$	0	1	1
69	$6\underline{mm}$	1	2	3
70	$\underline{6mm}$	0	0	1
71	622	0	2	1
72	$6\underline{22}$	1	1	3
73	$\underline{622}$	0	0	1
74	$6/mmm$	0	0	1
75	$6/m\underline{mm}$	0	1	0
76	$6/\underline{mm}m$	1	0	3
77	$6/\underline{mmm}$	0	2	0

TABLE VIII(c) (*concluded*)

No.	Class symbol	No. of independent constants		
		Pyro-magnetism	Magneto-electric polarizability	Piezo-magnetism
78	6/mmm	0	0	0
79	6/mmm	0	0	1
80	23	0	1	1
81	m3	0	0	1
82	m3	0	1	0
83	43m	0	0	0
84	43m	0	1	1
85	432	0	1	0
86	432	0	0	1
87	m3m	0	0	0
88	m3m	0	1	0
89	m3m	0	0	1
90	m3m	0	0	0

expansion and in particular the electro-optical effect represented by the first order term. The even power effects, however, can exist in centrosymmetric classes and in the present case they represent the Kerr effect. A point to be noted here is that in some crystals, it is possible for the higher order effects to exist even when the lower order effects are forbidden.

To give an example represented by an even rank axial tensor, we may mention the gyration tensor which represents the property of optical activity. The gyration tensor is a second rank axial tensor and, as is evident from the last column of Table VIII(a), the corresponding property of optical activity is forbidden in all the centrosymmetric classes.

In Table VII(c) are listed some magnetic properties and the appropriate tensors that represent them. The characters of conventional and complementary symmetry operations in the relevant tensor representation are also given. The numbers of independent constants needed to describe these properties in each of the 90 magnetic classes are given in Table VIII(c). In Tables VII(a), VII(b) and VII(c) $\pm$ is to be taken according as the symmetry operation R is a pure rotation or a rotation-reflection respectively.

7.4 A Formula for $\chi_\rho(R)$

The intrinsic symmetry of a physical property tensor $c_{ijk...}$ manifests itself as either the invariance or a change of sign of the tensor under certain permutations of its indices. The set of all such permutations evidently forms a permutation group which we shall denote by P. If the physical property represented by $c_{ijk...}$, which is invariant under a given group of permutations of its indices denoted by P, is observed in a crystal of point group G, the character $\chi_\rho(R)$ of an element R belonging to the ρth class in G is given by Lyubarskii[†] as

$$\chi_\rho(R) = \frac{1}{N_p} \Sigma \chi(R^m) \chi(R^n) \dots \chi(R^p). \tag{5}$$

In equation (5), N_p is the order of the group P, $\chi(R)$ is the character of R in the vector representation of the group G, i.e. $(2\cos\phi \pm 1)$ or $(\pm 2\cos\phi + 1)$, while $m, n, \dots, p$ are the cycle lengths of the permutations in P. The summation extends over all the elements in P.

We may note that the elements in a permutation group P may be odd or even according as the number of interchanges in the element under consideration is odd or even. If the tensor remains invariant under even permutations of P and changes sign under odd permutations of P, the above formula becomes (6).

$$\chi_\rho(R) = \frac{1}{N_p} \Sigma \pm \chi(R^m) \chi(R^n) \dots \chi(R^p). \tag{6}$$

We use the $\pm$ sign according as the permutation is even or odd. To illustrate the use of the above formulae, let us consider the tensor σ_{ij} which is symmetric with respect to its indices i, j. The group P consists of the two permutations $(1)(2)$ and (12). In this case, formula (5) takes the following form:

$$\chi_\rho(R) = \tfrac{1}{2}\{\chi(R) \cdot \chi(R) + \chi(R^2)\}$$
$$= \tfrac{1}{2}\{(2\cos\phi \pm 1)^2 + (2\cos 2\phi + 1)\} = 4\cos^2\phi \pm 2\cos\phi.$$

That $\chi_\rho(R) = 4\cos^2\phi \pm 2\cos\phi$ is a result already obtained earlier in this Chapter. If the tensor σ_{ij} is antisymmetric with respect to its indices i, j, that is $\sigma_{ij} = -\sigma_{ji}$, the group P again consists of the two permutations $(1)(2)$ and (12). In this case, formula (6) takes the following form:

$$\chi_\rho(R) = \tfrac{1}{2}\{\chi^2(R) - \chi(R^2)\}$$
$$= \tfrac{1}{2}\{(2\cos\phi \pm 1)^2 - (2\cos 2\phi + 1)\} = (\pm 2\cos\phi - 1).$$

† Lyubarskii, G. Ya., "The Application of Group Theory in Physics". Pergamon Press, Oxford (1960).

But $(\pm 2\cos\phi - 1)$ is the character in an axial vector representation. This result thus confirms that an antisymmetric tensor of second rank is equivalent to an axial vector. It is evident that if formulae (5) and (6) are to be used, the expression for $\chi_\rho(R)$ need not be evaluated in a complete form for the symmetry operation R. It is easier to substitute the values of the characters $\chi(R)$ for the particular R under consideration. To illustrate this, we take the elasticity tensor c_{ijkl} which has the intrinsic symmetry

$$(1)(2)(3)(4), \quad (12)(3)(4), \quad (34)(1)(2), \quad (13)(24),$$
$$(12)(34), \quad (14)(23), \quad (1423), \quad (1324).$$

By substitution in (5), we get

$$\chi_\rho(R) = \tfrac{1}{8}\{\chi^4(R) + 2\chi(R^2)\chi^2(R) + 3\chi^2(R^2) + 2\chi(R^4)\}.$$

Let this tensor be subject to point group symmetry D_{2h} which has symmetry elements $E, C_2, C_2', C_2'', i, \sigma_h, \sigma_v', \sigma_v''$. We have

$$\chi_\rho(E) = \tfrac{1}{8}\{3^4 + 2 \cdot 3^2 \cdot 3 + 3 \cdot 3^2 + 2 \cdot 3\} = 21$$
$$\chi_\rho(C_2) = \tfrac{1}{8}\{(-1)^4 + 2 \cdot 3(-1)^2 + 3 \cdot 3^2 + 2 \cdot 3\} = 5.$$

In the same manner, we can show that $\chi_\rho(i) = 21$ and $\chi_\rho(\sigma) = 5$. Substituting these values for $\chi_\rho(R)$ in the formula (1) which gives n_i the number of non-vanishing independent components, we get

$$n_i = \tfrac{1}{8}(21 + 5 + 5 + 5 + 21 + 5 + 5 + 5) = 9.$$

The elasticity tensor for a D_{2h} class crystal has thus 9 non-vanishing independent components, a result which has already been obtained.

The above formulae for $\chi_\rho(R)$ are stated for the two cases, namely, (a) the tensor is symmetric with respect to all the permutations of the group P and (b) the tensor is symmetric with respect to all the even permutations of P and antisymmetric with respect to all the odd permutations of P. It may be noted, however, that the general case of intrinsic symmetry, when the tensor is symmetric with respect to an interchange of certain of its indices and antisymmetric with respect to the interchange of certain other indices, can also be handled using the formula (6) and taking the $\pm$ sign according as the relevant permutation leaves the tensor invariant or changes its sign. The general case can also be handled in a slightly different way. The tensor itself is expressed as the direct product of two tensors, one of which is symmetric with respect to a group of permutations of some of its indices and the other is antisymmetric with respect to a group of permutations on the other indices. The tensor of row 6 in Table VII(b) namely ρ_{iklmn} is such a case. ρ_{iklmn} is antisymmetric with respect to the interchange of i and k and totally symmetric in lmn. It may be evaluated by using formula (6) with the modification relating to the interpretation of the sign $\pm$ as already mentioned, or from the outer product of an antisymmetric second rank tensor and a totally symmetric third rank tensor, using (5) and (6) to evaluate the character in the factor tensor representations separately and taking the product of the characters.

The intrinsic symmetry of ρ_{iklmn} is given by the following group of permutations denoted by P.

(1)(2)(3)(4)(5)	(12)(3)(4)(5)
(1)(2)(3)(45)	(12)(3)(45)
(1)(2)(4)(53)	(12)(4)(53)
(1)(2)(5)(34)	(12)(5)(34)
(1)(2)(345)	(12)(345)
(1)(2)(435)	(12)(435)

The first 6 permutations which leave the indices $1, 2$ invariant leave the tensor itself invariant. The second 6 permutations which interchange the indices $1, 2$ change the sign of the tensor. Taking the $+$ sign for the first 6 permutations and the $-$ sign for the second 6 permutations in formula (6), we obtain equations (8) and (9).

$$\chi_\rho(R) = \tfrac{1}{12}\{\chi^5(R) + 3\chi^3(R)\chi(R^2) + 2\chi^2(R)\chi(R^3)$$
$$- \chi^3(R)\chi(R^2) - 3\chi(R)\chi^2(R^2) - 2\chi(R^2)\chi(R^3)\} \qquad (8)$$
$$= \tfrac{1}{2}\{\chi^2(R) - \chi(R^2)\}\cdot\tfrac{1}{6}\{\chi^3(R) + 3\chi(R)\chi(R^2) + 2\chi(R^3)\}. \qquad (9)$$

ρ_{iklmn} connects an antisymmetric tensor of second rank and a totally symmetric tensor of third rank which have the intrinsic symmetries represented by the permutation groups (1)(2), (12) and (3)(4),(5), (3)(45), (4)(53), (5)(34), (345), (435), respectively. Evidently, the expression for $\chi_\rho(R)$ given in (9) is the product of characters in the representations formed by an antisymmetric second rank and a totally symmetric third rank tensor. The first factor has the same value whether we use $(2\cos\phi \pm 1)$ or $(\pm 2\cos\phi + 1)$ for $\chi(R)$. For evaluating the second factor, we have to take $\chi(R) = (\pm 2\cos\phi + 1)$ because the third rank tensor under consideration is obtained as the third power of an axial vector, namely the magnetic field. On substituting the proper values for $\chi(R)$ in (9), we obtain equation (10). As before, c stands for $\cos\phi$.

$$\chi_\rho(R) = (\pm 2c + 1)(\pm 8c^3 + 4c^2 \mp 2c). \qquad (10)$$

We could have obtained the same expression by substituting $\chi(R) = (\pm 2\cos\phi + 1)$ in (8) itself. The result contained in (10) is the same as that obtained by direct evaluation and is given in row 6 of Table VII(b).

CHAPTER 8

Classification of Physical Properties

8.1 Introduction

We have stated that a physical property of a crystal describes the relationship between two physical quantities. The physical quantities may be broadly classified as influences and effects. Usually a crystal subjected to the influence of a physical quantity exhibits several effects. Therefore it is necessary and useful to adopt a general point of view and consider the crystal as subjected to a number of external influences and simultaneously study its response in several aspects. More accurately speaking, we are studying a thermodynamic system, that is a portion of matter exhibiting physical properties under the influence of various physical quantities. We may call the physical quantities as system parameters. A state of the system under study may be completely specified by specifying all the independent system parameters.

We specify two kinds of systems, namely those which are in thermodynamic equilibrium and those which are in a steady state. The general thermodynamic principles applicable to such systems enable us to systematize and correlate the various apparently unconnected physical properties and draw useful conclusions regarding their intrinsic symmetry.

8.2 Systems in Equilibrium

The parameters that specify a thermodynamic system may be classified as intensive and extensive parameters. Each intensive parameter has always its corresponding extensive parameter such that their product has the dimensions of energy.

The extensive parameters are directly proportional to the mass, i.e. number of gram mols of the substance present. Some examples of extensive parameters are mass, entropy, internal energy, volume, etc. It can also be said that the extensive parameters are more closely associated with the material itself. By reducing the extensive parameters as referring to a unit volume of the substance we get the specific extensive parameters, namely specific entropy (entropy per unit volume), density, specific magnetic induction, etc.

Examples of intensive parameters are temperature, stress, magnetic field intensity, electric field intensity, pressure, etc. In Table IX are arranged some intensive parameters and the corresponding specific extensive parameters.

Every one of the extensive parameters is a function of all the intensive parameters. In practice, however, we concern ourselves with a few at a time, namely, those which are significant. However, we shall develop the theory in its generality and assume that all the variables

TABLE IX

Thermodynamic parameters

Intensive parameter		Specific extensive parameter	
Temperature	T	Specific entropy	s
Stress	τ	Strain	ε
Magnetic field	H	Specific magnetic induction	B
Electric field	E	Electric displacement	D
Pressure	P	Specific volume	v

are simultaneously involved. Thus if all the intensive parameters are varied simultaneously the extensive parameters also vary and to a first approximation a system of linear equations will result. The equations may be written

$$\mathrm{d}e_p = C_{pq}\,\mathrm{d}i_q \qquad (1)$$

where $\mathrm{d}e_p$ is a small change in the extensive parameter e_p and $\mathrm{d}i_q$ is a small change in the intensive parameter i_q and $C_{pq} = \partial e_p/\partial i_q$. The terms C_{pq} are physical properties of the crystal when it is in thermodynamic equilibrium with its environment and small reversible changes are effected. We have to understand that the intensive and extensive parameters as well as the coefficients in the above relations which are the physical properties are tensors of appropriate rank.

It is evident that the leading diagonal terms in the coefficient matrix (or the C-matrix) are what may be called the principal properties which connect an intensive variable with its corresponding extensive variable. Thus, for example, permittivity $\partial D/\partial E$, permeability $\partial B/\partial H$ and thermal capacitivity $\partial s/\partial T$ occur as diagonal terms in the C-matrix. The non-diagonal terms represent physical properties which connect different kinds of physical quantities. They are associated with what may be called the cross effects. For example, the thermal expansion coefficient $\partial 1/\partial T$, the piezoelectric stress coefficient $\partial D/\partial \tau$ and the electrocaloric coefficient $\partial s/\partial E$ are such cross effects, and occur as non-diagonal terms in the C-matrix. The coefficients of the C-matrix may be called compliances and the following notation to denote the physical properties may be adopted. We shall denote the coefficient which relates the extensive parameter e_p and the intensive parameter i_q by $C_{e_p i_q}$. For example, $C_{BH} = \partial B/\partial H$ and $C_{DE} = \partial D/\partial E$, and so on.

Let us consider a simple case confining ourselves to electrical and mechanical properties and neglecting other effects. The compliance matrix takes the form

$$\left\| \begin{array}{cc} C_{\varepsilon\tau} & C_{\varepsilon E} \\ C_{P\tau} & C_{PE} \end{array} \right\|.$$

The diagonal terms $C_{\varepsilon\tau}$ and C_{PE} are elasticity and electrical polarizability, respectively. The cross terms $C_{P\tau}$ and $C_{\varepsilon E}$ define, respectively, piezo-electricity and converse piezoelectricity. The compliances are tensors of appropriate rank as already pointed out. Equations (1) are concisely represented by a single matrix equation

$$\| de_p \| = \| C_{pq} \| \| di_q \|. \tag{2}$$

By solving the equations (1) for di_p, we obtain

$$\| di_p \| = \| R_{pq} \| \| de_q \| \tag{3}$$

which give small changes in the intensive parameters due to small arbitrary changes in the extensive parameters. The coefficient matrix R_{pq} or simply the R-matrix is called the rigidity matrix, and the coefficients are called rigidities. The term "rigidity" used here is not to be confused with the same term occurring in elasticity for describing a specific modulus of elasticity. Evidently

$$\| R_{pq} \| = \| C_{qp} \|^{-1}.$$

The rigidity matrix for the electric and mechanical properties takes the form

$$\left\| \begin{array}{cc} R_{\tau\varepsilon} & R_{\tau P} \\ R_{E\varepsilon} & R_{EP} \end{array} \right\|.$$

Among the diagonal terms in the above matrix, $R_{\tau\varepsilon}$ is the elastic stiffness coefficient and among the non-diagonal terms $R_{\tau P}$ is the piezoelectric coefficient.

Perhaps the most useful result of this general treatment is the fact that the compliance matrix as well as the rigidity matrix are symmetric. This may be proved in the following way. We know that $i_p \, de_p = du$, a small increase in internal energy, and it follows that $i_p = \partial u/\partial e_p$ where all the other extensive parameters are held constant. Differentiating with respect to e_q gives

$$\frac{\partial i_p}{\partial e_q} = \frac{\partial^2 u}{\partial e_p \, \partial e_q} = \frac{\partial^2 u}{\partial e_q \, \partial e_p} = \frac{\partial i_q}{\partial e_p}.$$

Consequently $R_{pq} = R_{qp}$. The proof that the compliance matrix is also symmetric similarly follows if we choose the thermodynamic potential instead of the internal energy.

From the above result it follows that the principal properties are represented by tensors which are symmetric with respect to interchange of indices of the influences and effects. Thus the elasticity tensor, which represents the relation between the two symmetric second rank tensors of stress and strain, has at most 21 independent components instead of 36. Similarly, the electrical polarizability tensor which relates the electric field and the electric moment vectors is a symmetric second rank tensor and can have at most 6 independent components instead of 9.

Another important result that follows from the symmetry of the compliance and rigidity matrices is that the symmetrically placed cross effects (with respect to the leading diagonal of the matrix) are equal to each other but not necessarily symmetric. Thus, from the C-matrix for the electrical and mechanical effects, it follows that $C_{\varepsilon E} = C_{P\tau}$, i.e. the matrix representing the direct piezoelectric effect is the same as the matrix representing the converse piezoelectric effect, but they are not necessarily symmetric.

8.3 Thermal, Elastic, Electric and Magnetic Effects

Along the lines of the general treatment of the simultaneous interaction of diverse physical quantities to produce various effects in crystals, we shall take up the particular group of equilibrium properties, namely, thermal, elastic, electric and magnetic properties. We shall consider the respective intensive parameters, namely, temperature T, electric field E_i and magnetic field H_i, stress τ_{ij}, as independent variables and the respective extensive parameters, namely, specific entropy S, specific electric polarization P_i, and intensity of magnetization I_i, strain ε_{ij}, as the dependent variables. Each one of the extensive parameters is a function of all the intensive parameters. The first order effects due to all possible interactions between these two sets of physical quantities are expressed by the following set of linear equations.

$$dS = C\, dT + p_i\, d\,E_i + q_i\, dH_i + e_{ij}\, d\tau_{ij}$$
$$dP_i = p'_i\, dT + \alpha_{ij}\, dE_j + \lambda_{ij}\, dH_j + d_{ijk}\, d\tau_{jk}$$
$$dI_i = q'_i\, dT + \lambda'_{ij}\, dE_j + \mu_{ij}\, dH_j + Q_{ijk}\, d\tau_{jk}$$
$$d\varepsilon_{ij} = e'_{ij}\, dT + d'_{ijk}\, dE_k + Q'_{ijk}\, dH_k + s_{ijkl}\, d\tau_{kl}.$$

S, P_i, I_i and ε_{ij} being, respectively, a scalar, a vector, a vector and a symmetric tensor of second rank, these are $1 + 3 + 3 + 6 = 13$ linear equations in 13 independent variables. The physical nature of the

5

problem requires these equations to be tensor equations which are independent of the coordinate system. It immediately follows from the quotient theorem that the coefficients are tensors of appropriate rank such that all terms on the right-hand side in an equation are of the same rank as the terms on the left-hand side. The notation used makes the rank of the particular coefficient evident. Each coefficient tensor relates two physical quantities and describes a relevant physical property, when all the other parameters (intensive parameters in the above equations) are held constant.

We have seen that the coefficient matrix which we referred to as the compliance matrix has to be symmetrical. For this reason we have chosen the same symbols for the symmetrically disposed coefficients and distinguished them with a dash. The names of the various effects are llisted in the following.

C	Specific heat	λ'_{ij}	Converse magnetoelectric polarizability
α_{ij}	Electric polarizability		
μ_{ij}	Magnetic susceptibility	e_{ij}	Piezocaloric effect (converse of thermal expansion)
s_{ijkl}	Elastic compliance		
Q_{ijk}	Piezomagnetism	e'_{ij}	Thermal expansion
Q'_{ijk}	Converse piezomagnetism	q_i	Magnetocaloric effect
d_{ijk}	Piezoelectricity	q'_i	Pyromagnetism (converse of magnetocaloric effect)
d'_{ijk}	Converse piezoelectricity		
λ_{ij}	Magnetoelectric polarizability	p_i	Electrocaloric effect
		p'_i	Pyroelectricity (converse of electrocaloric effect)

In the above notation, the symbols used and the effect shown against each property correspond with one another only when the physical quantities are appropriately chosen. This is so in α, μ, s, d, etc. On the other hand, in properties like C and q, additional quantities like the temperature and density enter if we wish to express the usually measured physical properties like specific heat and magnetocaloric effect in terms of the symbols chosen. All the diagonal terms in the matrix give rise to physical properties which may be designated as principal effects. In this case, they are the specific heat, electric polarizability, magnetic susceptibility and elasticity. Effects represented by the non-diagonal terms will be designated as cross effects.

It has already been stated that all the principal effects are represented by symmetric tensors. All the cross effects are in general represented by unsymmetric tensors and each such effect is numerically equal to its converse effect. Thus, for example, the coefficients of piezoelectric effect and its converse are equal to each other.

The scheme of equations gives all the possible first order interactions of the physical quantities mentioned. It does not follow that either the effects are possible in all crystals or that they are significant. Due to the interaction of various physical quantities the measurement of a particular physical quantity carried out under different conditions can be expected to give different values. It is therefore necessary to find expressions for such differences in values of a physical property. To illustrate this let us consider the thermoelastic behaviour of crystals neglecting other effects. Specializing from the more general relations given above, we obtain the constitutive equations for the thermoelastic behaviour as

$$dS = C^\tau \, dT + e_{ij}^T \, d\tau_{ij} \tag{4}$$

$$d\varepsilon_{ij} = e_{ij}'^\tau \, dT + s_{ijkl}^T \, d\tau_{kl} \tag{5}$$

where the subscripts indicate the parameters held constant. e' stands for the thermal expansion coefficient, the superscripts and subscripts indicating the appropriate conditions as per notation currently being explained. The relation between adiabatic and isothermal elastic compliances can be obtained as follows. Putting $dS = 0$ in (4), we have

$$dT = \frac{-e_{ij}^T \, d\tau_{ij}}{c^\tau} = \frac{-e_{kl}^T \, d\tau_{kl}}{c^\tau}$$

where we have changed the dummy suffixes from ij to kl. Substituting this value for dT in (5), we have

$$d\varepsilon_{ij} = s_{ijkl}^T \, d\tau_{kl} - \frac{e_{ij}'^\tau e_{kl}^T \, d\tau_{kl}}{c} \tag{6}$$

where S is held constant. Dividing (6) by $d\tau_{kl}$, and remembering that $e_{ij}'^\tau = e_{ij}^T$ due to the symmetry of the compliance matrix, we have

$$\left(\frac{\partial \varepsilon_{ij}}{\partial \tau_{kl}} \right)_S = s_{ijkl}^S = s_{ijkl}^T - \frac{e_{ij}'^\tau e_{kl}'^\tau}{c^\tau}$$

and

$$s_{ijkl}^S - s_{ijkl}^T = - \frac{e_{ij}'^\tau e_{kl}'^\tau}{c^\tau}. \tag{7}$$

From equation (4) it is evident that $c^\tau = (\partial S / \partial T)_\tau$ is the rate of change of entropy with temperature at constant stress. Therefore $T(\partial S / \partial T)_\tau = Tc^\tau$ is the rate of heat produced due to change in temperature at constant stress, i.e. heat capacity per unit volume at constant stress, which we shall denote by C. $e_{ij}'^\tau$ are the coefficients of thermal expansion at constant stress. We shall drop the superscripts because there is now little chance for confusion. Thus (7) takes the form

$$s_{ijkl}^S - s_{ijkl}^T = - \frac{e_{ij}' e_{kl}' T}{C}. \tag{8}$$

When the electrical effects are also taken into account the number of such conditions naturally increases. The relations between the various physical properties measured under different conditions are obtained in a way similar to the relation between adiabatic and isothermal elastic compliances given above. It may be pointed out that the differences between the coefficients measured under different conditions are in general small and amount to at most 1%. The difference between the pyroelectric effect at constant stress and constant strain which is of the order of 100% appears to be the only exception.

8.4 Systems in Steady State

We shall now consider systems not in thermodynamic equilibrium, but in steady state. We are here concerned with systems in which quantities like energy, mass, electric charge, etc. flow through the system under the influence of gradients of appropriate parameters. We, however, concern ourselves with systems in which these irreversible processes are taking place at steady rates only.

There exist a large number of phenomenological laws describing such transport phenomena; for example, the law that heat flow is proportional to temperature gradient, the law that diffusion of matter of one component in a mixture is proportional to its concentration gradient, Ohm's law which states that steady electric current is proportional to steady electric field, the law of chemical reaction connecting the reaction rate and chemical potentials, and the like. When two or more of these phenomena occur simultaneously, they interfere to give cross effects. The thermoelectric effect which arises due to a coupling between the electric and heat conductions is a well-known example of such a cross effect.

In all these phenomena we see that a number of influences cause transport of physical quantities like energy, mass, charge, etc. The causes are, for example, temperature gradient, concentration gradient, potential gradient, etc., respectively. These gradients of various physical quantities may be termed as "forces" and the effect of these forces on a crystal is to produce "fluxes". The "forces" and "fluxes" are both physical quantities. The relations between the "forces" and "fluxes" are characteristic of the crystalline medium under consideration and describe its transport properties. Thus each of the transport properties arises as describing the relation between two physical quantities, which are better denoted as forces and fluxes rather than as influences and effects. The forces and fluxes are represented by tensors of appropriate rank and consequently the transport properties are represented by tensors of appropriate rank.

Thus the physical properties which describe the transport phenomena also arise as relations between two appropriate physical quantities. The fluxes denoted by J_n are rates of flow of extensive quantities e_n and the forces are gradients of what are called entropy parameters. The entropy parameters are state variables, each one corresponding to an extensive variable. The entropy parameters themselves are intensive variables. If we write the first law of thermodynamics in the form

$$ds = \frac{1}{T} du - \sum_n \frac{i_n}{T} de_n \qquad (9)$$

then i_n/T are the entropy parameters we have referred to and may be denoted by F_n.

The entropy parameters act like pressures, driving various fluxes in a direction that will increase the entropy. Each of the fluxes J_n may be driven by the gradient of each of the pressures $\operatorname{grad} F_n$. This is because the various transport properties are in fact inter-related.

If the system is sufficiently near equilibrium, we can express this dependence of each of the fluxes on each of the pressures by a set of linear equations:

$$J_m = L_{mn} \operatorname{grad} F_n = L_{mn} X_n. \qquad (10)$$

In equation (10), $\operatorname{grad} F_n$ has been put equal to X_n and this set of equations expresses the phenomenological relations that govern the transport phenomena. The coefficients L_{mn} are the physical properties (transport properties) of the material and are represented by tensors of appropriate rank. L_{mn} may generally be called conductivities. The coefficients in the principal diagonal of the L-matrix are related to direct or principal effects whereas the non-diagonal terms are related to cross effects. That is to say, the coefficients L_{nn} are, for example, the heat conductivity, the ordinary diffusion coefficient, the electrical conductivity and the chemical drag coefficient and the like. The coefficients L_{mn} with $m \neq n$ are, for example, the thermal diffusion coefficient, the thermoelectric coefficient and the like.

To the above phenomenological relations is added Onsager's fundamental theorem of irreversible thermodynamics, which states that, provided a proper choice is made for the "fluxes" J_m and the "forces" X_m, the L-matrix is symmetric, i.e.

$$L_{mn} = L_{nm} \quad \text{for all } m, n. \qquad (11)$$

These identities are called Onsager reciprocity relations.

It is important to note that the Onsager reciprocity relations are valid only for a proper choice of fluxes and forces. We have given a procedure for selecting proper fluxes and forces using equation (9).

There is a certain amount of freedom in the choice of proper fluxes and forces.†

The theoretical justification for the principle is provided by statistical mechanics assuming the principle of microscopic reversibility. The assumption implied in the principle of microscopic reversibility is that if the velocities of all the particles in the system are simultaneously reversed the particles will retrace their former paths, i.e. that the symmetry of all mechanical equations of motion of individual particles with respect to time reversal is maintained. In other words, their invariance under the transformation $t \to -t$ is presumed. It is beyond the scope of the present treatise to go into the microscopic theory.

As an illustration of the usefulness of Onsager relations, we may cite the example of thermoelectric phenomena. The simultaneous linear relations which connect the electric current and heat flow with the electric field and temperature gradient may be easily formed. However, the Onsager relations are not directly applicable to the coefficient tensors in these relations. The problem of selecting a proper set of forces and fluxes so as to result in the Onsager relations being applicable has been discussed in Chapter 17. It can be seen even at this stage that the electrical conductivity and thermal conductivity which occur as diagonal terms in such relations will be represented by symmetric tensors, whereas the thermoelectric phenomena will be represented by tensors which do not possess such intrinsic symmetry.

The set of equations (10) can be solved for the forces in terms of the fluxes and the coefficient matrix in the resulting system of equations may be called the resistivity matrix and the coefficients called the resistivities. Here again, the term "resistivity" has a general meaning attached to it and is not to be confused with what occurs when we deal with the passage of an electric current through a conductor.

When the transport phenomena are influenced by an external magnetic field H, the conductivities will be functions of the magnetic field and the Onsager relations are modified. This is because the principle of microscopic reversibility fails for a charged particle moving in a magnetic field, unless we reverse the field as well as the velocity of the particle. These considerations lead to a different set of reciprocity relations:

$$L_{ij}(H) = L_{ji}(-H). \tag{12}$$

We shall defer a detailed discussion of the consequences of this to a later stage when we take up galvanomagnetic effects.

---

† De Groot, S. R., "Thermodynamics of Irreversible Processes". North-Holland Publishing Co., Amsterdam (1951).

CHAPTER 9

Strain

9.1 Deformation

When the particles that constitute a body are displaced relative to each other, the body is said to be deformed. If the body is such that its particles regain their original relative positions when the external influences that caused their displacements are removed, it is called an elastic body.

For a phenomenological treatment of elastic properties, a body is considered as continuous. A geometrical description of the body may be obtained by referring it to a cartesian system of coordinates OX_1, OX_2, OX_3 fixed with respect to its initial undeformed state. A deformation of the body is described by specifying to each point P of the body, the corresponding point P' to which it is displaced. Let x_1, x_2, x_3 be the coordinates of a typical point P in the initial undeformed state and x_1', x_2', x_3' be its coordinates in the final deformed state. The components of the displacement PP' are $(x_i' - x_i)$ and they are denoted by u_i. The displacement components u_i vary from point to point, i.e. they are functions of position. We may write

$$u_i = u_i(x_1, x_2, x_3). \tag{1}$$

We are interested in the change of displacement from point to point within the body, because mere displacement of all the points does not always result in a deformation. For example, in a rigid body motion, all the points are displaced but there is no deformation.

Let Q be a point in the neighbourhood of P and let its initial coordinates be $(x_i + dx_i)$. The point $P(x_1, x_2, x_3)$ is displaced to

$$P'\{(x_1 + u_1), (x_2 + u_2), (x_3 + u_3)\},$$

and the point $Q\{(x_1 + dx_1), (x_2 + dx_2), (x_3 + dx_3)\}$ is displaced to the point whose coordinates are:

$$(x_1 + dx_1) + u_1 + \frac{\partial u_1}{\partial x_1} dx_1 + \frac{\partial u_1}{\partial x_2} dx_2 + \frac{\partial u_1}{\partial x_3} dx_3 + \dots$$

$$(x_2 + dx_2) + u_2 + \frac{\partial u_2}{\partial x_1} dx_1 + \frac{\partial u_2}{\partial x_2} dx_2 + \frac{\partial u_2}{\partial x_3} dx_3 + \dots$$

$$(x_3 + dx_3) + u_3 + \frac{\partial u_3}{\partial x_1} dx + \frac{\partial u_3}{\partial x_2} dx + \frac{\partial u_3}{\partial x_3} dx + \dots \tag{2}$$

where we have neglected the terms of second and higher orders in dx's.

From equations (2), it follows that the changes in displacement components from a point P to its neighbouring point Q may be expressed as:

$$du_1 = \frac{\partial u_1}{\partial x_1}dx_1 + \frac{\partial u_1}{\partial x_2}dx_2 + \frac{\partial u_1}{\partial x_3}dx_3$$

$$du_2 = \frac{\partial u_2}{\partial x_1}dx_1 + \frac{\partial u_2}{\partial x_2}dx_2 + \frac{\partial u_2}{\partial x_3}dx_3$$

$$du_3 = \frac{\partial u_3}{\partial x_1}dx_1 + \frac{\partial u_3}{\partial x_2}dx_2 + \frac{\partial u_3}{\partial x_3}dx_3. \tag{3}$$

The quantities du_1, du_2, du_3 are displacements of a point which in the unstrained state is at $(x_1 + dx_1), (x_2 + dx_2), (x_3 + dx_3)$ relative to a point which in the unstrained state is at (x_1, x_2, x_3). Equations (3) take the particular form because we have neglected the second and higher order terms and express the fact that the relative displacements are linear functions of relative coordinates when the latter are small. It may be pointed out that the quantities $\partial u_i/\partial x_j$ are themselves functions of position and may vary from point to point.

The matrix $\left\| \dfrac{\partial u_i}{\partial x_j} \right\|$ can be expressed as the sum of a symmetric matrix and an antisymmetric matrix in the following way:

$$\left\| \frac{\partial u_i}{\partial x_j} \right\| = \left\| \frac{1}{2}\left(\frac{\partial u_i}{\partial x_j} + \frac{\partial u_j}{\partial x_i}\right) \right\| + \left\| \frac{1}{2}\left(\frac{\partial u_i}{\partial x_j} - \frac{\partial u_j}{\partial x_i}\right) \right\|. \tag{4}$$

It is convenient to introduce the following notation:

$$\frac{1}{2}\left(\frac{\partial u_i}{\partial x_j} + \frac{\partial u_j}{\partial x_i}\right) = \varepsilon_{ij}; \quad \frac{1}{2}\left(\frac{\partial u_i}{\partial x_j} - \frac{\partial u_j}{\partial x_i}\right) = \omega_{ij}. \tag{5}$$

9.2 Analysis of Strain

The quantities ε_{ij} are amenable to a direct and simple interpretation. By choosing a line element along the X_1-axis, we find from equations (2) that the increase in length of a linear element dx_1 due to deformation is $\varepsilon_{11} dx_1$. Hence ε_{11} is the elongation per unit length along the X_1-direction. Elongation per unit length is defined as longitudinal strain. Similar interpretation can be given for ε_{22} and ε_{33}.

A similar simple interpretation of the component ε_{12} may be given by considering two linear elements PQ $= dx_1$ and PR $= dx_2$ through P (Fig. 10). We can assume that the deformation is confined to the

X_1X_2-plane only and that there are no displacements in the X_3-direction. The point P is displaced to P'. The components u_1, u_2 of this displacement are shown in Fig. 10. P'Q' and P'R' show the displaced positions of the line elements PQ and PR due to deformation.

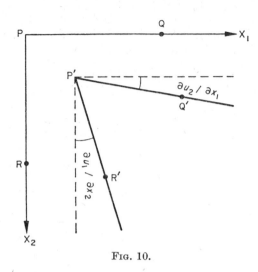

FIG. 10.

It is easily seen that P'Q' is inclined to the initial OX_1 direction by the small angle equal to $\partial u_2/\partial x_1$ and similarly P'R' is inclined to OX_2 by the small angle $\partial u_1/\partial x_2$. Thus the angle between dx_1 and dx_2, which is initially a right-angle, is diminished by

$$\left(\frac{\partial u_1}{\partial x_2}+\frac{\partial u_2}{\partial x_1}\right) = 2\varepsilon_{12}.$$

Thus ε_{12} is one-half of the change in the angle between the two directions along OX_1 and OX_2 through P. ε_{12} is called the shearing strain between the planes X_1X_3 and X_2X_3 at the point P. Similarly, ε_{23} and ε_{31} define the shearing strains between the planes X_1X_2 and X_1X_3 and the planes X_2X_3 and X_2X_1, respectively.

We shall show that, when the deformation is small, the quantities ε_{ij} at a point determine the change in length of every small linear element that passes through that point. Let l_1, l_2, l_3 be the direction cosines of a straight line passing through the point $P(x_1, x_2, x_3)$. The coordinates of a neighbouring point Q on this line at a small distance ds_0 are $(x_1+dx_1), (x_2+dx_2), (x_3+dx_3)$. Evidently

$$dx_1 = l_1\,ds_0; \quad dx_2 = l_2\,ds_0; \quad dx_3 = l_3\,ds_0.$$

After deformation the point P goes to P' whose coordinates are $(x_1+u_1), (x_2+u_2), (x_3+u_3)$. The neighbouring point Q goes to Q' after deformation, and its coordinates are given by equations (2) except that we replace $l_i\,ds_0$ for dx_i, which form is more useful in the present considerations. Equations (2) take the form:

$$x_i + l_i\,ds_0 + u_i + \frac{\partial u_i}{\partial x_j} l_j\,ds_0. \tag{6}$$

We denote the distance P′Q′ by ds and the following relation between ds and ds_0 can be obtained from (6).

$$(ds)^2 = (ds_0)^2\left[\left\{l_1\left(1+\frac{\partial u_1}{\partial x_1}\right) + l_2\frac{\partial u_1}{\partial x_1} + l_3\frac{\partial u_1}{\partial x_3}\right\}^2\right.$$
$$+\left\{l_1\frac{\partial u_2}{\partial x_1} + l_2\left(1+\frac{\partial u_2}{\partial x_2}\right) + l_3\frac{\partial u_2}{\partial x_3}\right\}^2$$
$$\left.+\left\{l_1\frac{\partial u_3}{\partial x_1} + l_2\frac{\partial u_3}{\partial x_2} + l_3\left(1+\frac{\partial u_3}{\partial x_3}\right)\right\}^2\right]. \tag{7}$$

Neglecting squares and products of quantities $\partial u_i/\partial x_j$, we can show that

$$ds = ds_0(1 + \varepsilon_{11} l_1^2 + \varepsilon_{22} l_2^2 + \varepsilon_{33} l_3^2 + \varepsilon_{23} l_2 l_3 + \varepsilon_{31} l_3 l_1 + \varepsilon_{12} l_1 l_2). \tag{8}$$

Defining longitudinal strain ε of a line element ds_0 as equal to $(ds - ds_0)/ds_0$ (change in length per unit original length), we see that

$$\varepsilon = \frac{ds - ds_0}{ds_0} = \varepsilon_{ij} l_i l_j. \tag{9}$$

Thus we find that the quantities ε_{ij} at a point give the change in length of every line element that passes through that point. It follows that ε_{ij} completely specify the changes of size and shape of all parts of a body when the deformations are small. It can also be shown that when the deformations are small the quantities ε_{ij} at a point determine change in the angle between any two linear elements passing through that point.

The quantities ω_{ij} of the antisymmetric matrix can be shown to have an interpretation in terms of a rigid body rotation of an elemental volume surrounding P. As already seen, the quantity $\partial u_1/\partial x_2$ gives the rotation of the linear element dx_2 in the anticlockwise sense and $\partial u_2/\partial x_1$ gives the rotation of the linear element dx_1 in the clockwise sense; therefore $-\partial u_2/\partial x_1$ gives its rotation in the anticlockwise sense. Therefore

$$\left(\frac{\partial u_1}{\partial x_2} - \frac{\partial u_2}{\partial x_1}\right)$$

characterizes the rotation of both the linear elements in the same direction and

$$\frac{1}{2}\left(\frac{\partial u_1}{\partial x_2} - \frac{\partial u_2}{\partial x_1}\right)$$

indicates the average or net rotation of the volume element around P. The relative displacements given in equations (3) can themselves be expressed as resultants of the symmetric and antisymmetric parts by writing $du_i = \varepsilon_{ij}\,dx_j + \omega_{ij}\,dx_j$. $\varepsilon_{ij}\,dx_j$ is the symmetric part of the displacements as shown above and gives rise to the deformation of the body. The antisymmetric part $\omega_{ij}\,dx_j$ represents a bodily rotation of amount $\sqrt{(\omega_{32}^2 + \omega_{13}^2 + \omega_{21}^2)}$ about an axis in the direction $(\omega_{32}, \omega_{13}, \omega_{21})$. For this reason, ω_{ij} are called the rotational components.

9.3 The Strain Tensor

The state of deformation of a body, which is characterized by the changes in the distances between its various points, is something independent of the coordinate system chosen to describe it. Thus we see from equation (9) that the quantity $\varepsilon_{ij}l_i l_j$ is a pure number, independent of the choice of coordinates. The quantities l_i are direction cosines, and they are in fact the components of an arbitrary unit vector. The products $l_i l_j$ therefore transform as products of coordinates, that is as the components of a second rank tensor. It follows from the quotient theorem that, since $\varepsilon_{ij}l_i l_j$ is an invariant, the quantities ε_{ij} form a second rank tensor. That ε_{ij} are symmetric in the suffixes i,j is evident from their very definition.

9.4 The Strain Quadric

It has been shown that

$$\varepsilon = \varepsilon_{ij}l_i l_j \tag{10}$$

gives the linear strain along any direction (l_1, l_2, l_3) passing through the point where the ε_{ij} are given. We shall choose that point as the origin O for convenience. If we take a point $P(x_1, x_2, x_3)$ in the neighbourhood at a short distance ds_0 from O, we have $ds_0\,l_i = x_i$. Multiplying both sides of equation (10) by $(ds_0)^2$ we obtain

$$\varepsilon.(ds_0)^2 = \varepsilon_{ij}\,x_i x_j. \tag{11}$$

Since we have chosen a particular point, we get the right-hand side expression equal to a constant number. Now

$$\varepsilon_{ij}\,x_i x_j = \text{constant} \tag{12}$$

where x_i are variables defines a quadric surface that passes through the point P. From equations (11) and (12), it follows that

$$\varepsilon.(ds_0)^2 = \varepsilon_{ij}\,x_i x_j = \text{constant}. \tag{13}$$

If we choose a typical point P on this quadric surface and join it to the origin O, we get a radius vector OP of the quadric. Equation (13) shows that the strain along OP is inversely proportional to the square of its length. Thus the linear strain along any direction is inversely proportional to the square of the radius vector of the strain quadric along that direction. Since x_i are small, $\varepsilon_{ij} x_j$ give the components of the relative displacement of the point P with respect to O. If we denote the expression $\varepsilon_{ij} x_i x_j$ by $G(x_i)$, we find that $\partial G/\partial x_i = \varepsilon_{ij} x_j$. But $\partial G/\partial x_i$ are the direction ratios of the normal to the surface $G(x_i) =$ constant at P. It follows that the relative displacement of P due to deformation is directed along the normal at that point to the quadric passing through that point. If the quadric is an ellipsoid, all the lines in all directions passing through O are contracted or all are extended. If the quadric is a hyperboloid some lines are extended while others are contracted.

The quadratic form $\varepsilon_{ij} x_i x_j$ can always be transformed into its canonical form by an orthogonal transformation. That is, we can find a cartesian system of coordinates in which the quadratic form transforms to $(\varepsilon_1 x_1^2 + \varepsilon_2 x_2^2 + \varepsilon_3 x_3^2)$ and the equation of the quadric assumes the form

$$\varepsilon_i x_i^2 = \text{constant.} \tag{14}$$

This happens when the coordinate axes coincide with the principal axes of the quadric. Since lengths of the radius vectors of the quadric along its principal axes have stationary values, it follows that the longitudinal strain has stationary values along these directions. These directions are called principal axes of strain and the corresponding planes principal planes of strain and the corresponding strains principal strains. It may be noted that the shear–strain components disappear from the equation for the quadric surface when it is referred to the principal axes. It follows that for any given deformation, there is a set of mutually perpendicular directions at each point in the body which remain mutually perpendicular after deformation. These directions are along the principal axes of the strain quadric at that point. A small rectangular parallelepiped with faces parallel to the principal planes remains a rectangular parallelepiped after deformation. The strain at a point is completely determined if we know the directions of the principal axes of strain and the magnitudes of the principal strains. Also it follows that any general strain is equivalent to three simple extensions along the principal axes at each point.

To determine the principal axes we proceed as follows. The relative displacements at the ends of the principal axes will be along the same direction as the axes. If x_i are the components of an axis, the relative displacement components δx_i of its end point are therefore proportional to x_i. If ε denotes the strain along the axis, it follows that $\delta x_i = \varepsilon x_i$.

Thus to find the directions of the principal axes we need seek those radius vectors x_i of the quadric for which the relative displacement components of the end points are proportional to x_i. From this it follows that the required x_i are solutions of the simultaneous equations

or

$$\varepsilon_{ij} x_j = \varepsilon x_i = \varepsilon \delta_{ij} x_j$$

$$(\varepsilon_{ij} - \varepsilon \delta_{ij}) x_j = 0.$$

This set of equations possesses a solution if, and only if, the determinant of the coefficients vanishes, i.e.

$$|\varepsilon_{ij} - \varepsilon \delta_{ij}| = 0.$$

This determinantal equation is a cubic in ε and it is known that its roots are all real because ε_{ij} are real and symmetric. Let its roots be $\varepsilon_1, \varepsilon_2, \varepsilon_3$ which are obviously strains along the principal axes. For each one of the ε_i we obtain a set of x_i from the above simultaneous equations which give the direction ratios of the corresponding principal axes. The determinantal equation can be expanded into the form

$$|\varepsilon_{ij} - \varepsilon \delta_{ij}| = -\varepsilon^3 + I_1 \varepsilon^2 - I_2 \varepsilon + I_3 = 0$$

where

$$I_1 = \varepsilon_1 + \varepsilon_2 + \varepsilon_3$$

$$I_2 = \varepsilon_2 \varepsilon_3 + \varepsilon_3 \varepsilon_1 + \varepsilon_1 \varepsilon_2$$

$$I_3 = \varepsilon_1 \varepsilon_2 \varepsilon_3.$$

The quantities I_1, I_2, I_3 are invariant under coordinate transformations and they are known as the invariants of the strain tensor. The expressions for these invariants in terms of the general strain components ε_{ij} are easily found. They are

$$I_1 = \varepsilon_{11} + \varepsilon_{22} + \varepsilon_{33}$$

$$I_2 = \begin{vmatrix} \varepsilon_{22} & \varepsilon_{23} \\ \varepsilon_{23} & \varepsilon_{33} \end{vmatrix} + \begin{vmatrix} \varepsilon_{11} & \varepsilon_{31} \\ \varepsilon_{31} & \varepsilon_{33} \end{vmatrix} + \begin{vmatrix} \varepsilon_{11} & \varepsilon_{12} \\ \varepsilon_{12} & \varepsilon_{22} \end{vmatrix}$$

$$I_3 = \begin{vmatrix} \varepsilon_{11} & \varepsilon_{12} & \varepsilon_{13} \\ \varepsilon_{21} & \varepsilon_{22} & \varepsilon_{23} \\ \varepsilon_{31} & \varepsilon_{32} & \varepsilon_{33} \end{vmatrix}.$$

Of these invariants, I_1 has a simple interpretation. If we consider a small cubical volume element of edge length l, with its edges along the principal axes of strain, the change δV in the volume V of the cube, neglecting terms of higher order in strains, is

$$\delta V = l^3 (1 + \varepsilon_1)(1 + \varepsilon_2)(1 + \varepsilon_3) - l^3$$

$$= l^3 (\varepsilon_1 + \varepsilon_2 + \varepsilon_3).$$

We have $\delta V/V = (\varepsilon_1 + \varepsilon_2 + \varepsilon_3)$. Thus, the invariant $I_1 = (\varepsilon_{11} + \varepsilon_{22} + \varepsilon_{33})$ represents the change in volume per unit original volume due to strain, and it is called the cubical dilatation or dilatation. It may also be noted that it is the divergence of the displacement vector.

9.5 Homogeneous Strain

When the strain components are constant throughout the body the strain is said to be homogeneous. The displacements corresponding to a homogeneous strain may therefore be given by equations of the form

$$u_i = a_{ij}x_j$$

where $a_{ij} = a_{ji}$ and where a_{ij} are constants. From the nature of the above equations we can infer that in a homogeneous strain, planes and straight lines remain plane and straight after deformation; parallel planes and parallel straight lines remain parallel; and a sphere is in general transformed into an ellipsoid.

9.6 Simple Examples of Strain

(i) *Uniform dilatation*

When the linear extension in every direction is the same, the strain is called uniform dilatation. In this case, the strain components

$$\varepsilon_{11} = \varepsilon_{22} = \varepsilon_{33} = \varepsilon \quad \text{and} \quad \varepsilon_{12} = \varepsilon_{23} = \varepsilon_{31} = 0$$

and the equation of the strain quadric is

$$\varepsilon(x_1^2 + x_2^2 + x_3^2) = \text{constant}.$$

It follows that in uniform dilatation, the change in volume per unit original volume equals three times the linear extension ϵ. We have

$$\frac{\delta V}{V} = K = (\varepsilon_{11} + \varepsilon_{22} + \varepsilon_{33}) = 3\varepsilon.$$

(ii) *Shearing strain*

Let us consider the case in which $\varepsilon_{11} = -\varepsilon_{22} = \varepsilon$ and the rest of the strain components are zero. The strain quadric is in the principal axes form and may be written,

$$\varepsilon x_1^2 - \varepsilon x_2^2 = \text{constant}.$$

This is the equation of a hyperbolic cylinder whose trace on the $X_1 X_2$-plane is a rectangular hyperbola having straight lines inclined at 45° to the X_1- and X_2-axes as asymptotes. In a different coordinate system, with the asymptotes as the X_1'- and X_2'-axes and the X_3'-axis coinciding with the X_3-axis, the strain quadric takes the form

$$2\varepsilon x_1' x_2' = \text{constant}.$$

From this it is evident that the strain is equivalent to a pure shear corresponding with the directions X_1' and X_2'. In other words, equal extension and contraction along two mutually perpendicular directions are together equivalent to a shearing strain, which is numerically equal to twice the extension or contraction and corresponds with directions bisecting the angles between the original directions, along which extension and contraction are applied. There is no cubical dilatation when the strain is a pure shear.

CHAPTER 10

Stress

10.1 The Notion of Stress

When an elastic body is deformed due to the action of external forces, internal forces arise which resist the deformation and which tend to return the body to its initial undeformed state. Consider an elastic body which is slightly deformed due to a system of external forces and which is in a state of equilibrium. We shall assume that body forces are not present and consider an interior portion separated from the rest of the body by an imaginary surface. This portion is in equilibrium under the action of the rest of the body on it. The nature of this action is assumed to be the same as the nature of mechanical action between two bodies in contact. They are assumed to be surface forces. For a complete specification of the system of such internal forces, we require to know, at each point in the body, the force per unit area across every elemental plane passing through that point. We shall show that the force per unit area at a point in magnitude and direction on an arbitrarily oriented plane through that point is determined if the forces per unit area in magnitude and direction on three coordinate planes passing through that point are given. Each of the forces on the coordinate planes are resolvable into three components along the coordinates. There are thus nine components involved in specifying the system of internal forces that are brought into play and they are defined as the components of a single physical quantity called stress. We shall show that, under very broad and justifiable assumptions, there are only six independent components of stress, and that stress is a symmetric tensor of second rank. A deformed elastic body is also referred to as a stressed body.

10.2 Analysis of Stress

Let O in Fig. 11 be any point in a stressed body. Let us determine the force across a plane passing through O and oriented in such a way that the direction cosines of its normal are (l_1, l_2, l_3). For this purpose we consider the equilibrium of a small tetrahedral portion of the body having its vertex at O, and the three edges that meet at O parallel to the coordinate axes. The fourth face of the tetrahedron is taken parallel to the plane under consideration at a small distance h from O, such that the (l_1, l_2, l_3) direction is directed outward with respect to the tetra-hedron. Let it meet the coordinate axes through O in A, B and C. The tetrahedron OABC is in equilibrium under the system of forces exerted on its faces by the rest of the body.

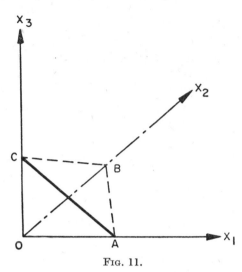

FIG. 11.

Because we are considering a small tetrahedron, we can take the forces acting on its faces as practically constant, or that their variation over the faces is of a higher order smallness and therefore neglected. Let Δ be the area of ABC and T_i the components of force acting on it. The areas of OBC, OCA and OAB are Δl_1, Δl_2 and Δl_3, respectively. Evidently, we require a two-suffix notation to denote the nine compo-nents of forces acting on these three faces. Let τ_{ij} denote the component of force on the face normal to the X_i-axis, acting in the direction of the X_j-axis. Assuming that there are no body forces, for equilibrium, the surface forces along the three coordinate axes must cancel out. For the X_1-direction, we have

$$\Delta T_1 - (\Delta l_1 \tau_{11} + \Delta l_2 \tau_{12} + \Delta l_3 \tau_{13}) = 0.$$

The τ_{ij} are taken with negative sign because the exterior normals to the faces of the tetrahedron are directed oppositely to the direction of the increasing X_j-coordinate. This is due to a convention we are going to adopt, regarding the signs of τ_{ij} which is explained in detail at a later stage in this section. In the same manner, the other two equations of equilibrium are obtained. Cancelling out the common factor Δ, these equations of equilibrium for the tetrahedron can be written

$$T_i = \tau_{ij} l_j. \tag{1}$$

It is not difficult to see that these equations are valid at the point O. If we had taken the force components T_i and τ_{ij} at the point O, the corresponding components on the faces of a small tetrahedron would vary from them by small quantities which tend to zero with the linear dimension h of the tetrahedron and, in the limit, the equations of equilibrium assume the form (1).

We shall now show that the presence of body forces does not effect the relations (1). Body forces are forces which are proportional to the mass contained in the volume element on which they are considered acting. The most common example that can be given for such forces is gravitation. If F_i are the components of the resultant of body forces per unit volume acting on the tetrahedral volume element OABC, the equation for equilibrium along the X_1-direction is

$$\Delta T_1 - (\Delta l_1 \tau_{11} + \Delta l_2 \tau_{12} + \Delta l_3 \tau_{13}) + F_1 \tfrac{1}{3}\Delta h = 0$$

where $\tfrac{1}{3}\Delta h$ is the volume of the tetrahedral element. After taking out the common factor Δ, the body force component is still multiplied by the small quantity h. In the limit as h tends to zero, $F_1 h$ will be equal to zero, i.e. the relations (1) are not altered and continue to be valid at the point O.

The τ_{ij} are called the stress components. The components $\tau_{11}, \tau_{22}, \tau_{33}$ are called the *normal components* of stress; the other components are called the *shear* or the *tangential components*.

The convention in regard to the signs of the quantities τ_{ij} is the following. Consider a small parallelepiped at O with edges along the axes. If one draws an exterior normal to a given face of the parallelepiped, then the components τ_{ij} are reckoned positive if the corresponding components of force act in the directions of increasing x_1, x_2, x_3, when the normal has the same sense as the positive direction of the axis to which the face is perpendicular. If, on the other hand, the exterior normal to a given face points in the direction opposite to that of the positive coordinate axis, then the positive values of the components τ_{ij} are associated with forces directed oppositely to the positive directions of the coordinate axes. It follows that positive values of the normal components are associated with tension, and the negative values with compression.

10.3 The Stress Tensor

Thus we have seen that the state of stress in a deformed elastic body is specified by the nine components of the physical quantity called stress. Equation (1) shows that the contracted product $\tau_{ij} l_j$, in which l_j are components of an arbitrary unit vector (the direction cosines of the normal to the surface element), is a vector T_i. From the quotient theorem it follows that τ_{ij} form a tensor of second rank.

Assuming that body moments and surface moments are not present, i.e. moments proportional to the volume and to the surface areas of the element (hence of the order h^3 and h^2, respectively, where h is the linear dimension of the element under consideration), we shall show that the quantities τ_{ij} are symmetric with respect to an interchange of indices i and j. Consider an elemental parallelepiped at O with edges dx_1, dx_2, dx_3. Take the moments of the forces acting on the element, about the coordinate axes. Contribution due to body forces can be neglected because, on reducing the dimensions of the element, the body forces which are proportional to the volume diminish as small quantities of higher order than surface forces, which are proportional to area. The contribution to the moments due to normal forces on the faces of the element arises only due to non-uniformity of their distribution within the element. This is again a quantity of higher order of smallness than the moments due to tangential forces on the faces. Therefore, taking moments about the X_1-axis, an equation for equilibrium of the parallelepiped is

$$\tau_{12}\,dx_1\,dx_2\,dx_3 = \tau_{21}\,dx_1\,dx_2\,dx_3.$$

The other two equations are obtained in the same manner. From these equations we find that

$$\tau_{ij} = \tau_{ji}. \tag{2}$$

It must be pointed out that the assumption that body moments are not present is not valid in cases where deformation of the body results in long-range force fields like the electric field and the magnetic field, in piezoelectric and piezomagnetic bodies, respectively. In such cases, the above arguments put forward are not adequate to show that stress is a symmetric tensor. It has been shown† that the presence of body couples does not alter the situation and the elastic behaviour is adequately described by a symmetric stress tensor. Moreover, from the symmetry of the compliance matrix (Chapter 8) it follows that the tensor which represents the piezoelectric property (relation between stress and the electric moment) must be equal to its converse effect which relates the strain and electric field. This is possible only if stress, like strain, is also a symmetric tensor. From the above arguments and from the fact that there is not enough experimental justification to support the arguments that in the presence of body moments the stress tensor is not symmetric, we shall take it in what follows that stress is represented by a symmetric tensor of second rank. We may leave the question of existence of surface moments and their effect on the symmetry of the stress tensor open for purposes of this work.

† Krishnan, R. S. and Rajagopal, E. S., *Ann. Phys. Lpz.* **7**, 177 (1960).

10.4 The Stress Quadric

Just as in the case of the strain tensor, a quadric surface called the stress quadric can be defined which is useful in studying the distribution of stress. Let O be a typical point in the stressed medium where the stress components are τ_{ij}. Let (l_1, l_2, l_3) be the direction cosines of the normal to an arbitrary plane element passing through the point O. If T_i are the components of the force per unit area on the plane element, we have $T_i = \tau_{ij} l_j$ and the normal component N of the force is given by $T_i l_i = \tau_{ij} l_i l_j$. If P is a point at a small distance r from O, lying on the normal to the plane element, $r l_i$ are the coordinates x_i of the point P in a coordinate system with O as origin and we have

$$N r^2 = \tau_{ij} x_i x_j = \text{constant}.$$

If $P(x_1, x_2, x_3)$ is a variable point satisfying the above equation, it evidently lies on a quadric surface with centre at O. The normal force N on a plane element which is perpendicular to the vector OP is inversely proportional to the square of its length. Denoting the quadratic expression $\tau_{ij} x_i x_j$ by $F(x_i)$, we find that

$$\frac{\partial F}{\partial x_i} = \tau_{ij} x_j = \tau_{ij} l_j r = T_i r.$$

Since $\partial F / \partial x_i$ are the direction ratios of the normal to the quadric at P, it follows that the force on the plane element passing through O, and having its normal directed along the central vector OP of the quadric, has its direction along the normal to the quadric surface at P.

Just as in the case of the strain quadric, the stress quadric can also be transformed into its canonical form by a principal axes transformation of coordinates. If (l_1, l_2, l_3) is along a principal axis to the quadric, from what is shown above it follows that the force on the plane element passing through O and normal to (l_1, l_2, l_3) is along the same direction, i.e. the force is entirely normal. In such a case T_i are proportional to l_i which fact may be expressed by writing $T_i = \tau l_i$. Therefore, to find the directions of principal axes, we have to find the directions which are such that the force on planes normal to them is entirely normal. For this we should equate the force components T_i on an arbitrarily oriented plane, expressed in terms of the direction cosines of its normal l_i and τ_{ij}, with l_i and determine l_i which satisfy those equations. Thus

$$\tau_{ij} l_j = \tau l_i = \tau \delta_{ij} l_j.$$

Therefore

$$(\tau_{ij} - \tau \delta_{ij}) l_j = 0. \tag{3}$$

The above set of three homogeneous equations in l_j has a solution if the determinant of the equations only is zero, i.e.

$$|\tau_{ij} - \tau \delta_{ij}| = 0. \tag{4}$$

The determinantal equation is a cubic in τ. τ_1, τ_2, τ_3, the roots of the cubic, are equal to the stresses along the axes of the quadric. They are called the principal stresses. Substituting each of the principal stresses τ_i in equation (3) we get the corresponding l_i, i.e. the direction cosines of the principal axis along which the normal stress is τ_i.

Equation (4) can be written as

$$|\tau_{ij} - \tau \delta_{ij}| = -\tau^3 + \theta_1 \tau^2 - \theta_2 \tau + \theta_3 = 0. \tag{5}$$

$\theta_1, \theta_2, \theta_3$, which are invariant under coordinate transformations, are known as the invariants of the stress tensor. In terms of the principal stresses τ_1, τ_2, τ_3, they are expressed as

$$\theta_1 = \tau_1 + \tau_2 + \tau_3$$

$$\theta_2 = \tau_1 \tau_2 + \tau_2 \tau_3 + \tau_3 \tau_1$$

$$\theta_3 = \tau_1 \tau_2 \tau_3. \tag{6}$$

The general expressions for the invariants $\theta_1, \theta_2, \theta_3$, in terms of τ_{ij}, are similar to those given for the strain invariants in terms of strain components.

10.5 Simple Examples of Stress

(i) *Hydrostatic pressure*

A purely normal stress is defined by equations

$$\tau_{11} = \tau_{22} = \tau_{33} = p \quad \text{and} \quad \tau_{12} = \tau_{23} = \tau_{31} = 0.$$

It corresponds to a stress quadric which is a sphere:

$$p(x_1^2 + x_2^2 + x_3^2) = \text{constant}.$$

This is a case of equal compression from all sides when p is negative, according to our convention. Such a stress is called hydrostatic pressure.

(ii) *Shearing stress*

The stress corresponding to a quadric of the form

$$\tau(x_1^2 - x_2^2) = \text{constant}$$

is obviously equal to a tension across one plane and an equal compression across a plane perpendicular to it. Just as in the case of pure shear strain, we can rotate the axes of coordinates about the X_3-axis by $45°$ and bring the stress quadric to assume the form

$$2\tau x_1' x_2' = \text{constant}$$

where primes denote the new coordinates. The above form for the quadric shows that the stress is a pure shearing stress of magnitude τ.

CHAPTER 11

Elasticity

11.1 Introduction

All solid bodies are deformed under the action of external forces. The response of various solid materials to external forces is varied and complex. We have seen that the deformation of a body is described by the physical quantity strain. The internal mechanical force system is described by the physical quantity stress. If a material is such that the deformation caused in it due to the action of external forces disappears after the removal of such forces, it is called an elastic material. There are several solid materials which are elastic in a limited range. If the external forces causing deformation do not exceed a certain limit, then they recover their original shape and size after the removal of such forces. In terms of the more precise physical quantities defined, we may state that a solid body is characterized as elastic if the strains produced on application of external forces completely disappear when the external forces are removed.

The physical property of elasticity may be understood as describing the relation between the stress field developed and the strains caused. The functional relation between stress and strain must reflect the property of complete recoverability from strain on removal of stress. It is therefore necessary that strain must be a unique homogeneous function of stress. As already pointed out, there are several materials which closely approximate to this ideal elastic behaviour, up to some limiting values of stress. Such a limiting value of stress is called an elastic limit of the material. Even among materials which are elastic, the relation between stress and strain is varied. In some cases it is very simple in the sense that the stress is linearly proportional to the strain, whereas in some cases it is not so.

11.2 The Generalized Hooke's Law

We shall first concern ourselves with the simple linear relation between stress and strain. This relation is arrived at as a generalization of the well-known Hooke's law. In its original form, Hooke's law gave the relation between the longitudinal strain ε and tensile stress τ of long thin rods. For several materials, it is found that, within the elastic limit, τ is proportional to ε. This relation may be written as

$$\tau = E\varepsilon \tag{1}$$

where E is called the Young's modulus. Our present considerations apply to the linear region of elastic behaviour of materials. The stress up to which the stress–strain relation is linear is called the proportional limit. A natural generalization of Hooke's law is to consider each one of the stress components as a linear homogeneous function of every one of the strain components. This may be written as

$$\tau_{ij} = c_{ijkl}\,\varepsilon_{kl}. \tag{2}$$

c_{ijkl} are called elastic moduli or *stiffnesses*. The converse relation which considers strains as linear homogeneous functions of stresses may be obtained by solving the equations (1) for ε_{ij}. These may be written as

$$\varepsilon_{ij} = s_{ijkl}\,\tau_{kl}. \tag{3}$$

s_{ijkl} are called elastic constants or *compliances*. Since we consider the medium as homogeneous, the stiffnesses and compliances do not vary from point to point in a body and they are constants.

Before we investigate the linear relations further, we may mention that there are materials for which the range in which the stress–strain relation is linear is very small, but still they are elastic. We do not consider such cases here.

11.3 The Strain Energy

When an elastic body undergoes a deformation, the external forces that cause the deformation do a certain amount of work. This work is done against the mutual forces between the particles or the elastic forces of the body and is stored as *potential energy of deformation* of the body. This is called the *strain energy*. The work done can be calculated by considering an elemental rectangular parallelepiped $dx_1\,dx_2\,dx_3$ when the elastic forces on it take it from a state of small strain given by ε_{ij} to a state of strain given by $\varepsilon_{ij}+d\varepsilon_{ij}$. The faces normal to the OX_1-axis are subjected to equal (neglecting the variations in τ_{11} within dx_1), but oppositely directed normal forces of magnitude $\tau_{11}\,dx_2\,dx_3$. The elongation of dx_1 is equal to $d\varepsilon_{11}\,dx_1$. Therefore the work done by the normal forces mentioned is equal to $\tau_{11}\,d\varepsilon_{11}\,dx_1\,dx_2\,dx_3$. Similarly, the work done by the normal forces on the other two pairs of faces and the work done by the tangential forces on the three pairs of faces may be calculated. Adding them all, we obtain the work done by the elastic forces on the parallelepiped during the small additional deformation as $\tau_{ij}\,d\varepsilon_{ij}\,dx_1\,dx_2\,dx_3$. This work is equal to the strain energy accumulated in the element, and the work done per unit volume of the body at the point where the parallelepiped is situated is $\tau_{ij}\,d\varepsilon_{ij}$. The total work done by the external forces on the body must therefore be equal to $\int_v \tau_{ij}\,d\varepsilon_{ij}\,dv$ taken over the volume of the body. This is accumulated as strain energy in the body. $\tau_{ij}\,d\varepsilon_{ij}$, which is the work done per unit volume by the external forces, may be taken as the differential $d\phi$ of a function ϕ of strains. We shall disregard all cross effects (like the piezoelectric effect) in our present considerations. We thus have

$$d\phi = \tau_{ij}\,d\varepsilon_{ij} \tag{4}$$

and

$$\frac{\partial \phi}{\partial \varepsilon_{ij}} = \tau_{ij} \tag{5}$$

and from the generalized Hooke's law (2) it follows that

$$d\phi = c_{ijkl}\,\varepsilon_{kl}\,d\varepsilon_{ij} \tag{6}$$

and that

$$c_{ijkl} = \frac{\partial^2 \phi}{\partial \varepsilon_{ij}\,\partial \varepsilon_{kl}} = \frac{\partial^2 \phi}{\partial \varepsilon_{kl}\,\partial \varepsilon_{ij}} = c_{klij}. \tag{7}$$

Since the strain is symmetric with respect to an interchange of its suffixes, it follows that the coefficients c_{ijkl} are subjected to the following relations:

$$c_{ijkl} = c_{jikl} = c_{ijlk} = c_{jilk} = c_{klij} = c_{lkij} = c_{klji} = c_{lkji}. \tag{8}$$

The above relations reduce the number of independent coefficients c_{ijkl} from 81 to 21. Integrating the relation (6) from the initial stress-free, strain-free state to the state given by ε_{ij}, we have

$$\phi = \tfrac{1}{2}c_{ijkl}\,\varepsilon_{ij}\,\varepsilon_{kl}. \tag{9}$$

It follows that

$$\phi = \tfrac{1}{2}s_{ijkl}\,\tau_{ij}\,\tau_{kl} \tag{10}$$

where the s_{ijkl} are compliances. The strain energy per unit volume is thus given as a quadratic form in strains or stresses.

We have introduced in the following Table, a one-suffix notation for the stresses and strains. A two-suffix notation follows for the coefficients c_{ijkl} and s_{ijkl}.

τ_{11}	τ_{22}	τ_{33}	τ_{23}	τ_{31}	τ_{12}	ε_{11}	ε_{22}	ε_{33}	$2\varepsilon_{23}$	$2\varepsilon_{31}$	$2\varepsilon_{12}$
τ_1	τ_2	τ_3	τ_4	τ_5	τ_6	ε_1	ε_2	ε_3	ε_4	ε_5	ε_6

In terms of the above notation, the equations (2) and (3) read

$$\tau_i = c_{ij}\,\varepsilon_j; \quad \varepsilon_i = s_{ij}\,\tau_j \tag{11}$$

and the equations (9) and (10) read

$$\phi = \tfrac{1}{2}c_{ij}\,\varepsilon_i\,\varepsilon_j = \tfrac{1}{2}s_{ij}\,\tau_i\,\tau_j. \tag{12}$$

In equations (2) and (3) and in (9) and (10), the suffixes i, j, k, l run from 1 to 3 whereas, in the corresponding equations (11) and (12), the suffixes i and j run from 1 to 6. In order that the format may remain so, the following relations have to be recognized:

$$s_{ijkl} = s_{mn} \quad \text{when } m \text{ and } n \text{ are 1, 2 or 3}$$

$$2s_{ijkl} = s_{mn} \quad \text{when either } m \text{ or } n \text{ is 4, 5 or 6}$$

$$4s_{ijkl} = s_{mn} \quad \text{when both } m \text{ and } n \text{ are 4, 5 or 6.}$$

In the case of cs, we have $c_{ijkl} = c_{mn}$ for all permissible values of the suffixes.

11.4 Effect of Symmetry on Elastic Coefficients

That the elastic stiffness coefficients c_{ijkl} and the elastic compliance coefficients s_{ijkl} form fourth rank tensors is obvious from the tensor equations (1) and (2) and the quotient theorem. The coefficient tensors are subjected to the intrinsic symmetry given in equations (12). Consequently there remain only 21 independent coefficients, all of which are given below in both the two-suffix and four-suffix notations. In

$$
\begin{array}{llllll}
c_{11} & c_{12} & c_{13} & c_{14} & c_{15} & c_{16} \\
c_{1111} & c_{1122} & c_{1133} & c_{1123} & c_{1113} & c_{1112} \\
x_1x_1x_1x_1 & x_1x_1x_2x_2 & x_1x_1x_3x_3 & x_1x_1x_2x_3 & x_1x_1x_1x_3 & x_1x_1x_1x_2 \\
\\
 & c_{22} & c_{23} & c_{24} & c_{25} & c_{26} \\
 & c_{2222} & c_{2233} & c_{2223} & c_{2213} & c_{2212} \\
 & x_2x_2x_2x_2 & x_2x_2x_3x_3 & x_2x_2x_2x_3 & x_2x_2x_1x_3 & x_2x_2x_1x_2 \\
\\
 & & c_{33} & c_{34} & c_{35} & c_{36} \\
 & & c_{3333} & c_{3323} & c_{3313} & c_{3312} \\
 & & x_3x_3x_3x_3 & x_3x_3x_2x_3 & x_3x_3x_1x_3 & x_3x_3x_1x_2 \\
\\
 & & & c_{44} & c_{45} & c_{46} \\
 & & & c_{2323} & c_{2313} & c_{2312} \\
 & & & x_2x_3x_2x_3 & x_2x_3x_1x_3 & x_2x_3x_1x_2 \\
\\
 & & & & c_{55} & c_{56} \\
 & & & & c_{1313} & c_{1312} \\
 & & & & x_1x_3x_1x_3 & x_1x_3x_1x_2 \\
\\
 & & & & & c_{66} \\
 & & & & & c_{1212} \\
 & & & & & x_1x_2x_1x_2
\end{array}
\tag{13}
$$

each case, the coordinate product which transforms like the corresponding coefficient is also given. In view of the importance of the subject
of elasticity and as this will serve the purpose of explaining the processes
involved in practically all other properties that we shall deal with in
the following chapters, the method of reduction by the application of
symmetry operations on the different crystal classes is given in some
detail.

(i) *The triclinic system*

The triclinic system has only a centre of inversion i as a symmetry
operation but the scheme of coordinate products is already centrosymmetric and therefore triclinic symmetry does not impose any further
restrictions on the components of the tensor. The crystals belonging to
this system can accordingly exhibit 21 independent coefficients.

(ii) *The monoclinic system*

We shall consider the crystal class m at the outset. We take a
coordinate system with the X_1X_2-plane as the plane of symmetry. The
operation of reflection in this plane corresponds to the transformation
$x_1 \to x_1, x_2 \to x_2, x_3 \to -x_3$. It follows that all the products which contain
x_3 an odd number of times will vanish leaving only the following 13
terms as non-vanishing.

$$x_1 x_1 x_1 x_1, \quad x_2 x_2 x_2 x_2, \quad x_3 x_3 x_3 x_3, \quad x_2 x_3 x_2 x_3,$$

$$x_1 x_3 x_1 x_3, \quad x_1 x_2 x_1 x_2, \quad x_1 x_1 x_2 x_2,$$

$$x_1 x_1 x_3 x_3, \quad x_1 x_1 x_1 x_2, \quad x_2 x_2 x_3 x_3,$$

$$x_2 x_2 x_1 x_2, \quad x_3 x_3 x_1 x_2, \quad x_2 x_3 x_1 x_3. \tag{14}$$

The independent non-vanishing coefficients admissible in the class m
correspond to these products. Regarding the class 2, if we take the
X_3-axis along the C_2-axis which is the convention, the transformation
corresponding to C_2 is $x_1 \to -x_1, x_2 \to -x_2, x_3 \to x_3$. On an application
of this transformation, the products which contain x_1 and x_2 together
an odd number of times vanish. As the products are of fourth power,
the above condition is equivalent to x_3 occurring an odd number of
times in the product. Thus for the class 2 also, the same scheme of
coefficients as (14) is obtained. The class $2/m$ cannot have a different
scheme as the operation i which corresponds to the transformation
$x_1 \to -x_1, x_2 \to -x_2, x_3 \to -x_3$ has already been seen to have no effect on
the products.

(iii) *The orthorhombic system*

Let us take the class mmm. If we take the three mirror planes
$\sigma_h, \sigma_v', \sigma_v''$ as coordinate planes, it is evident that only those products

which contain each of x_1, x_2, x_3 an even number of times survive. Since the operation i cannot have any further effect, we obtain the following scheme of 9 products.

$$x_1 x_1 x_1 x_1, \quad x_2 x_2 x_2 x_2, \quad x_3 x_3 x_3 x_3,$$

$$x_2 x_3 x_2 x_3, \quad x_1 x_3 x_1 x_3, \quad x_1 x_2 x_1 x_2,$$

$$x_1 x_1 x_2 x_2, \quad x_1 x_1 x_3 x_3, \quad x_2 x_2 x_3 x_3. \tag{15}$$

The class 222 cannot have a different scheme of products. This is so, because we can take the coordinate axes along the C_2-axes and, as already shown, the operation of a C_2 on the scheme of products (13) has the same effect as the operation of a plane of symmetry coinciding with the plane normal to the C_2-axis. Regarding the class 2mm the application of the two symmetry planes σ'_v, σ''_v reduces the scheme to the above form and the operation C_2 is only a product of σ'_v and σ''_v.

(iv) *The tetragonal system*

(a) The classes $4, \bar{4}, 4/m$: Taking the class 4, we see that the operation C_2 about the X_3-axis reduces the scheme of products to (14). The application of C_4 about the X_3-axis which corresponds to the transformation $x_1 \rightarrow x_2, x_2 \rightarrow -x_1, x_3 \rightarrow x_3$ to the scheme (14) yields the relations:

$$x_1 x_1 x_1 x_1 = x_2 x_2 x_2 x_2; \quad x_2 x_3 x_2 x_3 = x_1 x_3 x_1 x_3;$$

$$x_1 x_1 x_3 x_3 = x_2 x_2 x_3 x_3; \quad x_1 x_1 x_1 x_2 = -x_2 x_2 x_1 x_2;$$

$$x_3 x_3 x_1 x_2 = 0; \quad x_2 x_3 x_1 x_3 = 0.$$

We are left with the following 7 products:

$$x_1 x_1 x_1 x_1 = x_2 x_2 x_2 x_2, \quad x_3 x_3 x_3 x_3,$$

$$x_2 x_3 x_2 x_3 = x_1 x_3 x_1 x_3, \quad x_1 x_2 x_1 x_2,$$

$$x_1 x_1 x_3 x_3 = x_2 x_2 x_3 x_3, \quad x_1 x_1 x_2 x_2,$$

$$x_1 x_1 x_1 x_2 = -x_2 x_2 x_1 x_2. \tag{16}$$

(b) The classes $4mmm$, $\bar{4}2m$, 422 and $4/mmm$: The scheme of non-vanishing independent products corresponding to the class 422 is obtained as

$$x_1 x_1 x_1 x_1 = x_2 x_2 x_2 x_2, \quad x_3 x_3 x_3 x_3,$$

$$x_1 x_3 x_1 x_3 = x_2 x_3 x_2 x_3, \quad x_1 x_2 x_1 x_2,$$

$$x_1 x_1 x_3 x_3 = x_2 x_2 x_3 x_3, \quad x_1 x_1 x_2 x_2. \tag{17}$$

For reasons similar to those mentioned in the above systems, all the classes falling under this group have the same scheme of products.

(v, vi) *The trigonal and hexagonal systems*

The transformations corresponding to trigonal and hexagonal symmetries cannot be applied in a direct and simple way. In these cases we shall resort to the routine method of writing down the equations of transformation and find the relations between the coefficients. Details of the procedure given here follow Hearmon[†] closely. The application of a symmetry operation corresponds to a transformation of the kind $x_i' = a_{ij} x_j$. This induces a transformation of the components of the elasticity tensor c_{ijkl} which may be written as

$$c_{ijkl}' = a_{im} a_{jn} a_{ko} a_{lp} c_{mnop}. \tag{18}$$

The operation C_3 corresponds to a coordinate rotation by $2\pi/3$ about the X_3-axis. The coefficients of this transformation are $a_{11} = a_{22} = \cos(2\pi/3) = -\frac{1}{2}$; $a_{12} = -a_{21} = \sin(2\pi/3) = \sqrt{3}/2$; $a_{33} = 1$ and $a_{13} = a_{23} = a_{31} = a_{32} = 0$. If the operation is a C_6 which corresponds to a rotation by $2\pi/6$ about the X_3-axis again, the coefficients a_{ij} are: $a_{11} = a_{22} = \frac{1}{2}$, $a_{12} = -a_{21} = \sqrt{3}/2$, $a_{33} = 1$ and $a_{13} = a_{23} = a_{31} = a_{32} = 0$. Substituting these values for a_{ij} in (18) and adopting the two-suffix notation, we obtain for $c_{11}', c_{12}', c_{22}', c_{66}', c_{16}', c_{26}'$ the following expressions

$$c_{11} = \frac{1}{16} c_{11} + \frac{6}{16} c_{12} \mp \frac{4\sqrt{3}}{16} c_{16} + \frac{9}{16} c_{22} \mp \frac{12\sqrt{3}}{16} c_{26} + \frac{12}{16} c_{66} \tag{19}$$

$$c_{12} = \frac{3}{16} c_{11} + \frac{10}{16} c_{12} \mp \frac{4\sqrt{3}}{16} c_{16} + \frac{3}{16} c_{22} \pm \frac{4\sqrt{3}}{16} c_{26} - \frac{12}{16} c_{66} \tag{20}$$

$$c_{22} = \frac{9}{16} c_{11} + \frac{6}{16} c_{12} \pm \frac{12\sqrt{3}}{16} c_{16} + \frac{1}{16} c_{22} \pm \frac{4\sqrt{3}}{16} c_{26} + \frac{12}{16} c_{66} \tag{21}$$

$$c_{66} = \frac{3}{16} c_{11} - \frac{6}{16} c_{12} \mp \frac{4\sqrt{3}}{16} c_{16} + \frac{3}{16} c_{22} \pm \frac{4\sqrt{3}}{16} c_{26} + \frac{4}{16} c_{66} \tag{22}$$

$$c_{16} = \pm \frac{\sqrt{3}}{16} c_{11} \pm \frac{2\sqrt{3}}{16} c_{12} - \frac{8}{16} c_{16} \mp \frac{3\sqrt{3}}{16} c_{22} \qquad \pm \frac{4\sqrt{3}}{16} c_{66} \tag{23}$$

$$c_{26} = \pm \frac{3\sqrt{3}}{16} c_{11} \mp \frac{2\sqrt{3}}{16} c_{12} \qquad \mp \frac{\sqrt{3}}{16} c_{22} - \frac{8}{16} c_{26} \mp \frac{4\sqrt{3}}{16} c_{66} \tag{24}$$

where the upper sign in $\pm$ and $\mp$ refers to C_3 and the lower sign to C_6. We dropped the prime on the coefficients c_{ij} on the left-hand side because we are demanding invariance of the components under the transformation. Equations in this set are not independent. Adding the first four

[†] Hearmon, R. F. S., "An Introduction to Applied Anisotropic Elasticity. Oxford University Press, London (1961).

we obtain the result that $c_{16} = c_{26} = 0$. The first four equations then reduce to

$$-15c_{11} + 6c_{12} + 9c_{22} + 12c_{66} = 0 \qquad (25)$$

$$3c_{11} - 6c_{12} + 3c_{22} - 12c_{66} = 0 \qquad (26)$$

$$9c_{11} + 6c_{12} - 15c_{22} + 12c_{66} = 0. \qquad (27)$$

Adding (25) and (26) we get $c_{11} = c_{22}$ and, from this, $c_{66} = \frac{1}{2}(c_{11} - c_{12})$. From the expressions for c'_{13} and c'_{23} and c'_{36} we obtain the relations

$$c_{13} = \frac{1}{4}c_{13} + \frac{3}{4}c_{23} \mp \frac{\sqrt{3}}{2}c_{36} \qquad (28)$$

$$c_{23} = \frac{3}{4}c_{13} + \frac{1}{4}c_{23} \pm \frac{\sqrt{3}}{2}c_{36} \qquad (29)$$

$$c_{36} = \pm\frac{\sqrt{3}}{4}c_{13} \mp \frac{\sqrt{3}}{4}c_{23} - \frac{1}{4}c_{36} \qquad (30)$$

from which we find that

$$c_{13} = c_{23}; \quad c_{36} = 0.$$

From the expressions for $c'_{44}, c'_{45}, c'_{55}$ we have relations

$$c_{44} = \frac{1}{4}c_{44} \pm \frac{\sqrt{3}}{2}c_{45} + \frac{3}{4}c_{55} \qquad (31)$$

$$c_{45} = \mp\frac{\sqrt{3}}{4}c_{44} - \frac{1}{4}c_{45} \pm \frac{\sqrt{3}}{4}c_{55} \qquad (32)$$

$$c_{55} = \frac{3}{4}c_{44} \mp \frac{\sqrt{3}}{2}c_{45} + \frac{1}{4}c_{55} \qquad (33)$$

from which we find that

$$c_{44} = c_{55} \quad \text{and} \quad c_{45} = 0.$$

From the expressions for c'_{34} and c'_{35} we have

$$c_{34} = \mp\frac{1}{2}c_{34} - \frac{\sqrt{3}}{2}c_{35} \qquad (34)$$

$$c_{35} = \frac{\sqrt{3}}{2}c_{34} \mp \frac{1}{2}c_{35} \qquad (35)$$

from which we find that

$$c_{34} = c_{35} = 0.$$

From the expressions for $c'_{14}, c'_{15}, c'_{24}, c'_{25}, c'_{46}, c'_{56}$, we obtain the following relations.

$$c_{14} = \mp \frac{1}{8} c_{14} - \frac{\sqrt{3}}{8} c_{15} \mp \frac{3}{8} c_{24} - \frac{3\sqrt{3}}{8} c_{25} + \frac{\sqrt{3}}{4} c_{46} \pm \frac{3}{4} c_{56} \tag{36}$$

$$c_{15} = \frac{\sqrt{3}}{8} c_{14} \mp \frac{1}{8} c_{15} + \frac{3\sqrt{3}}{8} c_{24} \mp \frac{3}{8} c_{25} \mp \frac{3}{4} c_{46} + \frac{\sqrt{3}}{4} c_{56} \tag{37}$$

$$c_{24} = \mp \frac{3}{8} c_{14} - \frac{3\sqrt{3}}{8} c_{15} \mp \frac{1}{8} c_{24} - \frac{\sqrt{3}}{8} c_{25} - \frac{\sqrt{3}}{4} c_{46} \mp \frac{3}{4} c_{56} \tag{38}$$

$$c_{25} = \frac{3\sqrt{3}}{8} c_{14} + \frac{3}{8} c_{15} + \frac{\sqrt{3}}{8} c_{24} \mp \frac{1}{8} c_{25} \pm \frac{3}{4} c_{46} - \frac{\sqrt{3}}{4} c_{56} \tag{39}$$

$$c_{46} = -\frac{\sqrt{3}}{8} c_{14} \mp \frac{3}{8} c_{15} + \frac{\sqrt{3}}{8} c_{24} \pm \frac{3}{8} c_{25} \pm \frac{1}{4} c_{46} + \frac{\sqrt{3}}{4} c_{56} \tag{40}$$

$$c_{56} = \pm \frac{3}{8} c_{14} - \frac{\sqrt{3}}{8} c_{15} \mp \frac{3}{8} c_{24} + \frac{\sqrt{3}}{8} c_{25} - \frac{\sqrt{3}}{4} c_{46} \pm \frac{1}{4} c_{56} \tag{41}$$

In the above relations, as usual the upper sign in $\pm$ and $\mp$ refers to C_3 and the lower sign refers to C_6. From these relations we obtain for a C_3-axis, $c_{14} = -c_{24} = c_{56}$ and $-c_{15} = c_{25} = c_{46}$. For a C_6-axis we obtain

$$c_{14} = c_{15} = c_{24} = c_{25} = c_{46} = c_{56} = 0.$$

In addition we find that c_{33} is left unaltered by the operation C_3 or C_6.

(a) From the above results it follows that the classes 3 and $\bar{3}$ have the following non-vanishing coefficients.

$$c_{11}, c_{12}, c_{13}, c_{14}, c_{15}, c_{16} = 0,$$

$$c_{22} = c_{11}, \quad c_{23} = c_{13}, \quad c_{24} = -c_{14}, \quad c_{25} = -c_{15}, \quad c_{26} = 0,$$

$$c_{33}, c_{34} = 0, \quad c_{35} = 0, \quad c_{36} = 0, \quad c_{44},$$

$$c_{45} = 0, \quad c_{46} = -c_{15},$$

$$c_{55} = c_{44}, \quad c_{56} = c_{14}, \quad c_{66} = \tfrac{1}{2}(c_{11} - c_{12}). \tag{42}$$

(b) For the classes $3m, \bar{3}m, 32$, there is a C_2-axis normal to the C_3-axis, or an operation equivalent to it. Application of C_2 (or its equivalent) on the scheme given above is straightforward. We obtain that $c_{15} = 0$ in the above scheme as a result of a C_2-axis in the X_2-direction.

(c) The hexagonal system: We found that with the C_6-axis along X_3-axis, the scheme of coefficients is reduced to

$$c_{11}, c_{12}, c_{13}, c_{14} = 0, \quad c_{15} = 0, \quad c_{16} = 0,$$

$$c_{22} = c_{11}, \quad c_{23} = c_{12}, \quad c_{24} = 0, \quad c_{25} = 0,$$

$$c_{26} = 0, \quad c_{33}, c_{34} = 0, \quad c_{35} = 0, \quad c_{36} = 0,$$

$$c_{44}, c_{45} = 0, \quad c_{46} = 0,$$

$$c_{55} = c_{44}, \quad c_{56} = 0, \quad c_{66} = \tfrac{1}{2}(c_{11} - c_{12}) \tag{43}$$

in which there are 6 non-vanishing independent coefficients. All the classes in this system contain a C_6-axis as an element of symmetry, the application of which reduces the scheme of coefficients to the above. The group theoretical method tells us that all these classes have 6 independent non-vanishing coefficients. Therefore it follows that the same scheme applies to all the classes in this system.

(vii) *The cubic system*

Let us first take the class 23. We take the coordinate axes along the three cubic axes which are also 2-fold axes. This reduces the scheme of products to that of the orthorhombic system. An operation C_3 corresponds to the transformation $x_1 \to x_2, x_2 \to x_3, x_3 \to x_1$, which reduces the scheme further to

$$x_1 x_1 x_1 x_1 = x_2 x_2 x_2 x_2 = x_3 x_3 x_3 x_3$$

$$x_2 x_3 x_2 x_3 = x_1 x_3 x_1 x_3 = x_1 x_2 x_1 x_2$$

$$x_1 x_1 x_2 x_2 = x_1 x_1 x_3 x_3 = x_2 x_2 x_3 x_3 \tag{44}$$

showing that there are only 3 independent non-vanishing products.

All the other four classes in the cubic system contain 23 as a subgroup and we know from the group theoretical method that for the cubic system, we need only 3 independent non-vanishing coefficients. Thus the same scheme as in (44) should be applicable to every one of the cubic classes.

(viii) *Isotropic medium*

Since isotropy means invariance under the entire group of orthogonal transformations, the strain energy function for an isotropic medium can be expressed in terms of the strain invariants. The strain invariants I_1, I_2, I_3 are homogeneous expressions of first, second and third order products, respectively, in the strains. Since the strain energy expression is a quadratic form in strains it follows that it is not a function of I_3, and $\phi = \alpha I_1^2 + \beta I_2$, where α and β are constants, is its most general form. Thus the isotropic medium requires two independent elastic coefficients.

This result can be derived from the group theoretical method as well. To obtain the actual scheme of non-vanishing coefficients, we can superpose the hexagonal and cubic symmetries. This makes $c_{44} = \frac{1}{2}(c_{11} - c_{12})$ in the cubic scheme, and reduces it to a scheme of 2 independent constants which is the minimum for an isotropic medium. Since the isotropic medium should necessarily possess the cubic and hexagonal symmetries, it follows that the scheme obtained is the one applicable to the isotropic medium.

We have given below the schemes of non-vanishing independent elastic stiffness coefficients for the various crystal classes.

(i) TRICLINIC SYSTEM

$$
\begin{array}{cccccc}
c_{11} & c_{12} & c_{13} & c_{14} & c_{15} & c_{16} \\
 & c_{22} & c_{23} & c_{24} & c_{25} & c_{26} \\
 & & c_{33} & c_{34} & c_{35} & c_{36} \\
 & & & c_{44} & c_{45} & c_{46} \\
 & & & & c_{55} & c_{56} \\
 & & & & & c_{66}
\end{array}
$$

(ii) MONOCLINIC SYSTEM

$$
\begin{array}{cccccc}
c_{11} & c_{12} & c_{13} & 0 & 0 & c_{16} \\
 & c_{22} & c_{23} & 0 & 0 & c_{26} \\
 & & c_{33} & 0 & 0 & c_{36} \\
 & & & c_{44} & c_{45} & 0 \\
 & & & & c_{55} & 0 \\
 & & & & & c_{66}
\end{array}
$$

(iii) ORTHORHOMBIC SYSTEM

$$
\begin{array}{cccccc}
c_{11} & c_{12} & c_{13} & 0 & 0 & 0 \\
 & c_{22} & c_{23} & 0 & 0 & 0 \\
 & & c_{33} & 0 & 0 & 0 \\
 & & & c_{44} & 0 & 0 \\
 & & & & c_{55} & 0 \\
 & & & & & c_{66}
\end{array}
$$

(iv) (a) TETRAGONAL SYSTEM: CLASSES 4, $\bar{4}$, $4/m$

$$
\begin{pmatrix}
c_{11} & c_{12} & c_{13} & 0 & 0 & c_{16} \\
 & c_{11} & c_{13} & 0 & 0 & -c_{16} \\
 & & c_{33} & 0 & 0 & 0 \\
 & & & c_{44} & 0 & 0 \\
 & & & & c_{44} & 0 \\
 & & & & & c_{66}
\end{pmatrix}
$$

(iv) (b) TETRAGONAL SYSTEM: CLASSES $4mm$, $\bar{4}2m$, 422, $4/mmm$

$$
\begin{pmatrix}
c_{11} & c_{12} & c_{13} & 0 & 0 & 0 \\
 & c_{11} & c_{13} & 0 & 0 & 0 \\
 & & c_{33} & 0 & 0 & 0 \\
 & & & c_{44} & 0 & 0 \\
 & & & & c_{44} & 0 \\
 & & & & & c_{66}
\end{pmatrix}
$$

(v) (a) TRIGONAL SYSTEM: CLASSES 3, $\bar{3}$

$$
\begin{pmatrix}
c_{11} & c_{12} & c_{13} & c_{14} & c_{15} & 0 \\
 & c_{11} & c_{13} & -c_{14} & -c_{15} & 0 \\
 & & c_{33} & 0 & 0 & 0 \\
 & & & c_{44} & 0 & -c_{15} \\
 & & & & c_{44} & c_{14} \\
 & & & & & \tfrac{1}{2}(c_{11}-c_{12})
\end{pmatrix}
$$

(v) (b) TRIGONAL SYSTEM: CLASSES $3m$, 32, $\bar{3}m$

$$
\begin{pmatrix}
c_{11} & c_{12} & c_{13} & c_{14} & 0 & 0 \\
 & c_{11} & c_{13} & -c_{14} & 0 & 0 \\
 & & c_{33} & 0 & 0 & 0 \\
 & & & c_{44} & 0 & 0 \\
 & & & & c_{44} & c_{14} \\
 & & & & & \tfrac{1}{2}(c_{11}-c_{12})
\end{pmatrix}
$$

6

(vi) HEXAGONAL SYSTEM

$$
\begin{matrix}
c_{11} & c_{12} & c_{13} & 0 & 0 & 0 \\
 & c_{11} & c_{13} & 0 & 0 & 0 \\
 & & c_{33} & 0 & 0 & 0 \\
 & & & c_{44} & 0 & 0 \\
 & & & & c_{44} & 0 \\
 & & & & & \tfrac{1}{2}(c_{11}-c_{12})
\end{matrix}
$$

(vii) CUBIC SYSTEM

$$
\begin{matrix}
c_{11} & c_{12} & c_{12} & 0 & 0 & 0 \\
 & c_{11} & c_{12} & 0 & 0 & 0 \\
 & & c_{11} & 0 & 0 & 0 \\
 & & & c_{44} & 0 & 0 \\
 & & & & c_{44} & 0 \\
 & & & & & c_{44}
\end{matrix}
$$

(viii) ISOTROPIC MEDIUM

$$
\begin{matrix}
c_{11} & c_{12} & c_{12} & 0 & 0 & 0 \\
 & c_{11} & c_{12} & 0 & 0 & 0 \\
 & & c_{11} & 0 & 0 & 0 \\
 & & & \tfrac{1}{2}(c_{11}-c_{12}) & 0 & 0 \\
 & & & & \tfrac{1}{2}(c_{11}-c_{12}) & 0 \\
 & & & & & \tfrac{1}{2}(c_{11}-c_{12})
\end{matrix}
$$

The schemes for the stiffnesses c_{ij} have been derived and given in the previous pages. The schemes for the compliances s_{ij} are obtained from the above in the triclinic, monoclinic, orthorhombic, tetragonal and cubic systems by simple substitution of s_{ij} for c_{ij}. In the trigonal, hexagonal and isotropic systems, the s_{ij} schemes are obtained by the same process of substitution except that $s_{66} = 2(s_{11} - s_{12})$ and further in the trigonal system $s_{46} = -2s_{15}$ and $s_{56} = 2s_{14}$.

11.5 Brief Remarks on Experimental Methods and Results

As the subject is of great importance, a number of experimental methods for measuring the elastic constants using single crystals have been developed from time to time and results are available for many crystals, the list being inclusive of representative samples under practically all the crystal systems. In the more common systems like the cubic, the orthorhombic and so on, quite a large number of single crystals—metals, alloys, organic and inorganic substances and minerals —have been studied. Amongst the useful summary articles available in the literature, mention may be made of those by Bhagavantam,[†] Hearmon[‡] and Krishnan.[§]

In recent years, the trend of development in experimentation has been in the direction of employing high frequencies and suitably cut samples of small dimensions. Ultrasonic transmission methods, resonance methods, X-ray diffraction by the acoustic waves in the crystal, Brillouin scattering, etc. have all been pressed into service. The specific orientations along which rods or plates of a crystal have to be cut with a view to get all the independent coefficients depend both on the method chosen and symmetry system appropriate to the crystal under investigation. As these have been widely discussed in the available literature on the subject of elasticity, it is not proposed to go into details here. Tables of non-vanishing coefficients given in this chapter for each crystal system will be of great help in making suitable choice of cuts, restricting oneself to as small a number of cuts as possible and yet obtaining all the coefficients and a few checks.

Attempts have also been made to calculate the elastic constants from the atomic structure in non-metals and the electronic structure in metals by making suitable assumptions and to compare the values thus obtained with the experimental results. Work of this kind, besides being used for verifying various conclusions of the theories of elasticity, has also been extended by Hearmon to sheet materials, polycrystalline aggregates and composite structures with useful practical applications.

Metal crystals of the cubic system have been studied in some detail in the context of their electronic properties. From the schemes given in the foregoing for the elasticity tensor, we note that for an isotropic substance $c_{11} - c_{12} = 2c_{44}$. In fact, cubic crystals differ from the isotropic substances in regard to their elastic behaviour in this respect only, because such a relation need not be valid for them. We may say that the extent to which this relation holds good in the case of a particular cubic crystal may be taken as an indication of the extent of elastic isotropy which the crystal exhibits. To illustrate this point, the experimental values of c_{11}, c_{12} and c_{44} in units of 10^{11} dynes/cm^2 for

† Bhagavantam, S., *Proc. Indian Acad. Sci.* **41**, 72 (1955).
‡ Hearmon, R. F. S., *Phil. Mag.* **5**, 323 (1956).
t Krishnan, R. S., "Progress in Crystal Physics". (1958).

three typical metals, namely, sodium, nickel and aluminium single crystals, are given below.

	c_{11}	c_{12}	c_{44}	$\dfrac{2c_{44}}{c_{11}-c_{12}}$
Na	0·5	0·4	0·4	8·0
Ni	25·2	15·4	12·2	2·5
Al	11·2	6·6	2·8	1·0

From the results, it may be seen that sodium is highly anisotropic while aluminium is practically isotropic. Nickel is midway between the two extremes. Crystallographically, all the three belong to the same class, namely $m3m$. In the case of sodium, the results mean that a shear on any one of the cube faces will be resisted much more than the same shear on any one of its diagonal faces. In the case of aluminium, a given shearing stress will produce the same result irrespective of whether it is applied on a cube face or on a diagonal face. The internal electronic structure has evidently much to do with this result.

To bring out the usefulness of such experimental work, we shall cite another instance, namely the Cauchy relationships. As has already been mentioned, many attempts have been made to construct theories of elasticity on the basis of atomic structure. One can show that if all the interatomic lattice forces are assumed to be central, every atom in the lattice being located at an inversion point, certain additional relationships between the non-vanishing coefficients follow. These are called the Cauchy relationships and are over and above those imposed by crystal symmetry alone. For cubic crystals in particular, we should have $c_{12} = c_{44}$. We shall again give in the following Table illustrative experimental values for three typical crystals belonging to the cubic system. The units are 10^{11} dynes/cm², as in the earlier example.

	c_{11}	c_{12}	c_{44}	$\dfrac{c_{12}}{c_{44}}$
NaCl	4·83	1·26	1·26	1·0
LiF	11·30	4·50	5·64	0·8
MgO	28·60	8·70	14·80	0·6

The results show that Cauchy relationships are not true in general and one should therefore conclude that the assumption that interatomic forces are central is an over-simplification except in substances of the NaCl type.

As part of extended solid state physics programmes, many recent experiments on the elastic behaviour of chosen substances have been conducted, and these relate to a study of the pressure and thermal derivatives of elastic constants as well as their dependence on impurities introduced into the crystal lattices. We will, however, refrain from going into these details, as they are outside the scope of this book.

CHAPTER 12

Large Stresses and Strains

12.1 Finite Deformation

In Chapter 9 we described the classical theory of infinitesimal deformation where higher-order terms in the displacements and their derivatives are neglected. There are, however, many fundamental as well as engineering problems in which the deformation of bodies cannot be considered as small and the said approximation cannot be effected. Such a deformation is said to be finite.

To describe the finite deformation of a body we choose a cartesian coordinate system fixed with respect to the initial or unstrained state of the body. Let (x_1, x_2, x_3) be the coordinates of a typical point in its initial state while (x_1', x_2', x_3') be its coordinates in the final strained state. As in Section 9.1, let us denote the displacements by u_i and we have

$$x_i' = x_i + u_i.$$

A neighbouring point $(x_i + \mathrm{d}x_i)$ moves over after deformation to $(x_i' + \mathrm{d}x_i')$ and we have

$$\mathrm{d}x_i' = \mathrm{d}x_i + \mathrm{d}u_i. \tag{1}$$

The displacements u_i, and therefore the final coordinates x_i' and the relative displacements $\mathrm{d}u_i$, in general vary from point to point, i.e. they are functions of position. To be more specific we shall take them as functions of the initial coordinates x_i.

Consider a small element of a curve of length $\mathrm{d}s_0$ before deformation, passing through the point under study. After deformation the curve is deformed and displaced and let its final length be $\mathrm{d}s$. We have

$$\mathrm{d}s_0^2 = \mathrm{d}x_1^2 + \mathrm{d}x_2^2 + \mathrm{d}x_3^2 = \mathrm{d}x_i\,\mathrm{d}x_i \tag{2}$$

$$\mathrm{d}s^2 = \mathrm{d}x_1'^2 + \mathrm{d}x_2'^2 + \mathrm{d}x_3'^2 = \mathrm{d}x_i'\,\mathrm{d}x_i'. \tag{3}$$

If $\mathrm{d}s^2$ is equal to $\mathrm{d}s_0^2$ for all curves, it means that the body has not deformed due to the displacements that carried x_i to x_i'. It is apparent that the difference $(\mathrm{d}s^2 - \mathrm{d}s_0^2)$ characterizes the deformation of the body. We shall therefore define $\frac{1}{2}(\mathrm{d}s^2 - \mathrm{d}s_0^2)$ as measuring the strain of the elastic medium at the point under consideration. The factor $\frac{1}{2}$ is included for convenience which will be apparent in what follows. From equation (1) we have

$$dx_i' = \frac{\partial x_i'}{\partial x_i}\,dx_i = dx_i + \frac{\partial u_i}{\partial x_j}\,dx_j. \tag{4}$$

Equations (4) can be written in matrix notation, which formalism will be found to be more convenient in the present considerations. Thus

$$
\left\| \begin{array}{c} dx_1' \\ \\ dx_2' \\ \\ dx_3' \end{array} \right\|
=
\left\| \begin{array}{ccc} \dfrac{\partial x_1'}{\partial x_1} & \dfrac{\partial x_1'}{\partial x_2} & \dfrac{\partial x_1'}{\partial x_3} \\ \\ \dfrac{\partial x_2'}{\partial x_1} & \dfrac{\partial x_2'}{\partial x_2} & \dfrac{\partial x_2'}{\partial x_3} \\ \\ \dfrac{\partial x_3'}{\partial x_1} & \dfrac{\partial x_3'}{\partial x_2} & \dfrac{\partial x_3'}{\partial x_3} \end{array} \right\|
\left\| \begin{array}{c} dx_1 \\ \\ dx_2 \\ \\ dx_3 \end{array} \right\|
$$

$$
=
\left\| \begin{array}{ccc} 1+\dfrac{\partial u_1}{\partial x_1} & \dfrac{\partial u_1}{\partial x_2} & \dfrac{\partial u_1}{\partial x_3} \\ \\ \dfrac{\partial u_2}{\partial x_1} & 1+\dfrac{\partial u_2}{\partial x_2} & \dfrac{\partial u_2}{\partial x_3} \\ \\ \dfrac{\partial u_3}{\partial x_1} & \dfrac{\partial u_3}{\partial x_2} & 1+\dfrac{\partial u_3}{\partial x_3} \end{array} \right\|
\left\| \begin{array}{c} dx_1 \\ \\ dx_2 \\ \\ dx_3 \end{array} \right\|. \tag{5}
$$

In short,

$$\left\| dx_i' \right\| = \left\| \frac{\partial x_i'}{\partial x_j} \right\| \left\| dx_i \right\|$$

$$= \left\| \left(\delta_{ij} + \frac{\partial u_i}{\partial x_j} \right) \right\| \left\| dx_i \right\|. \tag{6}$$

The matrix

$$\left\| \frac{\partial x_i'}{\partial x_j} \right\| = \left\| \left(\delta_{ij} + \frac{\partial u_i}{\partial x_j} \right) \right\|$$

which is the Jacobian matrix

$$\frac{\partial(x_1', x_2', x_3')}{\partial(x_1, x_2, x_3)}$$

is denoted by J. In the matrix notation

$$dx_i'\,dx_i' = \| dx_i' \|^+ \| dx_i' \|$$

where $\| dx_i' \|^+$, the transpose of $\| dx_i' \|$, is a row matrix. Therefore we have

$$ds^2 = dx_i'\,dx_i' = \| dx_i' \|^+ \| dx_i' \| = \| dx_i \|^+ J^+ J \| dx_i \| \tag{7}$$

and

$$ds^2 - ds_0^2 = \| dx_i \|^+ J^+ J \| dx_i \| - \| dx_i \|^+ E_3 \| dx_i \|$$

$$= \| dx_i \|^+ (J^+ J - E_3) \| dx_i \| \tag{8}$$

where E_3 denotes the unit matrix in three dimensions. If we set,

$$\tfrac{1}{2}(J^+ J - E_3) = \eta \tag{9}$$

we have

$$\tfrac{1}{2}(ds^2 - ds_0^2) = \| dx_i \|^+ \eta \| dx_i \|. \tag{10}$$

The matrix η is called the strain matrix. To compute η, we make use of equation (9) which tells us to form the product $J^+ J$ and subtract unity from each of the diagonal elements. By halving each of the elements of this matrix, we obtain the elements of the η matrix. They are written out *in extenso* here.

$$\eta_{11} = \frac{\partial u_1}{\partial x_1} + \frac{1}{2}\left[\left(\frac{\partial u_1}{\partial x_1}\right)^2 + \left(\frac{\partial u_2}{\partial x_1}\right)^2 + \left(\frac{\partial u_3}{\partial x_1}\right)^2 \right]$$

$$\eta_{22} = \frac{\partial u_2}{\partial x_2} + \frac{1}{2}\left[\left(\frac{\partial u_1}{\partial x_2}\right)^2 + \left(\frac{\partial u_2}{\partial x_2}\right)^2 + \left(\frac{\partial u_3}{\partial x_3}\right)^2 \right]$$

$$\eta_{33} = \frac{\partial u_3}{\partial x_2} + \frac{1}{2}\left[\left(\frac{\partial u_1}{\partial x_2}\right)^2 + \left(\frac{\partial u_2}{\partial x_2}\right)^2 + \left(\frac{\partial u_3}{\partial x_3}\right)^2 \right]$$

$$\eta_{23} = \frac{1}{2}\left(\frac{\partial u_3}{\partial x_2} + \frac{\partial u_2}{\partial x_3}\right) + \frac{1}{2}\left[\frac{\partial u_1}{\partial x_2}\frac{\partial u_1}{\partial x_3} + \frac{\partial u_2}{\partial x_2}\frac{\partial u_2}{\partial x_3} + \frac{\partial u_3}{\partial x_2}\frac{\partial u_3}{\partial x_3}\right]$$

$$\eta_{31} = \frac{1}{2}\left(\frac{\partial u_1}{\partial x_3} + \frac{\partial u_3}{\partial x_1}\right) + \frac{1}{2}\left[\frac{\partial u_1}{\partial x_3}\frac{\partial u_1}{\partial x_1} + \frac{\partial u_2}{\partial x_3}\frac{\partial u_2}{\partial x_1} + \frac{\partial u_3}{\partial x_3}\frac{\partial u_3}{\partial x_1}\right]$$

$$\eta_{12} = \frac{1}{2}\left(\frac{\partial u_2}{\partial x_1} + \frac{\partial u_1}{\partial x_2}\right) + \frac{1}{2}\left[\frac{\partial u_1}{\partial x_1}\frac{\partial u_1}{\partial x_2} + \frac{\partial u_2}{\partial x_1}\frac{\partial u_2}{\partial x_2} + \frac{\partial u_3}{\partial x_1}\frac{\partial u_3}{\partial x_2}\right]. \tag{11}$$

There are only six independent terms as the η matrix is symmetric. That the η is a symmetric matrix is evident from the fact that $J^+ J$ is symmetric for every J, and E_3 is obviously symmetric; and the difference of two symmetric matrices is symmetric.

Equation (10) can be written in the following form as well:

$$\tfrac{1}{2}(ds^2 - ds_0^2) = \eta_{ij}\, dx_i\, dx_j \tag{12}$$

which shows that the right-hand side is an invariant under the transformation of the coordinates x_i. Since $dx_i\, dx_j$, which are products of the differentials of coordinates, transform as a second rank symmetric tensor, it follows from quotient theorem that η_{ij} transform as a second rank symmetric tensor.

It is evident that if we neglect the squares and products of the derivatives of the displacements, the new strain tensor η_{ij} reduces to the strain tensor ε_{ij} defined in the infinitesimal theory. The strain components η_{ij} are, however, not amenable to simple geometrical interpretations as in the case of ε_{ij}. It can only be shown that when the deformations are considered small, they possess interpretations analogous to the corresponding infinitesimal components. Consider a small linear element $ds_0 = dx_1$. The linear strain is defined as usual equal to $(ds - ds_0)/ds_0$, which we shall denote here by ε_1. We have

$$ds = (1 + \varepsilon_1)\, ds_0$$

and from equation (12), we have

$$ds^2 - ds_0^2 = 2\eta_{11}\, dx_1^2.$$

From the above two relations and after substituting ds_0 for dx_1, it follows that

$$(1 + \varepsilon_1)^2 = 1 + 2\eta_{11}.$$

Thus, we have

$$\varepsilon_1 = (1 + 2\eta_{11})^{\frac{1}{2}} - 1.$$

If η_{11} is small such that η_{11}^2 is negligible, we can obtain from the above equation, the relation

$$\varepsilon_1 = \eta_{11}.$$

That is, the component η_{11} reduces to the linear strain in the X_1-direction when the deformation is small. Similarly η_{22} and η_{33} give linear strains in the X_2- and X_3-directions when the deformation is small.

It can be shown under similar approximation that η_{ij} when $i \neq j$ reduce to one-half of the change in the angle between two linear elements which are along the X_i- and X_j-axes in the initial unstrained state.

Let dx_1, dx_2, dx_3 be a small volume element dV in the initial unstrained state. The deformation may be considered as a transformation of variables (x_1, x_2, x_3) to (x_1', x_2', x_3') and from the well-known formula for the transformation of volume element due to transformation of variables we have

$$dV' = dx_1'\, dx_2'\, dx_3' = \det \frac{\partial(x_1', x_2', x_3')}{\partial(x_1, x_2, x_3)}\, dx_1\, dx_2\, dx_3$$

$$= \det J\, dV.$$

Thus,

$$\frac{dV'}{dV} = \det J. \tag{13}$$

Squaring both sides of (13) we have

$$\left(\frac{\mathrm{d}V'}{\mathrm{d}V}\right)^2 = (\det J)^2 = J^+ J.$$

If we denote the cubical dilatation $(\mathrm{d}V' - \mathrm{d}V)/\mathrm{d}V$ by K, it follows that $\mathrm{d}V'/\mathrm{d}V = (K+1)$, and from the above equation we have

$$(K+1)^2 = J^+ J = (J^+ J - E_3) + E_3 = (2\eta + E_3).$$

When the deformation is small, K^2 can be neglected and we can substitute ε's in the place of η's. Under such an approximation, the above equation reduces to the familiar formula of the infinitesimal theory for dilatation, namely $K = \varepsilon_{11} + \varepsilon_{22} + \varepsilon_{33}$.

In the infinitesimal theory, the six components of the stress tensor τ_{ik} are obtained as the derivatives of the strain energy function ϕ with respect to the corresponding strain components. In the finite theory, the stresses are given as the elements in the matrix derived from the following formula due to Murnaghan.[†]

$$\tau = \frac{\rho'}{\rho} J \frac{\partial \phi}{\partial \eta} J^+.$$

Here ρ' is the density after deformation, while ρ is the density before the deformation. If V' and V be corresponding volumes per unit mass of the substance, we have the relations

$$\frac{\rho'}{\rho} = \frac{V}{V'} = \frac{1}{\det J}.$$

To obtain the stress tensor, we have to first write out the energy as a function of all the 9 strain components η_{ik}, disregarding the symmetry relation $\eta_{ik} = \eta_{ki}$. From this the energy derivative matrix $\partial \phi / \partial \eta_{ik}$ has to be obtained and the product matrix $J(\partial \phi / \partial \eta) J^+$ has to be formed. This has to be finally multiplied by

$$\frac{\rho'}{\rho} = \frac{1}{\det J}.$$

Such calculations are in general laborious.

12.2 Third Order Elasticity

In problems concerned with large elastic deformation of matter, the approximation adopted in limiting the components of the strain tensor to terms of first degree in the derivatives of the displacements is not justified. In such problems the general form of the strain tensor η_{ij} is adopted and the strain energy expansion is taken up to the third order

[†] Murnaghan, F. D., "Finite Deformation of an Elastic Solid", Wiley, New York (1951).

terms in the strain components η_{ij}. The strain energy is then written as

$$\phi = \phi_0 + \phi_1 + \phi_2 + \phi_3$$
$$= \phi_0 + c_{ij}\,\eta_{ij} + \tfrac{1}{2}c_{ijkl}\,\eta_{ij}\,\eta_{kl} + C_{ijklmn}\,\eta_{ij}\,\eta_{kl}\,\eta_{mn}. \tag{14}$$

If we assume, as before, that the initial energy is zero and that the strains are measured from a state of zero stress, we can drop the terms ϕ_0 and ϕ_1. The c_{ijkl} are elastic stiffnesses of which 21 are independent for a triclinic crystal. The coefficients C_{ijklmn} are called third order elastic coefficients. They obviously form a tensor of sixth rank.

Adopting the one-suffix notation proposed for the strains in Chapter 11, the third order coefficients are written in a three-suffix notation. In this shorter notation the strain energy expression (14) is written as

$$\phi = \tfrac{1}{2}c_{ij}\,\eta_i\,\eta_j + C_{ijk}\,\eta_i\,\eta_j\,\eta_k. \tag{15}$$

Relations similar to equation (8) of Chapter 11 which give the intrinsic symmetry of the third order elasticity tensor C_{ijklmn} can be written down. They show that the tensor is invariant with respect to interchange of i with j or k with l or m with n, and also to an interchange of any of the three pairs ij, kl and mn with another. A sixth rank tensor in three variables can in general have 729 components. The intrinsic symmetry reduces the maximum number of independent components permissible to 56. This reduction can be obtained by writing the tensor components in the three-suffix notation as C_{ijk}. It is immediately seen that the independent components are those C_{ijk} which have suffixes taking values from 1 to 6 such that $i \leqslant j \leqslant k$. The number of such coefficients is

$$\sum_{n=1}^{6} \frac{n(n+1)}{2} = 56.$$

Here we are obtaining the number of independent C_{ijk} where the digits involved are 1 to 6 and the tensor is total symmetric for any interchange amongst i, j and k. This is equivalent to writing down H_r^n, the number of ways in which n numbers can be written in groups of r, repetitions in any group being permitted. We have the relation

$$H_r^n = \frac{n(n+1)\dots(n+r-1)}{r!}.$$

For the second order elastic coefficients, $n = 6$ and $r = 2$. We have

$$H_2^6 = \frac{6 \times 7}{2 \times 1} = 21.$$

For the third order elastic coefficients, $n = 6$ and $r = 3$. We have

$$H_3^6 = \frac{6 \times 7 \times 8}{1 \times 2 \times 3} = 56.$$

12.3 Effect of Symmetry on Third Order Elastic Coefficients

Thus it follows that a triclinic crystal requires an additional 56 constants, besides the 21 constants pertaining to the second order terms in the strain energy, to describe its elastic behaviour when the deformations cannot be taken as infinitesimal. The number of independent third order coefficients necessary for each of the 32 crystal classes can be readily obtained. The results are given in column (12) of Table VIII(a) on page 92. It is significant that the 32 crystal classes fall into 11 subsystems. This is to be expected because elasticity which is a centrosymmetric property can distinguish only 11 classes, in which the symmetry operation of inversion explicitly occurs. These 11 are in fact the X-ray groups. By measurements on elasticity, we cannot further distinguish the subgroups of these 11 point groups. We may note that the elastic stiffness tensor c_{ijkl} fails to distinguish the two subsystems in the hexagonal system and the tetrahedral from the octahedral classes in the cubic system, because it has a higher symmetry than the third order elasticity tensor.

To derive the schemes of independent third order elastic coefficients, the same methods described in the case of second order elastic coefficients are applicable. We give here the results only in respect of cubic crystals and isotropic substances. For results in respect of all the 32 crystal classes, the original work of Hearmon[†] may be referred to. For the tetrahedral classes 23 and $m3$ in the cubic system, the following relations between the coefficients hold good. It will be noticed that for these classes, there are 8 independent coefficients. The coefficients not cited are all zero.

$$C_{111} = C_{222} = C_{333}, \quad C_{112} = C_{133} = C_{223},$$

$$C_{113} = C_{122} = C_{233}, \quad C_{123}, \quad C_{144} = C_{255} = C_{366},$$

$$C_{155} = C_{266} = C_{344}, \quad C_{166} = C_{244} = C_{355}, \quad C_{456}.$$

For the octahedral classes $\overline{4}3m$, 432 and $m3m$, there are 6 independent coefficients. These are obtained by putting $C_{112} = C_{113}$ and $C_{155} = C_{166}$ in the above relations. For isotropic substances, there are 3 independent coefficients. These are obtained by recognizing 3 relations amongst the 6 independent coefficients cited above. These relations are shown in (16).

$$C_{144} = 2C_{112} - C_{123}, \quad C_{155} = 3C_{111} - C_{112},$$

$$C_{456} = 6C_{111} - 6C_{112} + 2C_{123}. \tag{16}$$

[†] Hearmon, R. F. S., *Acta cryst.* **6**, 331 (1953).

12.4 Cubic Crystals

If we confine ourselves to the classes $\overline{4}3m$, 432 and $m3m$, we have seen that there are 6 independent elastic coefficients of the third order and they are C_{111}, C_{112}, C_{123}, C_{144}, C_{155} and C_{456}. The number reduces to 3 for an isotropic substance by the existence of relations (16) amongst the above 6 coefficients. By analogy with the second order coefficients in cubic crystals and isotropic substances, the satisfying or otherwise of relations (16) may be taken as indicating whether a crystal is elastically nearly isotropic or not in the region of third order elasticity.

We do not, however, have experimental values for all the individual constants in the case of any single crystal. Using the data obtained in respect of some cubic crystals up to hydrostatic pressures of 10,000 bars, Hearmon derived the orders of magnitude for 3 combinations of the 6 independent coefficients. The combinations C_a, C_b and C_d are given by

$$C_a = 6C_{111} + 4C_{112}; \quad C_b = C_{123} + 4C_{112};$$

$$C_d = \tfrac{1}{2}C_{144} + C_{155}.$$

In NaCl, for example, $C_a = -100 \times 10^{11}$; $C_b = -14 \times 10^{11}$ and $C_d = -11 \times 10^{11}$ dynes/cm^2. The corresponding values of the second order elastic constants of NaCl are $c_{11} = 4{\cdot}83 \times 10^{11}$; $c_{12} = 1{\cdot}26 \times 10^{11}$ and $c_{44} = 1{\cdot}26 \times 10^{11}$ dynes/cm^2. It may be noted that all the third order combinations are negative and numerically an order of magnitude larger than the second order coefficients.

Further, while the number of constants remains at 3 in respect of second order elasticity as we move from the three octahedral classes to the two tetrahedral classes of the cubic system, the corresponding number in respect of third order elasticity goes up from 6 to 8. That there is such a difference in respect of third order elastic coefficients between the two groups of classes in the cubic system was first obtained and pointed out by the author† with the help of group theoretical methods. This result is of significance and is analogous to what we shall discuss in greater detail when we consider the photoelastic tensor in a later Chapter.

12.5 Cubic Crystals Subject to Large Hydrostatic Pressures

A study of the elastic behaviour of crystals subject to large strains is in general complicated due to the large number of constants involved. For this reason, only such cases as are characterized by a high degree of symmetry, like the cubic and isotropic, have received attention. Of particular interest is the problem of the effect of large hydrostatic

† Bhagavantam, S. and Suryanarayana, D., *Nature, Lond.* **160**, 750 (1947).

pressures on the elastic constants of cubic crystals. We shall take up the derivation of expressions for the coefficients that specify the elastic behaviour of cubic crystals which are already subjected to large hydrostatic pressures.

In the power series expansion for the strain energy function ϕ given in (14), the constant term ϕ_0 is of no significance to us as we are ultimately interested only in the derivatives of ϕ. The first order term ϕ_1 is linear in the η's and may be expressed as follows in the one-suffix notation already introduced.

$$\phi_1 = c_i \eta_i \quad i = 1 \text{ to } 6. \tag{17}$$

The second order term ϕ_2 is quadratic in the η's and contains second order elastic constants. The third order term ϕ_3 is cubic in η's and contains third order elastic constants which come into play when the strains are large. For a substance of cubic symmetry the strain energy expression in the second and third order terms is given in (18). We shall in what follows refer to the strained state of a body given by strains η_i, $i = 1$ to 6 as the η state of the body.

$$\phi = \phi_2 + \phi_3$$

$$= \frac{c_{11}}{2}(\eta_1^2 + \eta_2^2 + \eta_3^2) + c_{12}(\eta_1\eta_2 + \eta_2\eta_3 + \eta_3\eta_1)$$

$$+ 2c_{44}(\eta_4^2 + \eta_5^2 + \eta_6^2) + C_{111}(\eta_1^3 + \eta_2^3 + \eta_3^3)$$

$$+ C_{112}\{\eta_1\eta_2(\eta_1 + \eta_2) + \eta_2\eta_3(\eta_2 + \eta_3) + \eta_3\eta_1(\eta_3 + \eta_1)\}$$

$$+ C_{123}\eta_1\eta_2\eta_3 + C_{456}\eta_4\eta_5\eta_6 + C_{144}(\eta_1\eta_4^2 + \eta_2\eta_5^2 + \eta_3\eta_6^2)$$

$$+ C_{155}\{\eta_1(\eta_5^2 + \eta_6^2) + \eta_2(\eta_4^2 + \eta_6^2) + \eta_3(\eta_4^2 + \eta_5^2)\}. \tag{18}$$

If on a cubic crystal already subjected to a large hydrostatic pressure P, we superpose infinitesimal strains $\delta\eta_i$ over the finite strains caused by the pressure P, we have the following first order term in the strain energy where compression is taken as negative:

$$\phi_1 = -P(\delta\eta_1 + \delta\eta_2 + \delta\eta_3). \tag{19}$$

A uniform hydrostatic pressure does not alter the symmetry of a crystal. Therefore the strain energy ϕ' accumulated in the cubic crystal due to the superposed infinitesimal strain is still given by an expression which involves $\delta\eta$'s only up to the second order. We may write

$$\phi' = -P(\delta\eta_1 + \delta\eta_2 + \delta\eta_3) + \tfrac{1}{2}b_{11}(\delta\eta_1^2 + \delta\eta_2^2 + \delta\eta_3^2)$$

$$+ b_{12}(\delta\eta_1\delta\eta_2 + \delta\eta_2\delta\eta_3 + \delta\eta_3\delta\eta_1)$$

$$+ 2b_{44}(\delta\eta_4^2 + \delta\eta_5^2 + \delta\eta_6^2). \tag{20}$$

The constants b_{11}, b_{12}, b_{44}, which specify the second order elastic behaviour of the crystal which still possesses cubic symmetry, are not in fact constants. They are in general different from c_{11}, c_{12}, c_{44} which specify its behaviour under initially stress-free conditions. They are functions of the usual second order and third order elastic constants as well as the finite strain on which the infinitesimal strain is superposed. The final state of the body may be referred to as the $\eta + \delta\eta$ state. The strain energy due to the final $\eta + \delta\eta$ strain, starting from a zero stress state, may be denoted by $\phi(\eta + \delta\eta)$.

The difference between the strain energies in the $\eta + \delta\eta$ state and the η state which can be directly evaluated must be equal to the strain energy ϕ' due to the infinitesimal strain superposed. We have, however, to take into account the fact that ϕ' given in (20) refers to a unit volume in the η state, whereas the difference $\phi(\eta + \delta\eta) - \phi(\eta)$ refers to a unit volume in the initial stress-free state.

We shall evaluate the strain energy in the η state, namely the state of uniform compression due to the hydrostatic pressure P. If a typical point (x_1, x_2, x_3) in the stress-free state is moved over to (x_1', x_2', x_3') after the finite uniform compression, we have

$$x_1' = (1+\eta)\,x_1; \quad x_2' = (1+\eta)\,x_2; \quad x_3' = (1+\eta)\,x_3$$

where

$$\eta = \frac{\partial u_1}{\partial x_1} = \frac{\partial u_2}{\partial x_2} = \frac{\partial u_3}{\partial x_3}.$$

The corresponding Jacobian of the transformation is given in (21), the strain and stress matrices in (22) and (23). Substituting for the strains in (18), we get the strain energy $\phi(\eta)$ due to the large uniform compression.

$$J_0 = \begin{Vmatrix} 1+\eta & 0 & 0 \\ 0 & 1+\eta & 0 \\ 0 & 0 & 1+\eta \end{Vmatrix}. \tag{21}$$

$$\begin{Vmatrix} \eta + \eta^{2/2} & 0 & 0 \\ 0 & \eta + \eta^{2/2} & 0 \\ 0 & 0 & \eta + \eta^{2/2} \end{Vmatrix}. \tag{22}$$

$$\begin{Vmatrix} \dfrac{\partial\phi/\partial\eta}{1+\eta} & 0 & 0 \\[3ex] 0 & \dfrac{\partial\phi/\partial\eta}{1+\eta} & 0 \\[3ex] 0 & 0 & \dfrac{\partial\phi/\partial\eta}{1+\eta} \end{Vmatrix}. \tag{23}$$

We shall next obtain the strain energy in the $\eta + \delta\eta$ state. Let the typical point be further moved to x_1'', x_2'', x_3'' from x_1', x_2', x_3'. The general relationship between x_i'' and x_i' may be given by

$$x_1'' = (1 + \delta_1)\, x_1' + \delta_6\, x_2' + \delta_5\, x_3'$$
$$x_2'' = \delta_6\, x_1' + (1 + \delta_2)\, x_2' + \delta_4\, x_3'$$
$$x_3'' = \delta_5\, x_1' + \delta_4\, x_2' + (1 + \delta_3)\, x_3'. \tag{24}$$

The Jacobian of the above transformation denoted by J_δ is given in (25).

$$J_\delta = \left\| \begin{array}{ccc} 1 + \delta_1 & \delta_6 & \delta_5 \\ \delta_6 & 1 + \delta_2 & \delta_4 \\ \delta_5 & \delta_4 & 1 + \delta_3 \end{array} \right\|. \tag{25}$$

In formulating J_δ in this symmetric form with 6 independent components, it is assumed that the rotations are removed beforehand. Now substituting $x_i' = (1 + \eta)\, x_i$, we finally get the transformation from the initial state x_i to the final state x_i'' as

$$x'' = Jx \quad \text{where} \quad J = (1 + \eta)\, J_\delta. \tag{26}$$

Forming $\frac{1}{2}(J^+ J - E_3)$, we obtain the strain matrix for this entire deformation $\eta + \delta\eta$ as

$$\left\| \begin{array}{ccc} R + q^2\, \delta\eta_1 & q^2\, \delta\eta_6 & q^2\, \delta\eta_5 \\ q^2\, \delta\eta_6 & R + q^2\, \delta\eta_2 & q^2\, \delta\eta_4 \\ q^2\, \delta\eta_5 & q^2\, \delta\eta_4 & R + q^2\, \delta\eta_3 \end{array} \right\| \tag{27}$$

where $R = \eta + \eta^2/2 = $ initial strain, $q = 1 + \eta$

$$\delta\eta_1 = \delta_1 + \tfrac{1}{2}(\delta_1^2 + \delta_5^2 + \delta_6^2) \quad \delta\eta_4 = \delta_4 + \tfrac{1}{2}(\delta_2\delta_4 + \delta_3\delta_4 + \delta_5\delta_6)$$
$$\delta\eta_2 = \delta_2 + \tfrac{1}{2}(\delta_2^2 + \delta_4^2 + \delta_6^2) \quad \delta\eta_5 = \delta_5 + \tfrac{1}{2}(\delta_1\delta_5 + \delta_3\delta_5 + \delta_4\delta_6)$$
$$\delta\eta_3 = \delta_3 + \tfrac{1}{2}(\delta_3^2 + \delta_4^2 + \delta_5^2) \quad \delta\eta_6 = \delta_6 + \tfrac{1}{2}(\delta_1\delta_6 + \delta_2\delta_6 + \delta_4\delta_5). \tag{28}$$

It should be noted here that we are maintaining the distinction between the δ matrix (25) which specifies the displacement, and the $\delta\eta$ matrix which is the strain matrix corresponding to the J_δ transformation. Further, while we have taken our additional deformation as infinitesimal, we are still keeping the square terms δ_1^2, etc. in the expression for $\delta\eta$. This is necessary because the energy of the infinitesimal deformation ϕ' will ultimately have terms up to squares and products of the displacement derivatives δ_1, δ_2, etc. If ϕ' contained only quadratic terms in the $\delta\eta$, it would have been wholly unnecessary to keep any square of the δ in the expression for $\delta\eta$. However, when an initial stress is present, ϕ' contains linear terms in the $\delta\eta$ which give rise to terms of the second degree in the δ's, as is evident from (28). Hence, we note the important point that, when an initial stress is present, even an infinitesimal strain thereon will have to be treated as a finite one only, no approximation being justifiable in the value for the strain element. After the energy expression is formed using the correct value of the strain component, terms higher than the second powers of the displacement derivatives could be neglected, to justify its classification as an infinitesimal deformation.

We can substitute the values of the strains from (27) to get the total energy in the $\eta + \delta\eta$ state. The difference $\phi(\eta + \delta\eta) - \phi(\eta)$ is then evaluated. This is the energy of the infinitesimal deformation when referred to a unit volume of the stress-free state. We multiply it by $1/\det J_0$ to refer it to a unit volume of the η state, i.e. by a factor $(1+\eta)^{-3}$. According to the energy method explained earlier, we equate this quantity to ϕ' to get

$$(1+\eta)^{-3}\left[\{R(c_{11}+2c_{12})+R^2(3C_{111}+6C_{112}+C_{123})\}(1+\eta)^2(\delta\eta_1+\delta\eta_2+\delta\eta_3)\right.$$

$$+\tfrac{1}{2}\{c_{11}+R(6C_{111}+4C_{112})\}(1+\eta)^4(\delta\eta_1^2+\delta\eta_2^2+\delta\eta_3^2)$$

$$+\{c_{12}+R.C_{123}+R.4C_{112}\}(1+\eta)^4(\delta\eta_1\delta\eta_2+\delta\eta_2\delta\eta_3+\delta\eta_3\delta\eta_1)$$

$$\left.+\tfrac{1}{2}\{4c_{44}+R(2C_{144}+4C_{155})\}(1+\eta)^4(\delta\eta_4^2+\delta\eta_5^2+\delta\eta_6^2)\right]$$

$$=\phi'=-P(\delta\eta_1+\delta\eta_2+\delta\eta_3)+\tfrac{1}{2}b_{11}(\delta\eta_1^2+\delta\eta_2^2+\delta\eta_3^2)$$

$$+b_{12}(\delta\eta_1\delta\eta_2+\delta\eta_2\delta\eta_3+\delta\eta_3\delta\eta_1)+2b_{44}(\delta\eta_4^2+\delta\eta_5^2+\delta\eta_6^2). \quad (29)$$

Equating the coefficient of $\delta\eta_1$ on either side, we immediately get

$$-P=(c_{11}+2c_{12})\frac{\eta+\tfrac{1}{2}\eta^2}{1+\eta}+\frac{(\eta+\tfrac{1}{2}\eta^2)^2}{1+\eta}(3C_{111}+6C_{112}+C_{123})$$

which, on development in powers of η and retaining up to η^2, becomes

$$-P=\eta(c_{11}+2c_{12})+\eta^2(3C_{111}+6C_{112}+C_{123}-\tfrac{1}{2}c_{11}-c_{12}). \quad (30)$$

In the same manner by equating coefficients of $\delta\eta_1^2$, $\delta\eta_1\delta\eta_2$ and $\delta\eta_4^2$ we get

$$b_{11}=c_{11}+\eta(c_{11}+6C_{111}+4C_{112})+\eta^2(9C_{111}+6C_{112}) \quad (31)$$

$$b_{12}=c_{12}+\eta(c_{12}+4C_{112}+C_{123})+\eta^2(6C_{112}+\tfrac{3}{2}C_{123}) \quad (32)$$

$$b_{44}=c_{44}+\eta(c_{44}+\tfrac{1}{2}C_{144}+C_{155})+\eta^2(\tfrac{3}{4}C_{144}+\tfrac{3}{2}C_{155}). \quad (33)$$

So far our task has been to derive an expression for the additional strain energy due to an infinitesimal deformation in powers of the strain components $\delta\eta$, each of which, however, involved not only terms linear in the δ_1, δ_2, etc., but the quadratic terms in them as well. For further discussion on the elastic behaviour of the substance from the η state, it will be necessary to express this energy in terms of $\delta_1, \ldots, \delta_6$. Substituting from (28) in (20) and retaining terms up to the second power of δ's only, we get

$$\phi' = -P(\delta_1 + \delta_2 + \delta_3) + \tfrac{1}{2}(b_{11} - P)\,(\delta_1^2 + \delta_2^2 + \delta_3^2)$$
$$+ b_{12}(\delta_1\delta_2 + \delta_2\delta_3 + \delta_3\delta_1) + (2b_{44} - P)\,(\delta_4^2 + \delta_5^2 + \delta_6^2). \tag{34}$$

The expression ϕ' refers to the total deformation energy which should be rendered available from external sources in order that the deformation η to $\eta + \delta\eta$ could be effected on a unit volume element in the η state. It has to be remembered, however, that an external force, namely the hydrostatic stress, is already present and there is the potential energy associated with this force. When displacements resulting in deformations $\delta_1, \delta_2, \delta_3$ take place, an amount of energy $\Delta W = -P(\delta_1 + \delta_2 + \delta_3)$ is released from this external potential energy. In other words, the work done by the existing external force in this displacement which is ΔW can go in as increase in internal energy, i.e. the strain energy, and thus meet the part of the total requirement ϕ'. Hence the extra energy, that should be made available in order that the deformation η to $\eta + \delta\eta$ may take place, is given by $\phi_e = \phi' - \Delta W$. ϕ_e, which is the effective elastic energy, represents the energy associated with an infinitesimal deformation which takes place from a state of finite strain, just as the usual elastic energy ϕ refers to a similar deformation of a state with zero initial strain. ϕ_e is thus obtained from ϕ' by the removal of the linear terms $-P(\delta_1 + \delta_2 + \delta_3)$. We have

$$\phi_e = \phi' - \Delta W = \phi' + P(\delta_1 + \delta_2 + \delta_3) = \tfrac{1}{2}c_{11}'(\delta_1^2 + \delta_2^2 + \delta_3^2)$$
$$+ c_{12}'(\delta_1\delta_2 + \delta_2\delta_3 + \delta_3\delta_1) + 2c_{44}'(\delta_4^2 + \delta_5^2 + \delta_6^2) \tag{35}$$

where

$$c_{11}' = b_{11} - P = c_{11} + \eta(2c_{11} + 2c_{12} + 6C_{111} + 4C_{112})$$
$$+ \eta^2(12C_{111} + 12C_{112} + C_{123} - \tfrac{1}{2}c_{11} - c_{12})$$
$$c_{12}' = b_{12} = c_{12} + \eta(c_{12} + 4C_{112} + C_{123}) + \eta^2(6C_{112} + \tfrac{3}{2}C_{123})$$
$$c_{44}' = b_{44} - \tfrac{1}{2}P = c_{44} + \eta(\tfrac{1}{2}c_{11} + c_{12} + c_{44} + \tfrac{1}{2}C_{144} + C_{155})$$
$$+ \eta^2(\tfrac{3}{2}C_{111} + 3C_{112} + \tfrac{1}{2}C_{123} + \tfrac{3}{4}C_{144}$$
$$+ \tfrac{3}{2}C_{155} - \tfrac{1}{4}c_{11} - \tfrac{1}{2}c_{12}). \tag{36}$$

The new constants $c_{11}', c_{12}', c_{44}'$ will be called the effective elastic constants. While ϕ_e could have been directly derived by substitution of relations such as $\delta\eta_1 = \delta_1 + \tfrac{1}{2}(\delta_1^2 + \delta_5^2 + \delta_6^2)$ in the function ϕ, the development of an intermediate function ϕ' as has been done in this Chapter helps us to retain $\delta\eta$ as it is, till a convenient stage is reached, whereafter ϕ_e could be easily deduced. This reduces the labour involved in a full substitution of $\delta\eta$ from the beginning itself.

The $\delta_1, \delta_2, \ldots, \delta_6$ are the displacement derivatives. In the infinitesimal theory, they are directly identified with the infinitesimal strain components themselves. We can therefore get the stresses required for effecting the δ deformation by the usual processes of differentiating the appropriate strain energy function, which in this case is ϕ_e. We thus obtain for the additional stresses $t_1, t_2, \ldots, t_6$ the relations

$$t_1 = c'_{11}\delta_1 + c'_{12}(\delta_2 + \delta_3) \tag{37}$$

with similar equations for t_2 and t_3 and

$$t_4 = 2c'_{44}\delta_4 \tag{38}$$

with similar equations for t_5 and t_6. Equations (37) and (38) are indicative of the linear relationships which connect the additional stresses with the additional strains through the effective elastic constants $c'_{11}, c'_{12}, c'_{44}$.

CHAPTER 13

Thermal Expansion

13.1 Nature of Thermal Expansion

At any given temperature T, the strain in a crystal will be fully described by a symmetric second rank tensor ε_{ij}. If there is a small change in temperature given by ΔT, the change taking place uniformly over the entire region of the crystal in which the strain has been designated as ε_{ij}, then the changes produced in all the components of ε are proportional to ΔT, the physical property connecting the two physical quantities strain and temperature being called thermal expansion. We have

$$\Delta \varepsilon_{ij} = e_{ij} \Delta T. \tag{1}$$

Since the left-hand side of equation (1) is a symmetric second rank tensor and ΔT is a scalar, e_{ij} should be a symmetric second rank tensor. We shall now refer to e_{ij} as the thermal expansion tensor.

As in the case of strain, we can now talk of a thermal expansion quadric, for which the equation will be

$$e_{ij} x_i x_j = 1. \tag{2}$$

The quadric (2) can obviously be referred to its principal axes so as to make the equation take the form

$$e_1 x_1^2 + e_2 x_2^2 + e_3 x_3^2 = 1 \tag{3}$$

where x_1, x_2, x_3 are taken along the principal axes of the ellipsoid of thermal expansion and e_1, e_2, e_3 are the principal coefficients of thermal expansion. They can be regarded, as in the case of principal strains, as the changes in length produced in unit original lengths along the principal directions when there is a uniform change of temperature of one unit in the crystal.

13.2 Effect of Crystal Symmetry on Thermal Expansion

It is evident that a triclinic crystal will need six distinct components in order that its thermal expansion properties may be fully described. In other crystals, the tensor is subject to restrictions imposed by Neumann's principle. The numbers required for different crystal systems have already been obtained and given under column 3 of

Table VIII(a). They, along with the schemes of tensor components, are reproduced below. The reference of the tensor components is to the crystallographic axes being chosen as the coordinate axes in accordance with the usual conventions wherever possible.

Crystal system	Number of independent coefficients	Tensor components		
Triclinic	6	e_{11}	e_{12}	e_{13}
			e_{22}	e_{23}
				e_{33}
Monoclinic	4	e_{11}	e_{12}	0
			e_{22}	0
				e_{33}
Orthorhombic	3	e_{11}	0	0
			e_{22}	0
				e_{33}
Tetragonal Trigonal Hexagonal	2	e_{11}	0	0
			e_{11}	0
				e_{33}
Cubic	1	e_{11}	0	0
			e_{11}	0
				e_{11}

As in the case of the strain quadric, the sum $e_{11} + e_{22} + e_{33}$ for any crystal is an invariant and this in fact represents the coefficient of volume expansion of the bulk crystal when its temperature is altered. The conventional definition of this quantity is the change in volume produced per unit original volume of the substance for one degree change in temperature. Thermal expansion coefficients have been measured for many crystals representing all the crystal systems. In all cases, the results agree with what is expected in the above analysis. There are some interesting substances such as calcite where one of the principal coefficients is negative, implying that the quadric is a hyperboloid. In most cases, all the coefficients are positive and the quadric is accordingly an ellipsoid. Substances like gypsum and graphite exhibit a marked anisotropy of thermal expansion.

13.3 Some General Remarks

Thermal expansion has been treated in the foregoing as an isolated physical property. That this is not strictly permissible for a thermodynamic system was pointed out and its implications discussed in detail in Chapter 8. In a more rigorous treatment, we have to take account of other parameters like stress, entropy and so on and related effects like elasticity, piezoelectricity, etc. will enter the discussion. In practice, however, the coupling between such cross effects is small and certain physical properties like the one under consideration may be dealt with in a satisfactory manner as if they are not connected with the others.

CHAPTER 14

Electrical Properties

14.1 Dielectric Properties of Crystals

If in a dielectric crystal plate, an electric field E_i is acting, the medium acquires an electric moment. The electric moment induced in unit volume is called the polarization and we may denote it by P_i. P_i and E_i are vectors related to each other by the physical property of electric polarizability or the dielectric susceptibility. This may easily be seen to be a symmetric tensor of the second rank in the general case. We have

$$P_i = \alpha_{ij} E_j. \tag{1}$$

If an external electric field E_0 is to cause the field E inside the crystal plate, assumed to be of large area and small thickness, the relationship between the usual electrical quantities is given by (2).

$$D = E_0 = KE = E + 4\pi P$$

or

$$K = D/E = 1 + 4\pi\alpha. \tag{2}$$

D is the electric displacement and K is the dielectric constant. K is simply related to α and has the same features as α for all crystalline media. In general, K is a symmetric tensor of the second rank and may be called the dielectric constant tensor.

We can study the effect of symmetry on these tensors straightaway. However, it is good to recall that we cannot regard the physical quantities involved and the physical property as isolated phenomena. For instance, if the crystal is piezoelectric, the presence of an electric field will cause strains. If strain is regarded as the extensive parameter, the corresponding intensive parameter is stress. It has been pointed out earlier that, while determining the elastic constants of crystals, one should specify the thermal conditions such as adiabatic or isothermal, under which the determinations are being made. Similarly, while determining the dielectric constants of crystals, one should specify the mechanical conditions such as constant strain or constant stress, under which the determinations are being made. In cases where there is no coupling between the electric field and the mechanical strain, as there will be in crystals which do not exhibit piezoelectricity, these considerations are not of any importance and we can simply talk of a dielectric constant. We shall, therefore, understand K_0, written for brevity as K, as referring to the dielectric constant in a state of no stress and no strain. K^τ and K^ϵ will be used to respectively represent the same quantity under conditions of constant stress and of constant strain. For most practical cases, the distinction is of little consequence because K^τ and K^ϵ differ only by very small amounts.

14.2 Effect of Symmetry on Dielectric Constants

K is a second rank symmetric tensor and all the six components will be needed to describe the dielectric behaviour of a triclinic crystal. The numbers needed for other crystal classes will be the same as for any other similar physical property like optical polarization or magnetic susceptibility represented by a second rank symmetric tensor. Being a second rank symmetric tensor, K_{ij} can always be referred to its principal axes. In crystals belonging to the triclinic, monoclinic and ortho-rhombic systems all the three principal values of the tensor are different. Such crystals are called biaxial. In the triclinic system the directions of the principal axes are not uniquely related to any directions in the crystal. In the monoclinic system one of the principal axes must coincide with the axis of symmetry or be perpendicular to the plane of symmetry of the crystal. In the orthorhombic system, all three principal axes are crystallographically fixed. In the crystals belonging to tetragonal, trigonal and hexagonal systems, two of the three principal values are equal. Such crystals are called uniaxial. One of the principal axes of the tensor coincides with the axis of symmetry of the crystals belonging to classes C_4, C_3 or C_6, but the directions of other principal axes can be arbitrarily chosen. In the cubic system, all the three principal values of the tensor are the same and the directions of principal axes are also the directions of the cube axes.

14.3 Pyroelectricity and Electrocaloric Effect

Certain crystals have the property of exhibiting electric polarization when the temperature is changed uniformly. This property is referred to as pyroelectricity and is the relation that connects temperature, a scalar physical quantity, with electric moment per unit volume which is a vector physical quantity. It is easy to study the effect of symmetry on this physical property. We may commence by stating that pyro-electricity can occur only in such crystals in which there is at least one direction which remains unchanged under all the symmetry operations of the crystal. This condition is satisfied in crystals whose groups of symmetry operations are generated by single axes of rotation. The condition is also satisfied in crystals having planes of symmetry besides the axes of rotation mentioned, which pass through the respective axes of rotation. The condition is not satisfied in crystals possessing the operation of inversion as a symmetry operation. The condition is also not satisfied if either two symmetry axes are mutually inclined or if a symmetry plane exists which does not contain a symmetry axis. Thus we arrive at the result that pyroelectricity is possible in the following classes only: $C_1, C_s, C_2, C_{2v}, C_4, C_{4v}, C_3, C_{3v}, C_6, C_{6v}$.

Electrocaloric effect is the name given to the converse phenomenon in which we expect to find a change of temperature produced when a change is effected in the electric polarization of a dielectric medium by withdrawing the electric field.

14.4 Piezoelectricity

A piezoelectric crystal is one in which electric polarization is produced when it is subjected to a stress. Quartz and tourmaline are two earliest known examples of such crystals. There are many others which exhibit this phenomenon and which have been extensively studied in recent years. Complete quantitative data are now available for more than 100 crystals. Some ceramic materials with marked piezoelectric properties have been developed and used in many practical contrivances. Piezoelectricity should be regarded as the physical property which connects the physical quantity stress, on the one hand, with the physical quantity of electric polarization, on the other. Stress is a symmetric second rank tensor and its components may be designated as $\tau_{11}(\tau_1)$, $\tau_{22}(\tau_2), \tau_{33}(\tau_3), \tau_{23}(\tau_4), \tau_{31}(\tau_5), \tau_{12}(\tau_6)$, the symbols in brackets being of the contracted one-suffix notation. If P_1, P_2 and P_3 are the components of the electric polarization moment per unit volume, we may write

$$P_i = d_{ijk} \tau_{jk} = d_{il} \tau_l \tag{3}$$

where i, j, k take the values $1, 2, 3$ and l takes the values 1 to 6. The d_{il}'s are 18 in number and constitute a tensor of rank 3 although the number of prefixes is reduced for convenience to two by shortening. They are called the piezoelectric stress coefficients.

As was shown in Chapter 8, it is also possible to conceive of the converse physical property by which a crystal when subjected to an electric field develops a strain. In such a case, the physical quantities involved are an electric field whose components are E_1, E_2 and E_3 and a strain whose components are ε_1 to ε_6. We may write

$$\varepsilon_1 = d_{li} E_i. \tag{4}$$

In equation (4) again, l takes the values 1 to 6 and i takes the values 1 to 3. The effect may be designated as the converse piezoelectric effect and the d's in equation (4) are the same as in (3).

It is also permissible to replace the stress components in equation (3) by the strain components. We will still get the same property, but the coefficients in that case have been termed the piezoelectric strain coefficients. The converse effect will also contain the same coefficients, but the strain components in equation (4) will be replaced by stress components. Such a change is equivalent to interchanging stress and strain in the compliance matrix of Chapter 8. It may be noted that there is no uniqueness of either choice.

The array of piezoelectric stress coefficients may be written in a matrix form as

$$\left\|\begin{array}{cccccc} d_{11} & d_{12} & d_{13} & d_{14} & d_{15} & d_{16} \\ d_{21} & d_{22} & d_{23} & d_{24} & d_{25} & d_{26} \\ d_{31} & d_{32} & d_{33} & d_{34} & d_{35} & d_{36} \end{array}\right\|.$$

P_1, P_2 and P_3 are obtained from the first, second and third rows, respectively, by forming the sums $d_{1l}\tau_l$, $d_{2l}\tau_l$ and $d_{3l}\tau_l$, as may be seen from equation (3). Similarly, equation (4) enables us to get ε_1 to ε_6 by forming the sums along each of the six columns in the above matrix.

14.5 Effect of Crystal Symmetry

Crystal symmetry reduces the number of independent piezoelectric moduli from 18 to 1 as we go from the triclinic asymmetric class to the cubic classes. In particular cases, special results may be obtained. The actual numbers are given in column 5 of Table VIII(a).

One noteworthy case is the crystal class possessing a centre of inversion. By the application of such a symmetry operation, the most general kind of stress remains invariant as we have assumed that it is a symmetry operation of the stress tensor. In order that the tensor equation connecting the electric moment, piezoelectricity and stress may remain invariant, it follows that the electric moment should remain unchanged on inverting the coordinate axes. This leads to $P_1 = -P_1$; $P_2 = -P_2$; $P_3 = -P_3$ and is possible only when $P_1 = P_2 = P_3 = 0$. Hence, we conclude that a crystal with a centre of symmetry cannot be piezo-electric.

Detailed schemes of non-vanishing tensor coefficients are given below for the 20 classes in which piezoelectricity is permissible on considerations of symmetry alone. In all cases of single crystals where the effect has been studied in detail, the results agree with what the schemes imply.

(i) TRICLINIC SYSTEM: CLASS 1

$$\begin{matrix} d_{11} & d_{12} & d_{13} & d_{14} & d_{15} & d_{16} \\ d_{21} & d_{22} & d_{23} & d_{24} & d_{25} & d_{26} \\ d_{31} & d_{32} & d_{33} & d_{34} & d_{35} & d_{36} \end{matrix}$$

(ii) (a) MONOCLINIC SYSTEM: CLASS m

$$\begin{matrix} d_{11} & d_{12} & d_{13} & 0 & 0 & d_{16} \\ d_{21} & d_{22} & d_{23} & 0 & 0 & d_{26} \\ 0 & 0 & 0 & d_{34} & d_{35} & 0 \end{matrix}$$

(ii) (b) MONOCLINIC SYSTEM: CLASS 2

$$\begin{matrix} 0 & 0 & 0 & d_{14} & d_{15} & 0 \\ 0 & 0 & 0 & d_{24} & d_{25} & 0 \\ d_{31} & d_{32} & d_{33} & 0 & 0 & d_{36} \end{matrix}$$

(iii) (a) ORTHORHOMBIC SYSTEM: CLASS $2mm$

$$\begin{matrix} 0 & 0 & 0 & 0 & d_{15} & 0 \\ 0 & 0 & 0 & d_{24} & 0 & 0 \\ d_{31} & d_{32} & d_{33} & 0 & 0 & 0 \end{matrix}$$

(iii) (b) ORTHORHOMBIC SYSTEM: CLASS 222

$$\begin{matrix} 0 & 0 & 0 & d_{14} & 0 & 0 \\ 0 & 0 & 0 & 0 & d_{25} & 0 \\ 0 & 0 & 0 & 0 & 0 & d_{36} \end{matrix}$$

(iv) (a) TETRAGONAL SYSTEM: CLASS 4

$$\begin{matrix} 0 & 0 & 0 & d_{14} & d_{15} & 0 \\ 0 & 0 & 0 & d_{15} & -d_{14} & 0 \\ d_{31} & d_{31} & d_{33} & 0 & 0 & 0 \end{matrix}$$

(iv) (b) TETRAGONAL SYSTEM: CLASS $\bar{4}$

$$\begin{matrix} 0 & 0 & 0 & d_{14} & d_{15} & 0 \\ 0 & 0 & 0 & -d_{15} & d_{14} & 0 \\ d_{31} & -d_{31} & 0 & 0 & 0 & d_{36} \end{matrix}$$

(iv) (c) TETRAGONAL SYSTEM: CLASS $4mm$

$$
\begin{matrix}
0 & 0 & 0 & 0 & d_{15} & 0 \\
0 & 0 & 0 & d_{15} & 0 & 0 \\
d_{31} & d_{31} & d_{33} & 0 & 0 & 0
\end{matrix}
$$

(iv) (d) TETRAGONAL SYSTEM: CLASS $\overline{4}2m$

$$
\begin{matrix}
0 & 0 & 0 & d_{14} & 0 & 0 \\
0 & 0 & 0 & 0 & d_{14} & 0 \\
0 & 0 & 0 & 0 & 0 & d_{36}
\end{matrix}
$$

(iv) (e) TETRAGONAL SYSTEM: CLASS 422

$$
\begin{matrix}
0 & 0 & 0 & d_{14} & 0 & 0 \\
0 & 0 & 0 & 0 & -d_{14} & 0 \\
0 & 0 & 0 & 0 & 0 & 0
\end{matrix}
$$

(v) (a) TRIGONAL SYSTEM: CLASS 3

$$
\begin{matrix}
d_{11} & -d_{11} & 0 & d_{14} & d_{15} & -2d_{22} \\
-d_{22} & d_{22} & 0 & d_{15} & -d_{14} & -2d_{11} \\
d_{31} & d_{31} & d_{33} & 0 & 0 & 0
\end{matrix}
$$

(v) (b) TRIGONAL SYSTEM: CLASS $3m$

$$
\begin{matrix}
0 & 0 & 0 & 0 & d_{15} & -2d_{22} \\
-d_{22} & d_{22} & 0 & d_{15} & 0 & 0 \\
d_{31} & d_{31} & d_{33} & 0 & 0 & 0
\end{matrix}
$$

(v) (c) TRIGONAL SYSTEM: CLASS 32

$$
\begin{matrix}
d_{11} & -d_{11} & 0 & d_{14} & 0 & 0 \\
0 & 0 & 0 & 0 & -d_{14} & -2d_{11} \\
0 & 0 & 0 & 0 & 0 & 0
\end{matrix}
$$

(vi) (a) HEXAGONAL SYSTEM: CLASS $\overline{6}$

$$
\begin{matrix}
d_{11} & -d_{11} & 0 & 0 & 0 & -2d_{22} \\
-d_{22} & d_{22} & 0 & 0 & 0 & -2d_{11} \\
0 & 0 & 0 & 0 & 0 & 0
\end{matrix}
$$

(vi) (b) HEXAGONAL SYSTEM: CLASS 6

Same scheme as Class 4.

(vi) (c) HEXAGONAL SYSTEM: CLASS $\bar{6}m2$

$$\begin{array}{cccccc} 0 & 0 & 0 & 0 & 0 & -2d_{22} \\ -d_{22} & d_{22} & 0 & 0 & 0 & 0 \\ 0 & 0 & 0 & 0 & 0 & 0 \end{array}$$

(vi) (d) HEXAGONAL SYSTEM: CLASS 6mm

Same scheme as Class 4mm.

(vi) (e) HEXAGONAL SYSTEM: CLASS 622

Same scheme as Class 422.

(vii) CUBIC SYSTEM: CLASSES 23 and $\bar{4}3m$

$$\begin{array}{cccccc} 0 & 0 & 0 & d_{14} & 0 & 0 \\ 0 & 0 & 0 & 0 & d_{14} & 0 \\ 0 & 0 & 0 & 0 & 0 & d_{14} \end{array}$$

CHAPTER 15

Magnetic Properties

15.1 Special Features of Magnetic Properties

A physical property is referred to as a magnetic property, if one or both of the interacting physical quantities involve the magnetic field or magnetic induction or magnetic moment as a part thereof. It has already been mentioned that the magnetic field, magnetic induction and magnetic moment are axial vectors, and physical quantities and physical properties which involve them are either polar tensors or axial tensors respectively, according as whether an odd or even multiple of magnetic vectors is involved in their definition. In dealing with physical properties represented by axial tensors, their special transformation properties should be borne in mind. This special feature is brought out in Table X

TABLE X

Special features of magnetic properties

Physical property	Action tensor	Effect tensor	Physical property tensor	Symbol used
Magnetic susceptibility	Magnetic field (axial vector)	Magnetic moment (axial vector)	Symmetric second rank polar tensor	μ_{ij}
Magnetoelectric polarizability and its converse	Electric field (polar vector)	Magnetic moment (axial vector)	Second rank axial tensor	λ_{ij}
Magnetocaloric effect and pyromagnetism	Magnetic moment (axial vector)	Temperature (scalar)	Axial vector	q_i
Piezomagnetism and its converse	Stress (polar tensor)	Magnetic moment (axial vector)	Third rank axial tensor	Q_{ijk}

in respect of some magnetic properties. It may be noted that except in the case of magnetic susceptibility, the action tensor and the effect tensor have to be interchanged and suitably interpreted where necessary, when we are dealing with the converse effect in each of the properties described in Table X. These special transformation properties have an effect on the physical property and influence the manner in which crystal symmetry affects the tensor components of the physical property. The procedure for taking this into account has been fully explained in Chapter 7 while deriving the appropriate characters in the group theoretical method.

Another special feature which we have to bear in mind is that the magnetic field, the magnetic induction and the magnetic moment, being represented by axial vectors, have the additional property of changing sign under the operation $\mathcal{R}$. The application of a complementary symmetry operation to such a vector is accomplished by first applying the conventional symmetry operation and then changing the sign of all its components. Since a physical property tensor is expressible as a product of a suitable number of vectors which may be polar or axial or magnetic, it follows that if the magnetic vector is involved an even number of times the operation $\mathcal{R}$ has no effect on the property. A symmetry operation and its complement transform such a tensor in the same manner. It follows that such a property cannot distinguish the 90 magnetic classes. With the help of such a property, we can recognize no more than the 32 crystal classes. However, if the magnetic vector is involved an odd number of times in the physical property, the transformation of the tensor representing the property due to a symmetry operation and that due to its complement are distinct. In fact they differ in sign. Such a physical property is observable only in the 90 magnetic classes and enables us to distinguish them as distinct from each other.

Thus, when dealing with magnetic properties, we have to take cognizance of the magnetic nature of the crystal in which they are observed. Crystals may be broadly classified in this regard as being diamagnetic, paramagnetic, ferromagnetic or antiferromagnetic. For example, when we consider the property of dia- or paramagnetic susceptibility, we should note that the corresponding tensor involves a magnetic vector an even number of times. Accordingly, we deal with the 32 conventional crystal classes when we study such properties. It is only for such substances that a unique relationship between the magnetic field and the magnetic moment exists and the property is defined by this unique relationship. On the other hand, ferromagnetism and antiferromagnetism imply the presence of a magnetic moment even in the absence of an external magnetic field. This is possible only if we take into account magnetic structures and the 90 magnetic classes as distinct from the 32 conventional classes which permit of dia- and paramagnetism only. Similarly, if a crystal has to exhibit a property like piezomagnetism, it has to possess a magnetic structure, i.e. it has to be either a ferromagnetic or an antiferromagnetic. In fact, piezomagnetism is observable only in antiferromagnetics since ferromagnetism is of such magnitude that, if present, it easily masks any piezomagnetism that may appear. Piezomagnetism is also a property which involves the magnetic moment vector in the first power and is, therefore, according to the above arguments, capable of distinguishing the 90 magnetic classes.

That properties like piezomagnetism are forbidden in the dia- or paramagnetic bodies can be inferred from symmetry consideration also. Such considerations follow from the generalized formalism adopted in Section 5.8 in categorizing the crystallographic point groups. We noted there that the introduction of the operation $\mathscr{R}$ has resulted in classifying the dia- and paramagnetic crystals under the 32 grey groups. Every grey group contains the element $\mathscr{R}$ explicitly and consequently contains the complements of all its elements. It follows that any physical property which involves an odd power of a magnetic vector is forbidden in such a crystal. This is easily seen to be so because for every R_i, $\chi(R_i) = -\chi(\underline{R}_i)$ and since a grey group contains the complements of all its elements, the number of independent non-vanishing coefficients computed using formula (1) of Chapter 7, turns out to be zero.

In the following sections of this Chapter, each of the magnetic properties mentioned in Table X is considered in some detail with a view to investigating the effect of symmetry on them.

15.2 Magnetic Susceptibility

For reasons already mentioned, although magnetic susceptibility is a magnetic property, the fact that the concerned physical property tensor is in every respect like a symmetric second rank tensor of the ordinary type results in the character of an operation R being the same as of its complementary operation $\underline{R}$. In this case, neither do we need to pay any attention to the special features that arise in the character evaluation for an axial tensor nor do we have to deal with 90 magnetic classes. This conclusion does not, however, apply to crystals in the ferromagnetic region. In fact the results to be expected for μ_{ij}, provided we confine ourselves to diamagnetic or paramagnetic susceptibilities, are exactly the same as for dielectric constant as described in Chapter 14.

15.3 Magnetocaloric Effect

This effect is concerned with the changes in temperature observed in a crystal by the withdrawal or introduction of an external magnetic field. It is of great practical importance as it has led to the production of very low temperatures by what has come to be known as adiabatic demagnetization. Its converse effect is known as pyromagnetism. Both are vectors and apart from the presence or otherwise of these effects as observable phenomena in specific crystals, the fact that the classes which can exhibit these properties are also those in which spontaneous magnetization in the absence of an external field can exist is of significance. This follows from the statements made earlier that irrespective of the detailed nature of the physical property under consideration, its behaviour under varying symmetry conditions will be the same as attributable to other physical properties of the same group in the sense that the properties in the group are all capable of being described by a tensor of one particular rank and type. In this case, ferromagnetism, pyromagnetism and magnetocaloric effect are all physical properties which can be described by an axial vector of the magnetic moment type. Thirty-one of the 90 magnetic classes are potentially capable of exhibiting these effects. These may be identified from Table VIII(c).

15.4 Magnetoelectric Polarizability

This phenomenon (or its converse) is the production of a magnetic moment I (or electric moment P) on the application of an electric field E (or magnetic field H) in a direction normal to it. Following a suggestion made by Landau and Lifshitz, Dzyaloshinskii[†] has shown that the effect is possible in crystals which possess a magnetic structure. The effect has been experimentally observed to occur in Cr_2O_3 and in Ti_2O_3 in the antiferromagnetic state. The relation between E and I is given by

$$I_i = \lambda_{ij} E_j.$$

λ_{ij} is the magnetoelectric polarizability tensor. Since E is a polar vector and I is an axial vector, λ_{ij} is a second rank tensor which transforms according to the representation formed by the product of the representations of E and I. The character, as has already been derived, of a symmetry operation R_ϕ in this representation is given by $(\pm 1 + 2\cos\phi)(1 \pm 2\cos\phi)$ where $+$ or $-$ is taken according as the symmetry operation is a pure rotation or a rotation-reflection. The character of a complementary operation $\underline{R}_\phi$ is the same as above multiplied by -1. The results for this and all other properties in this group, so far as mere numbers are concerned, are given against each of the magnetic crystal classes in Table VIII(c). That the magnetoelectric polarizability λ_{ij} is an axial tensor of second rank and is also magnetic

† Dzyaloshinskii, I. E., *Soviet Phys. JETP* **10**, 37 (1960).

is evident from the constitutive equations given above. Thirty-two of the 90 magnetic classes consist of conventional symmetry operations only. Under the conventional operations, λ_{ij} transforms as an axial tensor of second rank and it follows that it vanishes in the 11 centrosymmetric classes: $\bar{1}, 2/m, mmm, 4/m, 4/mmm, \bar{3}, \bar{3}m, 6/m, 6/mmm, m3$, $m3m$. The following 10 mixed groups in which i occurs as a conventional operation are magnetic variants of the above: $\underline{2}/m, m\underline{mm}, \underline{4}/m, 4/m\underline{mm}$, $\underline{4}/mm\underline{m}, \bar{3}\underline{m}, \underline{6}/\underline{m}, 6/m\underline{mm}, \underline{6}/m\underline{mm}, m3\underline{m}$.

For reasons similar to those which forbid an axial tensor of even rank in centrosymmetric classes, λ_{ij} is forbidden in these 10 classes as well. This result is evidently a general one and it may be stated that all axial tensors of even rank which are also magnetic are forbidden in the 21 magnetic classes given above. Therefore, we need consider only the remaining 69 classes. However, we find from Table VIII(c) that the tensor vanishes in the following 11 classes as well: $\bar{6}, \underline{6}, \underline{6}/m, \bar{6}m2, \bar{6}\underline{m}2$, $\underline{6}mm, \underline{6}22, \underline{6}/mm\underline{m}, \bar{4}3m, \underline{4}32, \underline{m}3m$.

Thus, we are left with 58 classes which are potentially capable of exhibiting this effect. The detailed schemes of coefficients under each of these classes are derived and listed below.

It is obvious that all the 9 coefficients remain in the classes $1, \bar{1}$.

Taking the class m, we note that the operation σ_h corresponds to the transformation of coordinates $x_1 \rightarrow x_1, x_2 \rightarrow x_2, x_3 \rightarrow -x_3$. This operation being a rotation-reflection and λ_{ij} being an axial tensor, we note that $\lambda_{13}, \lambda_{23}, \lambda_{31}, \lambda_{32}$ are non-vanishing. If C_2, which is a pure rotation, is taken along X_3, we have the transformation $x_1 \rightarrow -x_1, x_2 \rightarrow -x_2, x_3 \rightarrow x_3$, and this leaves $\lambda_{11}, \lambda_{12}, \lambda_{21}, \lambda_{22}, \lambda_{33}$ invariant and therefore as non-vanishing. It is evident that the above two sets of components are mutually exclusive. Now σ_h taken perpendicular to X_3 is equivalent to multiplying by -1 the transformed components obtained after the application of σ_h. Therefore all those components that are left invariant by σ_h vanish, and those left invariant by C_2 are left non-vanishing on the application of σ_h. Similarly by applying $\underline{C_2}$ we obtain the same non-vanishing components obtained by the application of σ_h. It follows that the groups 2, $\underline{m}$ and $2/\underline{m}$, the last one being generated by C_2 and $\underline{\sigma_h}$, possess the same scheme of coefficients, namely $\lambda_{11}, \lambda_{12}, \lambda_{21}, \lambda_{22}, \lambda_{33}$. Again the groups $\underline{2}$, m and $\underline{2}/m$, the last one being generated by $\underline{C_2}$ and σ_h, possess the same scheme namely $\lambda_{13}, \lambda_{23}, \lambda_{31}, \lambda_{32}$.

We next take a C_2 parallel to X_1, given by the transformation $x_1 \rightarrow x_1, x_2 \rightarrow -x_2, x_3 \rightarrow -x_3$. This, when applied to the scheme appropriate to the class 2, will leave $\lambda_{11}, \lambda_{22}, \lambda_{33}$ only as non-vanishing. Now C_2 parallel to X_3 and C_2 parallel to X_1 generate the class 222 and consequently $\lambda_{11}, \lambda_{22}, \lambda_{33}$ form the scheme of this class. We have seen above that the application of a C_2 to the tensor λ_{ij} is equivalent to applying σ_h perpendicular to that axis. It follows immediately that the classes $2\underline{mm}$ and $\underline{mmm}$ possess the same scheme as 222.

We next apply a $\underline{C_2}$ parallel to X_1 to the scheme appropriate to the class 2. This is complementary to C_2 parallel to X_1. Therefore the components left invariant by C_2 namely $\lambda_{11}, \lambda_{22}, \lambda_{33}$ will vanish and $\lambda_{12}, \lambda_{21}$ remain as non-vanishing. C_2 parallel to X_3 and C_2 parallel to X_1 generate the group 222. Since $\underline{C_2}$ is equivalent to a σ_h perpendicular to its axis, we conclude that the groups $2mm, \underline{mmm}$ also should possess the same scheme. A little reflection will show that the same scheme must apply to the class $\underline{2mm}$ if we take $\underline{C_2}$ parallel to X_1 and σ_h perpendicular to X_3.

We next take the class 4 with C_4 parallel to X_3. C_4 is given by $x_1 \to x_2, x_2 \to -x_1, x_3 \to x_3$. Since C_4 implies a C_2 about the same axis, we need apply the transformation to the scheme appropriate to class 2. We obtain the relations $\lambda_{12} = -\lambda_{21}, \lambda_{11} = \lambda_{22}$, between the coefficients appropriate to that class. Class $\bar{4}$ possesses the same scheme because the operation $\overline{C_4}$ is performed by multiplying twice with -1 the transformed coefficients obtained after the application of C_4: once because it is a rotation-reflection and a second time because it is a complementary operation. Since the C_2 implied in C_4 is equivalent to a σ_h perpendicular to it and since the C_4 and $\underline{\sigma_h}$ generate the group $4/\underline{m}$, we conclude that the class $4/\underline{m}$ also possesses the same scheme.

To apply C_3 and C_6, both taken parallel to X_3, we resort to equations (7.4). They are directly applicable because the operations are conventional pure rotations. We obtain the same scheme appropriate to class 4. Due to similar reasons advanced as in the case of class 4, it follows that the classes $3, \bar{3}, 6, \bar{6}, 6/m$ possess the same scheme.

The operation $\bar{C_4}$ parallel to X_3 also implies a C_2 about the same axis and we have only to multiply by -1, the transformed coefficients obtained after the application of C_4 and demand invariance. This gives the scheme $\lambda_{11} = -\lambda_{22}, \lambda_{12} = \lambda_{21}$. Application of $\underline{C_4}$ is effected by the same procedure as above. Thus the classes $\underline{4}, \bar{4}$ and $\underline{4}/m$ for reasons given in connection with the class $4/\underline{m}$ possess the same scheme.

If we apply a C_2 parallel to X_1 on the scheme appropriate to the class 4, we obtain that λ_{12} must vanish and $\lambda_{11} = \lambda_{22}, \lambda_{33}$ remain. These two elements generate the group 422. For reasons which are already advanced in connection with the previous cases, the classes $4\underline{mm}, \bar{4}\underline{2m}$, $4/\underline{mmm}, 32, 3m, \bar{3}m, 622, 6\underline{mm}, \underline{6m}2, 6/\underline{mmm}$ possess the same scheme as that of 422.

Similarly if we apply a C_2 parallel to X_1 on the scheme appropriate to $\bar{4}$, we obtain the scheme $\lambda_{11} = -\lambda_{22}$. $\bar{4}$ and C_2 generate the group $\bar{4}2m$.

For reasons which are obvious $4mm, 4/mmm$, $422, \bar{4}2m$ also possess the same scheme.

If we had applied a C_2 parallel to X_1 on the scheme appropriate to 4, we would be left with the coefficients that vanish due to the application of C_2 namely, $\lambda_{12} = -\lambda_{21}$. C_4 and C_2 generate 422. The classes $4mm, \bar{4}2m, 4/mmm, 32, 3m, \bar{3}m, 622, 6mm, \bar{6}m2, 6/mmm$ possess the same scheme.

To obtain the scheme appropriate to the class 23, we have only to apply a C_3 given by $x_1 \to x_2, x_2 \to x_3, x_3 \to x_1$ on the scheme appropriate to the class 222. The application of this transformation is effected by putting all the suffixes of the components in that scheme equal to each other. We obtain the relations $\lambda_{11} = \lambda_{22} = \lambda_{33}$. It is easy to see that the classes $23, m3, 432, \bar{4}3m, m3m$ possess the same scheme.

We thus obtain 11 distinct types of schemes. They are given on page 171 and against each scheme the corresponding magnetic classes are shown.

We may add here that the experimental observation of the magnetoelectric polarizability provides conclusive evidence in favour of recognizing the magnetic symmetry of crystals. Cr_2O_3 possesses the conventional symmetry appropriate to the class $\bar{3}m$ which is centrosymmetric and λ_{ij} is an axial tensor of even rank. From conventional arguments, we will arrive at the conclusion that this effect is forbidden in Cr_2O_3 crystals. On the other hand, the recognition of magnetic symmetry brings out the distinct features of the symmetry of the crystal in its antiferromagnetic state and the special transformation properties of the tensor λ_{ij}. This enables us to obtain the result that Cr_2O_3 in its antiferromagnetic state possesses the symmetry appropriate to the magnetic class $\bar{3}m$, and that magnetoelectric polarizability possesses two independent non-vanishing constants $\lambda_{11} = \lambda_{22}$ and λ_{33}. Experiment has confirmed this result. The converse effect of production of electrical polarization on the application of magnetic field has also been experimentally observed.

15.5 Piezomagnetism

Piezomagnetism is the appearance of a magnetic moment on the application of a stress. This effect, to which a reference has already been made in Chapter 6, has actually been discovered and experimentally measured only recently by Borovik-Romanov[†] in CoF_2 and MnF_2 crystals in their antiferromagnetic state. The appropriate tensor Q_{ijk} is of rank 3 and is axial as well as magnetic in nature. The character of a symmetry operation R_ϕ in this representation is given

† Borovik-Romanov, A. S., *Soviet Phys. JETP* **9**, 1390 (1959).

Magnetic class	Magnetoelectric polarizability tensor
$1,\ \underline{\bar{1}}$	$\begin{matrix} \lambda_{11} & \lambda_{12} & \lambda_{13} \\ \lambda_{21} & \lambda_{22} & \lambda_{23} \\ \lambda_{31} & \lambda_{32} & \lambda_{33} \end{matrix}$
$\underline{2},\ m,\ \underline{2}/m$	$\begin{matrix} 0 & 0 & \lambda_{13} \\ 0 & 0 & \lambda_{23} \\ \lambda_{31} & \lambda_{32} & 0 \end{matrix}$
$2,\ \underline{m},\ 2/\underline{m}$	$\begin{matrix} \lambda_{11} & \lambda_{12} & 0 \\ \lambda_{21} & \lambda_{22} & 0 \\ 0 & 0 & \lambda_{33} \end{matrix}$
$222,\ 2\underline{mm},\ \underline{mmm}$	$\begin{matrix} \lambda_{11} & 0 & 0 \\ 0 & \lambda_{22} & 0 \\ 0 & 0 & \lambda_{33} \end{matrix}$
$\underline{222},\ 2mm,\ \underline{2}m\underline{m},\ \underline{m}mm$	$\begin{matrix} 0 & \lambda_{12} & 0 \\ \lambda_{21} & 0 & 0 \\ 0 & 0 & 0 \end{matrix}$
$4,\ \underline{\bar{4}},\ 4/\underline{m},\ 3,\ \underline{\bar{3}},\ 6,\ \underline{\bar{6}},\ 6/\underline{m}$	$\begin{matrix} \lambda_{11} & \lambda_{12} & 0 \\ -\lambda_{12} & \lambda_{11} & 0 \\ 0 & 0 & \lambda_{33} \end{matrix}$
$\underline{4},\ \bar{4},\ \underline{4}/\underline{m}$	$\begin{matrix} \lambda_{11} & \lambda_{12} & 0 \\ \lambda_{12} & -\lambda_{11} & 0 \\ 0 & 0 & 0 \end{matrix}$
$422,\ 4\underline{mm},\ \bar{4}2m,\ 4/\underline{mmm},$ $32,\ 3\underline{m},\ \underline{\bar{3}m},\ 622,\ 6\underline{mm},$ $\underline{\bar{6}}m2,\ 6/\underline{mmm}$	$\begin{matrix} \lambda_{11} & 0 & 0 \\ 0 & \lambda_{11} & 0 \\ 0 & 0 & \lambda_{33} \end{matrix}$
$\underline{4}\underline{2}2,\ \underline{4}mm,\ \bar{4}2m,\ \bar{4}\underline{2}\underline{m},$ $4/m\underline{mm}$	$\begin{matrix} \lambda_{11} & 0 & 0 \\ 0 & -\lambda_{11} & 0 \\ 0 & 0 & 0 \end{matrix}$
$422,\ 4mm,\ \bar{4}2m,\ 4/\underline{m}mm,$ $3\underline{2},\ 3m,\ \bar{3}m,\ 6\underline{22},\ 6mm,$ $\bar{6}m\underline{2},\ 6/\underline{m}mm$	$\begin{matrix} 0 & \lambda_{12} & 0 \\ -\lambda_{12} & 0 & 0 \\ 0 & 0 & 0 \end{matrix}$
$23,\ \underline{m}3,\ 432,\ \bar{4}3\underline{m},\ \underline{m}3\underline{m}$	$\begin{matrix} \lambda_{11} & 0 & 0 \\ 0 & \lambda_{11} & 0 \\ 0 & 0 & \lambda_{11} \end{matrix}$

by $(4\cos^2\phi \pm 2\cos\phi)(1 \pm 2\cos\phi)$; + and − signs are to be taken with the usual convention. The character of a complementary operation R_ϕ is the same but multiplied by -1. The results obtained, in respect of numbers alone, for the 90 magnetic crystal classes are given in Table VIII(c). It may be noted that such an effect gets masked if ferromagnetism is simultaneously present.

A general result is apparent here. We know that a polar tensor of odd rank vanishes in the 11 conventional centrosymmetric classes. The effect of the operation i on a polar tensor of odd rank can be seen to be equivalent to the effect of the operation $\underline{i}$ on an axial tensor of odd rank. It follows that any axial magnetic tensor of odd rank and in particular Q_{ijk} which is one such vanishes in all those magnetic classes which contain $\underline{i}$. There are 21 such classes and they are given below.

$$\overline{1}, 2/\underline{m}, \underline{2}/m, \underline{m}\underline{m}\underline{m}, \underline{m}mm, 4/\underline{m}, \underline{4}/\underline{m}, \underline{4}/\underline{m}\underline{m}\underline{m},$$

$$4/\underline{m}mm, 4/\underline{m}\underline{m}\underline{m}, \overline{3}, \overline{3}\underline{m}, \overline{3}\underline{m}, 6/\underline{m}, \underline{6}/m, 6/\underline{m}mm,$$

$$6/\underline{m}\underline{m}\underline{m}, \underline{6}/mm\underline{m}, \underline{m}3, \underline{m}3\underline{m}, \underline{m}3m$$

From Table VIII(c), it is seen that Q_{ijk} vanishes in 3 more classes, namely $\overline{4}3m, 432, m3m$. Detailed schemes of non-vanishing tensor coefficients are given below for the remaining 66 classes in which piezomagnetism is permissible.

15.6 Magnetostriction

Converse piezomagnetism may be looked upon as the physical property which relates a magnetic field H as the action tensor and a strain ε in the crystal as the effect tensor. In a simple linear form, this connection will be represented by

$$\varepsilon_{ij} = Q_{ijk} H_k. \tag{1}$$

If we recognize that each strain component may also be made up of terms of the second order in H in addition to those of the first order, equation (1) will have to be written as

$$\varepsilon_{ij} = Q_{ijk} H_k + Q_{ijkl} H_k H_l. \tag{2}$$

Q_{ijkl} has the intrinsic symmetry of $ij = ji$ and $kl = lk$. It is a fourth rank polar tensor and different views have been expressed in the literature regarding its symmetry for the transposition of ij with kl.†
We note that the magnetic field is appearing in its even power. We do not, therefore, have to consider the magnetic classes separately for

† Shuvalov, L. A., and Tavger, B. A., Soviet Phys. Crystallography **3**, 765 (1958–60); Landau, L. D. and Lifshitz, E. M., "Electrodynamics of Continuous Media." Pergamon Press, Oxford (1960).

Magnetic class	Piezomagnetism tensor					
$1, \bar{1}$	Q_{11}	Q_{12}	Q_{13}	Q_{14}	Q_{15}	Q_{16}
	Q_{21}	Q_{22}	Q_{23}	Q_{24}	Q_{25}	Q_{26}
	Q_{31}	Q_{32}	Q_{33}	Q_{34}	Q_{35}	Q_{36}
$m, 2, 2/m$	0	0	0	Q_{14}	Q_{15}	0
	0	0	0	Q_{24}	Q_{25}	0
	Q_{31}	Q_{32}	Q_{33}	0	0	Q_{36}
$\underline{m}, \underline{2}, 2/\underline{m}$	Q_{11}	Q_{12}	Q_{13}	0	0	Q_{16}
	Q_{21}	Q_{22}	Q_{23}	0	0	Q_{26}
	0	0	0	Q_{34}	Q_{35}	0
$2mm, 222, mmm$	0	0	0	Q_{14}	0	0
	0	0	0	0	Q_{25}	0
	0	0	0	0	0	Q_{36}
$\underline{2}m\underline{m}, 2\underline{m}\underline{m}, \underline{2}\underline{2}2, m\underline{m}\underline{m}$	0	0	0	0	Q_{15}	0
	0	0	0	Q_{24}	0	0
	Q_{31}	Q_{32}	Q_{33}	0	0	0
$4, \bar{4}, 4/m, 6, \bar{6}, 6/m$	0	0	0	Q_{14}	Q_{15}	0
	0	0	0	Q_{15}	$-Q_{14}$	0
	Q_{31}	Q_{31}	Q_{33}	0	0	0
$\underline{4}, \underline{\bar{4}}, \underline{4}/m$	0	0	0	Q_{14}	Q_{15}	0
	0	0	0	$-Q_{15}$	Q_{14}	0
	Q_{31}	$-Q_{31}$	0	0	0	Q_{36}
$422, 4mm, \bar{4}2m, 4/mmm,$ $622, 6mm, \bar{6}m2, 6/mmm$	0	0	0	Q_{14}	0	0
	0	0	0	0	$-Q_{14}$	0
	0	0	0	0	0	0
$\underline{4}\underline{2}2, \underline{4}\underline{m}\underline{m}, \underline{\bar{4}}2\underline{m}, \underline{\bar{4}}2m,$ $\underline{4}/mm\underline{m}$	0	0	0	Q_{14}	0	0
	0	0	0	0	Q_{14}	0
	0	0	0	0	0	Q_{36}
$4\underline{2}\underline{2}, 4\underline{m}\underline{m}, \bar{4}2\underline{m}, 4/m\underline{m}\underline{m},$ $6\underline{2}\underline{2}, 6\underline{m}\underline{m}, \bar{6}m\underline{2}, 6/m\underline{m}\underline{m}$	0	0	0	0	Q_{15}	0
	0	0	0	Q_{15}	0	0
	Q_{31}	Q_{31}	Q_{33}	0	0	0
$3, \bar{3}$	Q_{11}	$-Q_{11}$	0	Q_{14}	Q_{15}	$-2Q_{22}$
	$-Q_{22}$	Q_{22}	0	Q_{15}	$-Q_{14}$	$-2Q_{11}$
	Q_{31}	Q_{31}	Q_{33}	0	0	0
$32, 3m, \bar{3}m$	Q_{11}	$-Q_{11}$	0	Q_{14}	0	0
	0	0	0	0	$-Q_{14}$	$-2Q_{11}$
	0	0	0	0	0	0
$3\underline{2}, 3\underline{m}, \bar{3}\underline{m}$	0	0	0	0	Q_{15}	$-2Q_{22}$
	$-Q_{22}$	Q_{22}	0	Q_{15}	0	0
	Q_{31}	Q_{31}	Q_{33}	0	0	0

Magnetic class	Piezomagnetism tensor					
$\underline{6}$, $\bar{6}$, $6/\underline{m}$	Q_{11}	$-Q_{11}$	0	0	0	$-2Q_{22}$
	$-Q_{22}$	Q_{22}	0	0	0	$-2Q_{11}$
	0	0	0	0	0	0
$\underline{622}$, $6\underline{mm}$, $\bar{6}m2$, $\bar{6}m\underline{2}$, $6/\underline{m}m\underline{m}$	Q_{11}	$-Q_{11}$	0	0	0	0
	0	0	0	0	0	$-2Q_{11}$
	0	0	0	0	0	0
23, $m3$, $\underline{432}$, $\bar{4}3\underline{m}$, $m3\underline{m}$	0	0	0	Q_{14}	0	0
	0	0	0	0	Q_{14}	0
	0	0	0	0	0	Q_{14}

evaluating the numbers of non-vanishing coefficients as we cannot distinguish an operation and its complement by the use of this physical property. The detailed schemes and the numbers of non-vanishing constants in respect of the 32 classes will be identical with those given for the elasticity tensor if we assume that Q_{ijkl} is symmetric with respect to an interchange of ij with kl. On the other hand, if we do not make such an assumption, the schemes will be identical with those given for the photoelasticity tensor. This is a typical example of a second order magnetic property but not requiring the consideration of magnetic symmetry in crystal classes for the purpose of evaluating the numbers and the schemes of non-vanishing coefficients. It may be noted, however, that in practice the effect becomes measurable only when there is a large magnetic moment involved such as in a ferromagnetic substance.

15.7 Ferromagnetism and Antiferromagnetism

Ferromagnetism and antiferromagnetism are terms which refer more to the nature of the structure of a crystal than to their being physical properties in the sense which constitutes the basis of our study of physical properties in this book. However, it is possible to find out the magnetic classes to which the ferromagnetic structures belong, using simple symmetry considerations and the results already obtained. We have given in what follows formal definitions and explanation of the terms involved and obtained the possible ferromagnetic classes.

A ferromagnetic substance is one which can possess a magnetic moment even in the absence of an applied magnetic field. For each such substance there is a definite temperature T_C, called the Curie temperature or the Curie point, above which the substance passes into a paramagnetic state. The variation of susceptibility with absolute temperature T in the paramagnetic state is governed by the Curie–Weiss law which is expressed by

$$\chi = \frac{C}{T - T_C} \tag{3}$$

where C is called the Curie constant and T_C is the Curie point. Below the Curie point, the magnetic moments of individual atoms in a ferromagnetic crystal are locked in parallel orientations resulting in a non-zero net magnetic moment per unit cell. This gives rise to a macroscopic magnetic moment in the crystal, the exact value of which is determined by the temperature, internal field and so on. The magnetic behaviour of such a substance below the Curie point T_C becomes rather complex.

The susceptibility versus temperature curve for several paramagnetic substances sometimes shows another well-defined turning point. This turning point defines the transition temperature below which the paramagnetic substance passes into what is called an antiferromagnetic state. The transition temperature is called the antiferromagnetic Curie point. This is also known as the Neel temperature. In the antiferromagnetic state, the individual atomic magnetic moments are locked in an antiparallel arrangement such that the net magnetic moment of a unit cell vanishes. Consequently, there is no spontaneous macroscopic magnetic moment of the crystal. The transition is also marked by anomalies in properties like the heat capacity and thermal expansion coefficient of the crystal. The relation between the susceptibility and temperature in such cases is expressed by

$$\chi = \frac{C}{T + \theta} \tag{4}$$

where θ is related to the transition temperature T_C. In the simple situation when the lattice of paramagnetic ions can be divided into two interpenetrating sublattices such that all nearest neighbours of an ion on a sublattice lie on the other sublattice, we have $\theta = T_C$. In the more general case, θ and T_C are different from each other.

Figure 12 shows some of the distinguishing features of paramagnetism, ferromagnetism and antiferromagnetism. There is substantial evidence from neutron diffraction studies by which to establish the existence of parallel and antiparallel locking of the individual atomic magnetic moments in the ferromagnetic and antiferromagnetic states of crystals respectively.

The determination of crystal classes in which ferromagnetism is possible necessarily involves taking the 90 magnetic classes into account. The ferromagnetic crystals, or the ferromagnetics as they are often referred to, may be defined as those which are capable of possessing a spontaneous magnetic moment. They should thus belong to the magnetic classes whose symmetry operations are such that they leave one or more components of the axial vector magnetic moment invariant.

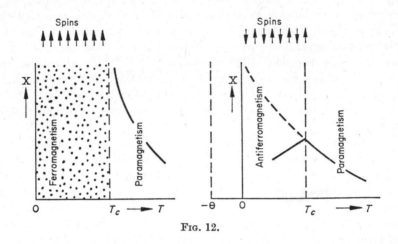

Fig. 12.

It is evident that ferromagnetism is possible only in those crystal classes in which pyromagnetism is also possible. These are shown in Table VIII(c) and they are 31 in number. In Table XI, the ferromagnetic classes arranged in a different manner are again given and the admissible direction of magnetic moment in each case is shown in a separate column.[†]

Crystal classes which possess a magnetic structure, i.e. which belong to a class of magnetic symmetry, not listed in the ferromagnetic classes of Table XI, are all to be regarded as capable of exhibiting antiferromagnetism. It does not, however, mean that those are the only antiferromagnetic classes. An arrangement of atomic magnetic moments giving rise to antiferromagnetism is possible in all magnetic classes, including those which are potentially capable of exhibiting ferromagnetism. For instant, NiF_2, which crystallizes with the magnetic symmetry $m\underline{m}m$ (a ferromagnetic class), exhibits antiferromagnetism because the spin moments are locked in an antiparallel arrangement.

15.8 Weak Ferromagnetism in Antiferromagnetics

It may happen that, although a crystal has an antiferromagnetic distribution of spins, a close examination of the structure sometimes

[†] Tavger, B. A., *Soviet Phys. Crystallography* **3**, 341 (1958).

discloses the possibility of spontaneous magnetization occurring as a result of a small rotation of the spins without deviating from the symmetry class. This phenomenon is called the weak ferromagnetism of antiferromagnetics because it results in a small spontaneous magnetic

TABLE XI

Ferromagnetic magnetic classes

Classes	Admissible direction of magnetic moment
$1, \bar{1}$	Any direction
2	Along the axis
$\underline{2}$	Perpendicular to axis
m	Perpendicular to plane
$\underline{m}$	Along the plane
$2/m$	Along the axis
$\underline{2/m}$	Perpendicular to axis
$2\underline{2}2, 2\underline{mm}$	Along the 2-fold axis
$\underline{2mm}$	Perpendicular to $\underline{2}$-axis and to plane m
$m\underline{m}m$	Perpendicular to plane m
$4, \underline{4}2\underline{2}, 4/m, 4\underline{mm}, 4/m\underline{mm}, \bar{4}, \bar{4}2\underline{m},$ $3, 3\underline{2}, 3\underline{m}, \bar{3}, \bar{3}\underline{m}, \bar{6}, \bar{6}\underline{m}2, 6,$ $62\underline{2}, 6/m, 6\underline{mm}, 6/m\underline{mm}$	Along the principal direction in each case

moment. The phenomenon is of some importance and has been experimentally observed in several substances amongst which are $\alpha\text{-Fe}_2\text{O}_3$ above 250°K, NiF_2, MnCO_3 and CoCO_3.

These cases are briefly cited here as the occurrence of the phenomenon is intimately connected with the magnetic symmetry of the crystal in which it is exhibited. We can immediately recognize that for weak ferromagnetism to appear in an antiferromagnetic crystal, it is necessary that its class should be one of the 31 classes of Table XI. This is only a necessary condition and is not sufficient. For instance, $\alpha\text{-Fe}_2\text{O}_3$ below 250°K has a crystal structure whose magnetic symmetry class is $\bar{3}m$. Cr_2O_3, in its antiferromagnetic state, has a crystal structure whose magnetic symmetry class is $\bar{3}\underline{m}$. FeCO_3 has the same magnetic symmetry class as $\alpha\text{-Fe}_2\text{O}_3$ and behaves like $\alpha\text{-Fe}_2\text{O}_3$. The spins are locked in an antiparallel arrangement in all these substances and they are all antiferromagnetic. It may be noted that neither the class $\bar{3}m$ nor the class $\bar{3}\underline{m}$ is listed in Table XI. Thus, symmetry considerations alone rule out

the appearance of a magnetic moment and therefore of weak ferromagnetism in these crystals belonging to the symmetry classes $\bar{3}m$ and
$\bar{3}\underline{m}$. Above 250°K and in the range up to 950°K, α-Fe$_2$O$_3$, however,
undergoes a phase transition and the appropriate magnetic point group
is $2/m$. It will be noticed from Table XI that ferromagnetism is
possible in this group and, in fact, α-Fe$_2$O$_3$ has been found to exhibit
weak ferromagnetism above 250°K.

NiF$_2$ is another interesting case as in the classical point group
description, this substance, along with three other fluorides, namely,
MnF$_2$, FeF$_2$ and CoF$_2$, possesses the same symmetry $4/mmm$ of the

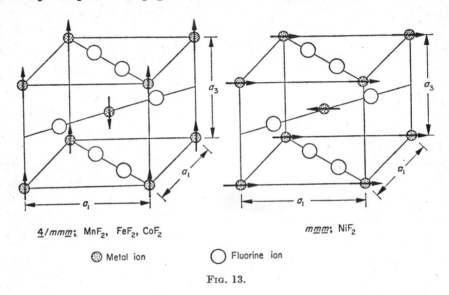

4/$mm\underline{m}$; MnF$_2$, FeF$_2$, CoF$_2$ $m\underline{m}\underline{m}$; NiF$_2$

⊛ Metal ion   ◯ Fluorine ion

Fɪɢ. 13.

well-known rutile structure. However, the recognition of magnetic
symmetry places NiF$_2$ in the magnetic class $m\underline{m}\underline{m}$ whereas MnF$_2$, FeF$_2$
and CoF$_2$ belong to the magnetic class $\underline{4}/mm\underline{m}$. In Fig. 13, these two
structures are shown along with the spin magnetic moment orientations.
The spins in $\underline{4}/mm\underline{m}$ are parallel and antiparallel to the 4-fold axis.
In fact, the group is incapable of sustaining a spontaneous magnetic
moment and hence MnF$_2$, FeF$_2$ and CoF$_2$ cannot exhibit weak ferromagnetism. In NiF$_2$, the spins are parallel and antiparallel to a 2-fold
axis and a rotation of each spin on either side of this axis, without
destroying the 2-fold symmetry, is possible. This is equivalent to
saying that the class $m\underline{m}m$ is a ferromagnetic class and so a rotation of
the spins in this structure preserves the symmetry and produces a
small spontaneous magnetic moment. NiF$_2$ thus exhibits weak ferromagnetism. It may also be noted from Table XI that while $m\underline{m}\underline{m}$ is a

ferromagnetic class, $\underline{4}/mm\underline{m}$ is not. This at once explains the experimentally observed fact that while all these fluorides are normally antiferromagnetic, NiF_2 alone exhibits the phenomenon of weak ferromagnetism.

Similarly, the weak ferromagnetism of the antiferromagnetic $MnCO_3$ and $CoCO_3$ and the fact that the isomorphous $FeCO_3$, which is also antiferromagnetic, does not exhibit weak ferromagnetism can be explained from considerations of magnetic symmetry. The difference between these substances is similar to what obtains as a difference between the high temperature modification and the low temperature modification of α-Fe_2O_3. In $FeCO_3$, the spins are parallel and antiparallel to the 3-fold axis and any rotation of the spins therefrom destroys the symmetry. The magnetic class is not capable of sustaining a spontaneous magnetic moment. In $MnCO_3$ and $CoCO_3$, the spins do not cancel by being parallel and antiparallel to the 3-fold axis. Thus, in a manner similar to that in NiF_2, they can rotate a little from the position of cancellation and cause the appearance of weak ferromagnetism. The direction of spontaneous magnetic moment relating to the weak ferromagnetism will be parallel to the 3-fold axis.

In the particular case of antiferromagnetic structures in which the spins are all parallel to a single direction, the magnetic classes admitting weak ferromagnetism are readily derived. Firstly, we note that these classes must be among the 31 given in Table XI. Next, we note that the direction of spontaneous magnetization of an antiferromagnetic belonging to the particular type mentioned cannot coincide with the direction to which the spins are all parallel. We may now choose from Table XI the 19 classes which contain a 3-fold or higher axis and note that they can exhibit spontaneous magnetization, but its direction should be parallel to the principal direction in each class. From considerations of symmetry, it is also seen that for these 19 classes if the spins have to be parallel to a single direction, that direction must again coincide with the principal direction in each class. From the above two mutually exclusive conclusions, it follows that weak ferromagnetism cannot appear in these 19 classes if the spins cancel by being parallel to a single direction. In other words, we can conclude from considerations of symmetry that weak ferromagnetism in antiferromagnetics, for which the spins cancel by being aligned parallel to a single direction, is possible only in the first 12 classes of Table XI.

We have here established elementary theorems which link up the phenomena of weak ferromagnetism in antiferromagnetics with the considerations of magnetic symmetry. The establishment of the complete set of necessary and sufficient conditions for weak ferromagnetism to exist in antiferromagnetics is a complex matter and outside the scope of the present treatise which is confined to the tensor properties of crystals. Reference may be made to a recent work by Turov† wherein this problem is discussed in great detail.

† Turov, E. A. "Physical Properties of Magnetically Ordered Crystals". Academic Press, New York (1965).

CHAPTER 16

Optical Properties

16.1 Optical Birefringence

We have seen in Chapter 14 that the dielectric constant K is a second rank symmetric tensor. If α denotes the polarizability or the electric moment induced per unit volume by a unit incident electric field, we have

$$K = 1 + 4\pi\alpha.$$

If we are dealing with the spectral region of optical frequencies, the relation $\sqrt{K} = n$ easily follows where n is the refractive index of the medium and we may conclude that all the features which the K tensor exhibits will also be exhibited by the refractive index tensor. Thus, the refractive index tensor is also a second rank symmetric tensor.

In the general case of an unsymmetrical crystal, it is customary to utilize the six independent coefficients for defining an ellipsoid called the index ellipsoid or the indicatrix by writing its equation as

$$B_{11} x_1^2 + B_{22} x_2^2 + B_{33} x_3^2 + 2B_{23} x_2 x_3 + 2B_{31} x_3 x_1 + 2B_{12} x_1 x_2 = 1. \qquad (1)$$

We can refer the B tensor to the principal axes and rewrite equation (1) as

$$B_1 x_1^2 + B_2 x_2^2 + B_3 x_3^2 = 1. \qquad (2)$$

It may be noted that X_1-, X_2-, X_3-axes in equation (2) are the principal axes and are different from those used in equation (1), although for simplicity we have not placed the superscripts for differentiating between them. The relationship between the B's and the n's is given in (3).

$$B_1 = \frac{1}{n_1^2} = \frac{1}{K_1}; \quad B_2 = \frac{1}{n_2^2} = \frac{1}{K_2}; \quad B_3 = \frac{1}{n_3^2} = \frac{1}{K_3}. \qquad (3)$$

n_1, n_2 and n_3 are called the principal refractive indices. However, every triclinic crystal needs six independent coefficients to describe its optical birefringence properties. In this notation, one can see that they are the three principal refractive indices and three other angles, say the Eulerian angles specifying the position of the principal axes system of coordinates X_1, X_2, X_3 with reference to the crystallographic axes of the crystal. The crystal in such a case is said to be doubly refracting, will have three principal refractive indices differing from each other and therefore designated biaxial, its indicatrix being an ellipsoid.

The effect of symmetry on the refractive index tensor will be the same as on the dielectric constant tensor. In the case of monoclinic crystals, the number of coefficients needed reduces to 4. These may be interpreted as the three principal refractive indices and one angle which determines the position of the two principal axes in the plane of symmetry. The 2-fold axis is always one of the principal axes of the indicatrix. In the case of orthorhombic crystals, 3 coefficients are needed and these may be chosen as the three principal refractive indices, the three 2-fold axes being coincident with the three principal axes of the indicatrix. In the hexagonal, tetragonal and trigonal systems, two of the principal refractive indices become equal and only two independent coefficients in the tensor remain non-vanishing. These crystals are designated as uniaxial because the unique axis is always an optic axis and the plane perpendicular to the same is a circular section of the indicatrix. In the cubic system of crystals, there is only one independent non-vanishing coefficient, and this is so because all the three principal refractive indices become equal making the indicatrix a sphere. It is easy to obtain all these results by successive imposition of symmetry operations on the second rank symmetric tensor. The results are contained in column (3) of Table VIII(a) for all the 32 crystal classes.

16.2 Photoelasticity

The optical properties of a crystal are affected by the application of stress. Isotropic substances like glasses and cubic crystals which are initially optically isotropic become birefringent under the application of a stress. In the case of substances in which birefringence already exists, it is altered by the stress. This phenomenon is known as photoelasticity and is a physical property arising from an action and effect relation between a symmetric second rank tensor and another symmetric second rank tensor. It was first observed experimentally by Brewster and was studied theoretically by Pockels.

The index ellipsoid of a crystal, in the most general case characterized by the absence of all symmetry, may be written as

$$B_{11}^0 x_1^2 + B_{22}^0 x_2^2 + B_{33}^0 x_3^2 + 2B_{23}^0 x_2 x_3 + 2B_{31}^0 x_3 x_1 + 2B_{12}^0 x_1 x_2 = 1. \quad (4)$$

Equation (4) is the same as equation (1) except that the 6 different Bs have been used with the superscript 0 indicating reference to the normal state of a crystal free from stress or strain. Pockels postulated that when a stress is applied, the 6 coefficients undergo changes.

If the changed coefficients are written by dropping the superscript 0, we have, for the index ellipsoid,

$$B_{11} x_1^2 + B_{22} x_2^2 + B_{33} x_3^2 + 2B_{23} x_2 x_3 + 2B_{31} x_3 x_1 + 2B_{12} x_1 x_2 = 1. \quad (5)$$

Adopting the one-suffix notation used for stress and strain in Chapter 11 for the B's as well, we may express the differences between the two sets of coefficients by

$$
\begin{Vmatrix} B_1 - B_1^0 \\ B_2 - B_2^0 \\ B_3 - B_3^0 \\ B_4 - B_4^0 \\ B_5 - B_5^0 \\ B_6 - B_6^0 \end{Vmatrix} = \| p_{ik} \| \begin{Vmatrix} \varepsilon_1 \\ \varepsilon_2 \\ \varepsilon_3 \\ \varepsilon_4 \\ \varepsilon_5 \\ \varepsilon_6 \end{Vmatrix} = \| -q_{ik} \| \begin{Vmatrix} \tau_1 \\ \tau_2 \\ \tau_3 \\ \tau_4 \\ \tau_5 \\ \tau_6 \end{Vmatrix}.
$$

εs are the strain components and τ's are the stress components. p_{ik} and q_{ik}, where i and k run from 1 to 6 are, respectively, known as the strain-optical and stress-optical coefficients and describe the behaviour of the index ellipsoid in the presence of strain or stress.

The strain-optical coefficients and the stress-optical coefficients are related between themselves as

$$p_{ik} = q_{ij} c_{jk}; \quad q_{ik} = p_{ij} s_{jk}.$$

The cs and the ss are, respectively, the elastic stiffnesses and elastic compliances. It is to be noted that the relations $p_{ik} = p_{ki}$ or $q_{ik} = q_{ki}$ do not hold good in the case of photoelasticity, unlike in the case of elasticity. Therefore, in the general unsymmetrical case, there are 36 independent photoelastic coefficients. For similar reasons as in the case of the elastic stiffnesses and compliances, the passage from the four-suffix notation to the two-suffix notation implies that the following relationships have to be recognized.

$q_{ijkl} = q_{mn}$ when m is 1 to 6 and n is 1, 2 or 3.

$2q_{ijkl} = q_{mn}$ when m is 1 to 6 and n is 4, 5 or 6.

$p_{ijkl} = p_{mn}$ for all permissible values of the suffixes.

16.3 Effect of Symmetry on the Photoelastic Tensor

The numbers of independent non-vanishing coefficients for each of the crystal classes in respect of this tensor, which is a fourth rank cross property type, have been given in column (8) of Table VIII(a). In view of the importance of photoelasticity and as the same schemes are applicable to a few other properties, namely, piezoresistance, magneto-resistance and magnetothermal conductivity, the full schemes for all the 32 crystal classes are given below.

(i) TRICLINIC SYSTEM

$$
\begin{array}{cccccc}
q_{11} & q_{12} & q_{13} & q_{14} & q_{15} & q_{16} \\
q_{21} & q_{22} & q_{23} & q_{24} & q_{25} & q_{26} \\
q_{31} & q_{32} & q_{33} & q_{34} & q_{35} & q_{36} \\
q_{41} & q_{42} & q_{43} & q_{44} & q_{45} & q_{46} \\
q_{51} & q_{52} & q_{53} & q_{54} & q_{55} & q_{56} \\
q_{61} & q_{62} & q_{63} & q_{64} & q_{65} & q_{66}
\end{array}
$$

(ii) MONOCLINIC SYSTEM

$$
\begin{array}{cccccc}
q_{11} & q_{12} & q_{13} & 0 & 0 & q_{16} \\
q_{21} & q_{22} & q_{23} & 0 & 0 & q_{26} \\
q_{31} & q_{32} & q_{33} & 0 & 0 & q_{36} \\
0 & 0 & 0 & q_{44} & q_{45} & 0 \\
0 & 0 & 0 & q_{54} & q_{55} & 0 \\
q_{61} & q_{62} & q_{63} & 0 & 0 & q_{66}
\end{array}
$$

(iii) ORTHORHOMBIC SYSTEM

$$
\begin{array}{cccccc}
q_{11} & q_{12} & q_{13} & 0 & 0 & 0 \\
q_{21} & q_{22} & q_{23} & 0 & 0 & 0 \\
q_{31} & q_{32} & q_{33} & 0 & 0 & 0 \\
0 & 0 & 0 & q_{44} & 0 & 0 \\
0 & 0 & 0 & 0 & q_{55} & 0 \\
0 & 0 & 0 & 0 & 0 & q_{66}
\end{array}
$$

(iv) (a) TETRAGONAL SYSTEM: CLASSES 4, $\bar{4}$, $4/m$

$$
\begin{array}{cccccc}
q_{11} & q_{12} & q_{13} & 0 & 0 & q_{16} \\
q_{12} & q_{11} & q_{13} & 0 & 0 & -q_{16} \\
q_{31} & q_{31} & q_{33} & 0 & 0 & 0 \\
0 & 0 & 0 & q_{44} & q_{45} & 0 \\
0 & 0 & 0 & -q_{45} & q_{44} & 0 \\
q_{61} & -q_{61} & 0 & 0 & 0 & q_{66}
\end{array}
$$

(iv) (b) TETRAGONAL SYSTEM: CLASSES $4mm$, $\bar{4}2m$, 422, $4/mmm$

$$
\begin{matrix}
q_{11} & q_{12} & q_{13} & 0 & 0 & 0 \\
q_{12} & q_{11} & q_{13} & 0 & 0 & 0 \\
q_{31} & q_{31} & q_{33} & 0 & 0 & 0 \\
0 & 0 & 0 & q_{44} & 0 & 0 \\
0 & 0 & 0 & 0 & q_{44} & 0 \\
0 & 0 & 0 & 0 & 0 & q_{66}
\end{matrix}
$$

(v) (a) TRIGONAL SYSTEM: CLASSES 3, $\bar{3}$

$$
\begin{matrix}
q_{11} & q_{12} & q_{13} & q_{14} & q_{15} & -2q_{61} \\
q_{12} & q_{11} & q_{13} & -q_{14} & -q_{15} & 2q_{61} \\
q_{31} & q_{31} & q_{33} & 0 & 0 & 0 \\
q_{41} & -q_{41} & 0 & q_{44} & q_{45} & -2q_{51} \\
q_{51} & -q_{51} & 0 & -q_{45} & q_{44} & 2q_{41} \\
q_{61} & -q_{61} & 0 & -q_{15} & q_{14} & (q_{11}-q_{12})
\end{matrix}
$$

(v) (b) TRIGONAL SYSTEM: CLASSES $3m$, 32, $\bar{3}m$

$$
\begin{matrix}
q_{11} & q_{12} & q_{13} & q_{14} & 0 & 0 \\
q_{12} & q_{11} & q_{13} & -q_{14} & 0 & 0 \\
q_{31} & q_{31} & q_{33} & 0 & 0 & 0 \\
q_{41} & -q_{41} & 0 & q_{44} & 0 & 0 \\
0 & 0 & 0 & 0 & q_{44} & 2q_{41} \\
0 & 0 & 0 & 0 & q_{14} & (q_{11}-q_{12})
\end{matrix}
$$

(vi) (a) HEXAGONAL SYSTEM: CLASSES $\bar{6}$, 6, $6/m$

$$
\begin{matrix}
q_{11} & q_{12} & q_{13} & 0 & 0 & -2q_{61} \\
q_{12} & q_{11} & q_{13} & 0 & 0 & 2q_{61} \\
q_{31} & q_{31} & q_{33} & 0 & 0 & 0 \\
0 & 0 & 0 & q_{44} & q_{45} & 0 \\
0 & 0 & 0 & -q_{45} & q_{44} & 0 \\
q_{61} & -q_{61} & 0 & 0 & 0 & (q_{11}-q_{12})
\end{matrix}
$$

(vi) (b) HEXAGONAL SYSTEM: CLASSES $\bar{6}m2$, $6mm$, 622, $6/mmm$

$$
\begin{pmatrix}
q_{11} & q_{12} & q_{13} & 0 & 0 & 0 \\
q_{12} & q_{11} & q_{13} & 0 & 0 & 0 \\
q_{31} & q_{31} & q_{33} & 0 & 0 & 0 \\
0 & 0 & 0 & q_{44} & 0 & 0 \\
0 & 0 & 0 & 0 & q_{44} & 0 \\
0 & 0 & 0 & 0 & 0 & (q_{11}-q_{12})
\end{pmatrix}
$$

(vii) (a) CUBIC SYSTEM: CLASSES 23, $m3$

$$
\begin{pmatrix}
q_{11} & q_{12} & q_{13} & 0 & 0 & 0 \\
q_{13} & q_{11} & q_{12} & 0 & 0 & 0 \\
q_{12} & q_{13} & q_{11} & 0 & 0 & 0 \\
0 & 0 & 0 & q_{44} & 0 & 0 \\
0 & 0 & 0 & 0 & q_{44} & 0 \\
0 & 0 & 0 & 0 & 0 & q_{44}
\end{pmatrix}
$$

(vii) (b) CUBIC SYSTEM: CLASSES $\bar{4}3m$, 432, $m3m$

$$
\begin{pmatrix}
q_{11} & q_{12} & q_{12} & 0 & 0 & 0 \\
q_{12} & q_{11} & q_{12} & 0 & 0 & 0 \\
q_{12} & q_{12} & q_{11} & 0 & 0 & 0 \\
0 & 0 & 0 & q_{44} & 0 & 0 \\
0 & 0 & 0 & 0 & q_{44} & 0 \\
0 & 0 & 0 & 0 & 0 & q_{44}
\end{pmatrix}
$$

(viii) ISOTROPIC MEDIUM

$$
\begin{pmatrix}
q_{11} & q_{12} & q_{12} & 0 & 0 & 0 \\
q_{12} & q_{11} & q_{12} & 0 & 0 & 0 \\
q_{12} & q_{12} & q_{11} & 0 & 0 & 0 \\
0 & 0 & 0 & (q_{11}-q_{12}) & 0 & 0 \\
0 & 0 & 0 & 0 & (q_{11}-q_{12}) & 0 \\
0 & 0 & 0 & 0 & 0 & (q_{11}-q_{12})
\end{pmatrix}
$$

The schemes for the strain-optical coefficients p_{ij} are identical with the above schemes in triclinic, monoclinic, orthorhombic, tetragonal and cubic systems. In the trigonal and hexagonal systems, the schemes for p's can be obtained from those of q's by keeping all the coefficients in the first five columns unchanged and dividing the coefficients in the sixth column by a factor 2. In the schemes for an isotropic medium, whereas $q_{44} = q_{11} - q_{12}$ for the q's, $p_{44} = \frac{1}{2}(p_{11} - p_{12})$ for the p's.

Photoelasticity is of some special interest. It is in regard to this physical property that the application of group theoretical methods first revealed the errors that crept into the schemes of non-vanishing coefficients as determined by the older methods. Table XII gives all such differences between the results of earlier work and the results obtained by applying group theoretical methods.

TABLE XII

Photoelastic constants of some crystal classes

No.	Crystal class	Earlier work	Group theory	Extra constants
1	$3, \bar{3}$	11	12	q_{61}
2	$4, \bar{4}, 4/m$	9	10	q_{45}
3	$\bar{6}, 6, 6/m$	6	8	q_{61}, q_{45}
4	$23, m3$	3	4	$q_{12} \neq q_{13}$

Of the 10 classes mentioned in Table XII, 2 of the classes, T(23) and $T_h(m3)$, belong to the cubic system and they should have 4 constants. The other 3 classes in the cubic system, namely $T_d(\bar{4}3m)$, O(432) and $O_h(m3m)$ should have only 3 constants, as may be seen from the detailed schemes. The two schemes merge into each other if $q_{12} = q_{13}$. The results obtained originally by Pockels implied that $q_{12} = q_{13}$ for all the classes in the cubic system. That $q_{12} \neq q_{13}$ in crystals of classes T and T_h has been experimentally verified in several instances and in fact a difference of as much as 70% between the two q's has been observed in one or two crystals. We shall deal with individual cases in greater detail in Chapter 18.

16.4 Optical Activity

Quartz and sodium chlorate are familiar examples of crystals exhibiting optical activity. When plane polarized light of a specific wave length passes through a quartz crystal along its optic axis or through sodium chlorate along any direction, the plane of polarization is rotated through a certain angle, the total rotation being proportional to the distance traversed in the medium. The convention in regard to the sign of optical activity is to call the substance a right-handed one and define it as positive when the plane of polarization is rotated in the clockwise direction when seen by an observer whose eye is looking at the incoming beam of light. If under these conditions, the plane of polarization is rotated in the anticlockwise direction, we call the substance a left-handed one and define it as negative. With these definitions, it is easy to see that a positive optical activity becomes negative if we reflect the parameters in a plane perpendicular to the axis along which light is travelling. In addition to this, G the magnitude of rotation is found to be a linear function of the products of the direction cosines l_1, l_2, l_3, taken two at a time, of the wave normal in respect of the polarized light wave travelling in the medium. We may thus write

$$G = g_{11} l_1^2 + g_{22} l_2^2 + g_{33} l_3^2 + 2g_{23} l_2 l_3 + 2g_{31} l_3 l_1 + 2g_{12} l_1 l_2.$$

In tensor notation, this will be

$$G = g_{ij} l_i l_j$$

where g_{ij} is a set of nine quantities with the relation $g_{ij} = g_{ji}$ holding good. g_{ij} may be taken as the coefficients which describe the optical activity in the general case for the choice of coordinates in respect of which the direction cosines of the wave normal are l_1, l_2, l_3. g_{ij} may be called the gyration tensor and we note that it is a second rank symmetric axial tensor. We have already seen that its character is $\pm (4\cos^2\phi \pm 2\cos\phi)$, the plus or minus sign being chosen according as the symmetry operation is a simple rotation or a rotation-reflection.

16.5 Effect of Symmetry on the Gyration Tensor

This is a typical instance of an axial tensor defining the physical property but for which we do not have to consider the 90 magnetic classes as there is no magnetic field or magnetic moment involved. We need apply group theoretical methods to the 32 crystal classes only. The results in regard to the numbers of non-vanishing coefficients are given in the last column of Table VIII(a). Detailed schemes of non-vanishing coefficients are given below. Gyration tensor becomes zero in all crystal classes not listed.

(i) TRICLINIC SYSTEM: CLASS 1

$$g_{11} \quad g_{12} \quad g_{13}$$
$$g_{22} \quad g_{23}$$
$$g_{33}$$

(ii) (a) MONOCLINIC SYSTEM: CLASS m

$$\begin{matrix} 0 & 0 & g_{13} \\ & 0 & g_{23} \\ & & 0 \end{matrix}$$

(ii) (b) MONOCLINIC SYSTEM: CLASS 2

$$\begin{matrix} g_{11} & g_{12} & 0 \\ & g_{22} & 0 \\ & & g_{33} \end{matrix}$$

(iii) (a) ORTHORHOMBIC SYSTEM: CLASS $2mm$

$$\begin{matrix} 0 & g_{12} & 0 \\ & 0 & 0 \\ & & 0 \end{matrix}$$

(iii) (b) ORTHORHOMBIC SYSTEM: CLASS 222

$$\begin{matrix} g_{11} & 0 & 0 \\ & g_{22} & 0 \\ & & g_{33} \end{matrix}$$

(iv) (a) TETRAGONAL SYSTEM: CLASSES 4, 422

$$\begin{matrix} g_{11} & 0 & 0 \\ & g_{11} & 0 \\ & & g_{33} \end{matrix}$$

(iv) (b) TETRAGONAL SYSTEM: CLASS $\bar{4}$

$$\begin{matrix} g_{11} & g_{12} & 0 \\ & -g_{11} & 0 \\ & & 0 \end{matrix}$$

(iv) (c) TETRAGONAL SYSTEM: CLASS $\bar{4}2m$

$$\begin{matrix} 0 & g_{12} & 0 \\ & 0 & 0 \\ & & 0 \end{matrix}$$

(v) and (vi) TRIGONAL AND HEXAGONAL SYSTEMS: CLASSES: 3, 32, 6, 622

$$
\begin{matrix}
g_{11} & 0 & 0 \\
 & g_{11} & 0 \\
 & & g_{33}
\end{matrix}
$$

(vii) CUBIC SYSTEM: CLASSES 432, 23

$$
\begin{matrix}
g_{11} & 0 & 0 \\
 & g_{11} & 0 \\
 & & g_{11}
\end{matrix}
$$

It may be noted that 15 of the 32 classes are capable of exhibiting optical activity. No crystal with a centre of symmetry can exhibit optical activity. In the classes $4mm$, $3m$, $\bar{6}$, $\bar{6}m2$, $6mm$ and $\bar{4}3m$, although there is no centre of symmetry, there is no possibility of observing optical activity.

CHAPTER 17

Transport Phenomena

17.1 Thermal Conductivity

The dependence of the rate of flow of heat through a crystalline medium on the temperature gradient in the absence of electric current is governed by the generalized Fourier's law

$$q_i = -K_{ij}(\text{grad}\,T)_j \tag{1}$$

where q_i is the heat flux and T is the temperature. q_i and $(\text{grad}\,T)_i$ being vectors, K_{ij} is a second rank tensor. Long before Onsager put forward the reciprocity relations, it was experimentally established that the thermal conductivity represented by K_{ij} is a symmetric second rank tensor. It follows from Onsager relations as well that $K_{ij} = K_{ji}$. A component like K_{ij} measures the rate of heat flow along the X_i direction due to a unit negative temperature gradient along the X_j direction. Just as in the case of any physical property represented by a second rank symmetric tensor, a thermal conductivity quadric may be defined. The quadric is an ellipsoid because the principal conductivities are always positive.

A thermal resistivity tensor r_{ij} is defined by the following equations which are reciprocal to (1).

$$(\text{grad}\,T)_i = -r_{ij}q_j.$$

It is evident that r_{ij} are the elements of the matrix $\|K_{ij}\|^{-1}$. It follows that r_{ij} is a second rank symmetric tensor and it can be referred to its principal axes. It is not difficult to see that the principal axes of the resistivity ellipsoid coincide with those of the conductivity ellipsoid, and that the principal resistivities are reciprocals of the principal conductivities. Thus the principal axes of the resistivity ellipsoid are proportional to the principal conductivities. From the properties of the representation quadric, it follows that the resistivity ellipsoid is similar to the isothermal surfaces due to a point source of heat in the crystal. $\text{grad}\,T$ is along the normal to the isothermal surfaces. The heat flux direction coincides with the temperature gradient only along the principal axes.

The effect of symmetry on the tensors K_{ij} and r_{ij} is the same as that on any second rank symmetric tensor. The results given earlier for such properties, as for instance the polarizability tensor, apply to K_{ij} and r_{ij} as well.

17.2 Electrical Conductivity

The electric current through a crystalline conductor at a uniform temperature is governed by the generalized Ohm's law

$$j_i = - \sigma_{ik}(\text{grad}\,\phi)_k = \sigma_{ik} E_k \tag{2}$$

where ϕ is the electric potential and E_k is the electric field intensity. σ_{ik} is the electrical conductivity tensor and is obviously a second rank tensor. The relations reciprocal to (2) may be written as

$$E_i = \rho_{ik} j_i$$

where ρ_{ik} is the electrical resistivity tensor and $\| \rho_{ik} \| = \| \sigma_{ik} \|^{-1}$. Onsager reciprocity relations give that σ_{ik} and ρ_{ik} are symmetric tensors of second rank. The effect of crystal symmetry on the tensors σ_{ik} and ρ_{ik} is again the same as that on any second rank symmetric tensor and in particular on polarizability tensor.

17.3 Thermoelectric Phenomena

The simultaneous presence of thermal and electric currents in a homogeneous crystalline medium gives rise to thermoelectric effects. The relations that give the electric current j_i and the heat flux q_i in terms of the gradients of potential and of temperature may be put down as

$$j_i = - a_{ik}(\text{grad}\,\phi)_k - b_{ik}(\text{grad}\,T)_k$$
$$q_i = - c_{ik}(\text{grad}\,\phi)_k - d_{ik}(\text{grad}\,T)_k. \tag{3}$$

In (3), ϕ and q_i have been suitably defined to obtain the constitutive equations in the above form. When there are no temperature gradients, ϕ reduces to the ordinary electric potential. When there are no electric currents, q_i reduces to the ordinary heat flux. Unless a proper choice of fluxes and forces is made, Onsager reciprocity relations cannot be applied to the coefficients in equations (3). For such a consideration it is convenient, for the sake of simplicity, to suppose the material to be isotropic. The coefficients, which are tensors of second rank in the general case of an asymmetric crystal, become scalars for an isotropic material.

The equations for electric current and heat flux in linear isotropic conductors may be written as

$$j = - a\,\text{grad}\,\phi - b\,\text{grad}\,T$$
$$q = - c\,\text{grad}\,\phi - d\,\text{grad}\,T. \tag{4}$$

For a small element of volume of the material, we can put down the Gibbs equation as

$$T\,dS = dU - \phi\,de \tag{5}$$

where S is specific entropy, U is specific energy and e is electric charge. From considerations outlined in Section 8.4 it follows that $1/T$ and $-\phi/T$ are entropy parameters and $\mathrm{grad}\,(1/T)$ and $\mathrm{grad}\,(-\phi/T)$ are a choice of forces. The corresponding fluxes are the energy current U and electric current j. The rate of creation of entropy per unit volume dS/dt is given by the divergence of entropy current vector S. From (5) we can see that the following vector relation holds between the energy current, the entropy current and the electric current.

$$S = \frac{1}{T}U - \frac{\phi}{T}j.$$

Taking the divergence of the above equation and noting that $\mathrm{div}\,U$ and $\mathrm{div}\,j$ vanish, we get

$$\frac{dS}{dt} = U\cdot\mathrm{grad}\left(\frac{1}{T}\right) + j\cdot\mathrm{grad}\left(\frac{-\phi}{T}\right). \tag{6}$$

We can use the vector relation $U = q + \phi j$ and write (6) as

$$\frac{dS}{dt} = (q + \phi j)\cdot\mathrm{grad}\left(\frac{1}{T}\right) + j\cdot\mathrm{grad}\left(\frac{-\phi}{T}\right)$$

$$= (q + \phi j)\cdot\mathrm{grad}\left(\frac{1}{T}\right) + j\cdot\frac{-\mathrm{grad}\,\phi}{T} - \phi j\cdot\mathrm{grad}\left(\frac{1}{T}\right)$$

$$= q\cdot\mathrm{grad}\left(\frac{1}{T}\right) - j\cdot\frac{\mathrm{grad}\,\phi}{T}. \tag{7}$$

From (7) it follows that $\mathrm{grad}\,(1/T)$ and $-\mathrm{grad}\,\phi/T$ may be taken as the forces if q and j are to be taken as the corresponding fluxes. Equations (4) may be recast as follows:

$$j = aT\frac{-\mathrm{grad}\,\phi}{T} + bT^2\,\mathrm{grad}\left(\frac{1}{T}\right)$$

$$q = cT\frac{-\mathrm{grad}\,\phi}{T} + dT^2\,\mathrm{grad}\left(\frac{1}{T}\right). \tag{8}$$

The Onsager reciprocity relations are applicable to the system of equations (8) from which it follows that

$$bT^2 = cT \quad\text{or}\quad bT = c. \tag{9}$$

Using the first of equations (8) to express $-\mathrm{grad}\,\phi$ in terms of j and grad T, and substituting in the second of equations (8), we have (10) for the heat flux q.

$$q = \frac{b}{a} T j - \left(d - \frac{b^2}{a} T \right) \operatorname{grad} T. \qquad (10)$$

In (10) we can identify $(d - (b^2/a) T)$ as the ordinary thermal conductivity in the absence of electric current and write

$$\left(d - \frac{b^2}{a} T \right) = K.$$

To find the heat flux flowing into a point in the material, we compute the negative of divergence of the energy flux $(q + \phi j)$ using equation (10), which is in fact a vector equation.

$$- \operatorname{div}(q + \phi j) = - \operatorname{div}\left(\frac{b}{a} T + \phi \right) j + \operatorname{div}(K \operatorname{grad} T)$$

$$= - \operatorname{grad} \phi . j - \frac{b}{a} \operatorname{grad} T . j - T j . \operatorname{grad}\left(\frac{b}{a} \right) + \operatorname{div}(K \operatorname{grad} T).$$

Substituting for $- \operatorname{grad} \phi$ from (4) we have

$$- \operatorname{div}(q + \phi j) = \frac{j . j}{a} - T j . \operatorname{grad} \frac{b}{a} + \operatorname{div}(K \operatorname{grad} T). \qquad (11)$$

The first term in (11) gives the Joule heat and the last term gives the heat flux due to thermal conduction. The second term, which is called the Thomson heat, is due to the thermoelectric effects. In a homogeneous medium, b/a can be taken as a function of T only and $\operatorname{grad}(b/a)$ can be put equal to $\{ \mathrm{d}(b/a)/\mathrm{d}T \} \operatorname{grad} T$. $- T \{ \mathrm{d}(b/a)/\mathrm{d}T \}$ is called the Thomson coefficient. The Thomson heat depends on the first power of j and changes sign when the current is reversed.

From equations (8) we may put down the phenomenological relations for the thermoelectric effects in crystalline media in a form suitable for the application of Onsager relations. They are

$$j_i = a_{ik} T \left(\frac{-1}{T} \frac{\partial \phi}{\partial x_k} \right) + b_{ik} T^2 \frac{\partial}{\partial x_k}\left(\frac{1}{T} \right)$$

$$q_i = c_{ik} T \left(\frac{-1}{T} \frac{\partial \phi}{\partial x_k} \right) + d_{ik} T^2 \frac{\partial}{\partial x_k}\left(\frac{1}{T} \right). \qquad (12)$$

From the Onsager relations we have

$$c_{ik} = b_{ik}{}' T. \qquad (13)$$

Including (13) into (12) and expressing $E_i = -\partial\phi/\partial x_i$ and q_i in terms of j_i and $(\partial/\partial x_i)(1/T)$, we obtain

$$E_i = a_{ik}^{-1} j_k + a_{il}^{-1} b_{lk} \frac{\partial T}{\partial x_k}$$

$$q_i = b_{il} a_{lk}^{-1} T j_k - (d_{ik} - b_{il} a_{lm}^{-1} b_{mk} T) \frac{\partial T}{\partial x_k} \tag{14}$$

where a_{ik}^{-1} denote the elements of the matrix $\|a_{ik}\|^{-1}$. These may be concisely written as

$$E_i = \rho_{ik} j_k - \alpha_{ik} \frac{\partial T}{\partial x_k}$$

$$q_i = -\beta_{ik} j_k - K_{ik} \frac{\partial T}{\partial x_k}. \tag{15}$$

In equations (15), ρ_{ik} is the electrical resistivity tensor and K_{ik} is the thermal conductivity tensor. The tensors α_{ik} and β_{ik} are related. $\beta_{ik} = T\alpha_{ik}$, and they are affected by symmetry in an identical manner. α_{ik} and β_{ik} determine the thermoelectric properties of the crystal. They are second rank polar tensors. They may be called the thermoelectric tensors and α_{ik} in particular may be called the thermoelectric power tensor. The schemes of non-vanishing coefficients of α_{ik} for the various crystal classes are given below.

(i) TRICLINIC SYSTEM

$$
\begin{array}{ccc}
\alpha_{11} & \alpha_{12} & \alpha_{13} \\
\alpha_{21} & \alpha_{22} & \alpha_{23} \\
\alpha_{31} & \alpha_{32} & \alpha_{33}
\end{array}
$$

(ii) MONOCLINIC SYSTEM

$$
\begin{array}{ccc}
\alpha_{11} & \alpha_{12} & 0 \\
\alpha_{21} & \alpha_{22} & 0 \\
0 & 0 & \alpha_{33}
\end{array}
$$

(iii) ORTHORHOMBIC SYSTEM

$$
\begin{array}{ccc}
\alpha_{11} & 0 & 0 \\
0 & \alpha_{22} & 0 \\
0 & 0 & \alpha_{33}
\end{array}
$$

(vi) (a) TETRAGONAL, TRIGONAL, HEXAGONAL SYSTEMS: CLASSES 4, $\bar{4}$, $4/m$, 3, $\bar{3}$, 6, $\bar{6}$, $6/m$

$$\begin{array}{ccc} \alpha_{11} & \alpha_{12} & 0 \\ -\alpha_{12} & \alpha_{11} & 0 \\ 0 & 0 & \alpha_{33} \end{array}$$

(iv) (b) TETRAGONAL, TRIGONAL, HEXAGONAL SYSTEMS: CLASSES 422, $4mm$, $\bar{4}2m$, $4/mmm$, 32, $3m$, $\bar{3}m$, 622, $6mm$, $\bar{6}m2$, $6/mmm$

$$\begin{array}{ccc} \alpha_{11} & 0 & 0 \\ 0 & \alpha_{11} & 0 \\ 0 & 0 & \alpha_{33} \end{array}$$

(v) CUBIC SYSTEM AND ISOTROPIC MEDIUM

$$\begin{array}{ccc} \alpha_{11} & 0 & 0 \\ 0 & \alpha_{11} & 0 \\ 0 & 0 & \alpha_{11} \end{array}$$

17.4 Galvanomagnetic and Thermomagnetic Effects

The presence of an external magnetic field affects the electrical, thermal and thermoelectric properties of a conducting crystal in several important ways. The phenomenological description of the influence of the magnetic field on the thermal, electrical and thermoelectric properties is given by the same set of tensor equations as (15) of the previous article, except that the coefficient tensors are to be regarded as functions of H. They may be written in the form

$$E_i = \rho_{ik}(H)j_k + \alpha_{ik}(H)G_k$$
$$q_i = -\beta_{ik}(H)j_k + K_{ik}(H)G_k \tag{16}$$

where G_k stands for the negative temperature gradient $-\partial T/\partial x_k$. The Onsager reciprocity relations are altered in the presence of a magnetic field and consequently we have the following relations between the coefficients in (16).

$$\rho_{ik}(H) = \rho_{ki}(-H)$$
$$K_{ik}(H) = K_{ki}(-H)$$
$$\alpha_{ik}(H) = T\beta_{ki}(H). \tag{17}$$

This means that the resistivity tensor ρ_{ik} and thermal conductivity tensor K_{ik} which are symmetric in the absence of a magnetic field are no longer symmetric. Any tensor of second rank can be expressed as the sum of a symmetric part and an antisymmetric part. In particular, we can write

$$\rho_{ik} = s_{ik} + a_{ik} \tag{18}$$

where s_{ik} is the symmetric part and a_{ik} is the antisymmetric part. By definition

$$s_{ik}(H) = s_{ki}(H) \quad \text{and} \quad a_{ik}(H) = -a_{ki}(H). \tag{19}$$

From (17) and (19), it follows that

$$s_{ik}(H) = s_{ki}(-H) = s_{ik}(-H); \tag{20}$$

$$a_{ik}(H) = a_{ki}(-H) = -a_{ik}(-H); \tag{21}$$

which means that the symmetric part s_{ik} is an even function of H and the antisymmetric part a_{ik} is an odd function of H. The antisymmetric part a_{ik} corresponds to an axial vector a defined by the relations

$$a_1 = a_{23}, \quad a_2 = -a_{13}, \quad a_3 = a_{12}. \tag{22}$$

We have, in the absence of a temperature gradient,

$$E_i = \rho_{ik} j_k = s_{ik} j_k + a_{ik} j_k \tag{23}$$

which may be expressed in terms of the axial vector a as

$$E_i = s_{ik} j_k + (j \times a)_i. \tag{24}$$

To obtain the Joule heat generated, we compute the scalar product $j \cdot E$. Since the vectors $(j \times a)$ and j are mutually perpendicular, their scalar product is zero and we have from (24)

$$j \cdot E = s_{ik} j_i j_k \tag{25}$$

which means that the Joule heat is determined only by the symmetric part of the resistivity tensor. From the term $(j \times a)$ in equation (24), it follows that a magnetic field perpendicular to an electric current gives rise to an electric field in a direction perpendicular to itself and to the current. This phenomenon is known as the Hall effect.

If we expand the resistivity tensor components as power series in H_i, the symmetric part of the tensor is given by terms of even powers in H_i and the antisymmetric part of the tensor is given by the terms of odd powers in H_i. Taking up to the second power terms, we may write

$$\rho_{ik}(H) = \rho_{ik}^0 + \rho_{ikl} H_l + \rho_{iklm} H_l H_m. \tag{25a}$$

It follows that

$$s_{ik}(H) = \rho_{ik}^0 + \rho_{iklm} H_l H_m \tag{26}$$

and

$$a_{ik}(H) = \rho_{ikl} H_l. \tag{27}$$

As we have already seen, the Hall effect is due to the antisymmetric part of the resistivity tensor. The antisymmetric part is given here by the first order terms in H_i. The tensor ρ_{ikl} is called the Hall tensor. The Hall tensor relates an antisymmetric tensor of second rank a_{ik} with an axial vector H_i as in equation (27). Thus, it is equivalent to a second rank polar tensor. The change due to an external magnetic field H in the symmetric part of the resistivity tensor which is responsible for the Joule heating as in equation (26) is known as the magnetoresistance effect. It is given here by the second order terms in H_i. The tensor ρ_{iklm} is called the magnetoresistance tensor. This tensor relates a symmetric tensor of second rank s_{ik} with vector products like $H_l H_m$ and is symmetric with respect to interchange of suffixes i with k and l with m. We may regard it as relating two symmetric tensors, each of rank 2.

Exactly similar analysis can be carried out for the electrical conductivity tensor σ_{ik}. We obtain the following relations similar to (23) and (24).

$$j_i = \sigma_{ik} E_k = s'_{ik} E_k + a'_{ik} E_k$$
$$= s'_{ik} E_k + (E \times a')_i \tag{28}$$

where we denoted the symmetric and antisymmetric parts of σ_{ik} by s'_{ik} and a'_{ik} and the axial vector equivalent to a'_{ik} by a'. Equation (28) shows that a magnetic field perpendicular to an electric field gives rise to a current in a direction perpendicular to itself and the electric field and it will not contribute to the Joule heating. This transverse current which is determined by the antisymmetric part is known as the Hall current. The symmetric part is called magnetoelectrical conductivity.

The conventional definitions of Hall effect and the associated phenomena are given for the isotropic medium. In an isotropic medium the ordinary electrical resistivity ρ^0_{ik} and the Hall tensor ρ_{ikl} are isotropic, i.e. possess only a single non-vanishing independent component, and the magnetoresistance tensor ρ_{iklm} possesses two such components. It follows that for an isotropic medium, the axial vector as defined by relations (22) is parallel to H and that the Hall field is perpendicular to the current as well as the magnetic field. The relation between ρ, a and H may be written as

$$\rho(H) = a(H) = -RH$$

where R, the only non-vanishing independent component, is called the Hall constant. From the fact that the only vectors linear in j and quadratic in H which can be constructed from j and H are $H^2 j$ and $(j.H)H$, it follows that the expression for E up to second order terms in H should in general take the form

$$E = \rho_0 j + R(H \times j) + \beta_1 H^2 j + \beta_2 (j.H) H. \tag{29}$$

If we take the magnetic field to be along the X_3-axis only, we have from (29)

$$E_1 = (\rho_0 + \beta_1 H_3^2) j_1 - R H_3 j_2$$

$$E_2 = R H_3 j_1 + (\rho_0 + \beta_1 H_3^2) j_2$$

$$E_3 = [\rho_0 + (\beta_1 + \beta_2) H_3^2] j_3. \tag{30}$$

In (30), the coefficient $(\rho_0 + \beta_1 H_3^2)$ is the resistance measured in the direction of the current when the magnetic field is perpendicular to the current and thus it gives the longitudinal effect in a transverse magnetic field. It is denoted by $\rho_\perp$. Similarly, $R H_3$ gives the transverse effect in a transverse field and in fact it gives the Hall effect. $[\rho_0 + (\beta_1 + \beta_2) H_3^2]$ gives the longitudinal effect in a longitudinal field and is denoted by $\rho_\parallel$. The quantities

$$\frac{\rho_\perp - \rho_0}{\rho_0} = \frac{\Delta\rho_\perp}{\rho_0} \quad \text{and} \quad \frac{\rho_\parallel - \rho_0}{\rho_0} = \frac{\Delta\rho_\parallel}{\rho_0}$$

are called the transverse and longitudinal magnetoresistance respectively.

The effect of magnetic field on thermal conductivity tensor K_{ik} may be likewise analysed. The effect of Onsager relations on K_{ik} is similar to what is given for ρ_{ik} in relations (19), (20) and (21). The first order effect of the magnetic field on thermal conductivity is analogous to the Hall effect. A transverse temperature gradient is produced when a magnetic field is imposed in a direction perpendicular to the heat flux and it is called the Leduc–Righi effect. A magnetothermal conductivity is defined analogously to the magnetoresistance by the second order terms in the magnetic field.

The tensor α_{ik} represents the relation between the electric field E_i and the (negative) temperature gradient G_i in the absence of electric current and it is a function of H when a magnetic field is present. This relation may be obtained by putting j_i equal to zero in the first of relations (16) as

$$E_i = \alpha_{ik}(H) G_k. \tag{31}$$

Similarly, β_{ik} represents the relation between the thermal flux q_i and the electric current in the absence of temperature gradient which may be obtained from the second of relations (16) as

$$q_i = -\beta_{ik}(H) j_k. \tag{32}$$

The Onsager relations (17) for α_{ik} and β_{ik} are different from those for ρ_{ik} and K_{ik}. As a result of this the symmetric and antisymmetric parts of α_{ik} and β_{ik} are not even and odd functions of H, respectively. Relations similar to (24) can be obtained for α_{ik} and β_{ik}, which show that the

8

antisymmetric parts give rise to transverse effects. However, since the antisymmetric parts are not equivalent to the odd parts of the functions, we cannot conclude that the principal (first order) effects are entirely transverse effects as in the case of ρ_{ik} and K_{ik}. We can obtain a power series expansion for α_{ik} and β_{ik} similar to (25a). For example,

$$\alpha_{ik}(H) = \alpha_{ik}^0 + \alpha_{ikl} H_l + \alpha_{iklm} H_l H_m \qquad (33)$$

where terms up to the second power are considered. Substituting this expansion for $\alpha_{ik}(H)$ in (31) we obtain

$$E_i = (\alpha_{ik}^0 + \alpha_{ikl} H_l + \alpha_{iklm} H_l H_m) G_k. \qquad (34)$$

The tensor of α_{ikl} is thus seen to be analogous to the Hall tensor but does not entirely represent a transverse effect as the Hall tensor does. A similar remark applies to β_{ikl}. The related transverse effects in an isotropic medium are the Nernst effect and the Ettingshausen effect. The Nernst effect is the appearance of transverse voltage difference when a magnetic field is applied perpendicular to a longitudinal thermal current. The tensor α_{ikl} may be considered as a generalization of this effect to a crystalline medium even though the generalization is not exact. α_{ikl} is therefore called the Nernst tensor. The component α_{ikl} gives the change in the i-component of the thermoelectric field due to a k-component of the (negative) temperature gradient, on the imposition of an l-component of magnetic field. The Ettingshausen effect is the appearance of temperature difference in a direction perpendicular to both longitudinal electric current and the applied magnetic field. The tensor β_{ikl} may be considered as a generalization of this effect to a crystalline medium, and it may be called the Ettingshausen tensor. The Nernst tensor α_{ikl} and the Ettingshausen tensor β_{ikl} each relate a second order polar tensor and an axial vector.

The related second order effects are given by the tensors α_{iklm} and β_{iklm}. They each relate a second order polar tensor to a second order symmetric tensor. The tensor α_{iklm} may be called the magnetothermo-electric power.

The effects of magnetic field on the electrical and thermoelectric properties in the absence of a temperature gradient are called galvano-magnetic effects. Thus the Hall effect, the magnetoresistance effect, the Ettingshausen effect and their related higher order effects are galvanomagnetic effects. The effects of magnetic field on the thermo-electric and thermal properties in the absence of an electric current are called thermomagnetic effects. Thus the Nernst effect, the magneto-thermoelectric power, the Leduc–Righi effect and the magnetothermal conductivity and their related higher order effects are thermomagnetic effects. As already mentioned, the conventional definitions of the galvanomagnetic and thermomagnetic effects are given for isotropic media. The related effects in single crystals are complex, and the definitions given for the isotropic case are applicable only in the case of certain simple orientations of the crystal with respect to the physical quantities, namely, the forces, the fluxes and the magnetic field. In what follows, we shall give a systematic general formulation of the effects in single crystals.

17.5 Systematic Enumeration of the Effects of Various Orders in Single Crystals

It has already been pointed out that the galvanomagnetic and thermomagnetic effects in single crystals are complex and a straightforward generalization of the conventionally measured effects cannot be effected. A general formulation and a systematic enumeration of these effects of various orders are given in this section. The basis for such a formulation is the set of tensor equations (16) of this Chapter. The coefficient tensors which are functions of magnetic field are expanded as follows into power series involving the magnetic field components.

$$\rho_{ik}(H) = \rho_{ik}^0 + \rho_{ikl}\,H_l + \rho_{iklm}\,H_l\,H_m + \rho_{iklmn}\,H_l\,H_m\,H_n$$
$$+ \rho_{iklmnp}\,H_l\,H_m\,H_n\,H_p + \dots$$

$$K_{ik}(H) = K_{ik}^0 + K_{ikl}\,H_l + K_{iklm}\,H_l\,H_m + K_{iklmn}\,H_l\,H_m\,H_n$$
$$+ K_{iklmnp}\,H_l\,H_m\,H_n\,H_p + \dots$$

$$\alpha_{ik}(H) = \alpha_{ik}^0 + \alpha_{ikl}\,H_l + \alpha_{iklm}\,H_l\,H_m + \alpha_{iklmn}\,H_l\,H_m\,H_n$$
$$+ \alpha_{iklmnp}\,H_l\,H_m\,H_n\,H_p + \dots$$

$$\beta_{ik}(H) = \beta_{ik}^0 + \beta_{ikl}\,H_l + \beta_{iklm}\,H_l\,H_m + \beta_{iklmn}\,H_l\,H_m\,H_n$$
$$+ \beta_{iklmnp}\,H_l\,H_m\,H_n\,H_p + \dots.$$

We shall consider the galvanomagnetic and thermomagnetic effects up to fourth power in H, and therefore limit the development of the tensors to terms of fourth power in H. The coefficient of a particular power in H in the development of a tensor gives that particular order effect of magnetic field on the physical property represented by the tensor. For example, the first term ρ_{ik}^0 in the development of $\rho_{ik}(H)$ in powers of H is independent of H and represents the electrical resistivity in the absence of H. The coefficient ρ_{ikl} in the second terms gives the first order effect of H on electrical resistivity. Thus ρ_{ikl} tensor represents the Hall effect.

The quantities $\rho_{ik}^0, \rho_{ikl}, \rho_{iklm}, \rho_{iklmn}, \ldots$ and $\beta_{ik}^0, \beta_{ikl}, \beta_{iklm}, \beta_{iklmn}, \ldots$ are called galvanomagnetic coefficients. The quantities $K_{ik}^0, K_{ikl}, K_{iklm},$ $K_{iklmn}, \ldots$ and $\alpha_{ik}^0, \alpha_{ikl}, \alpha_{iklm}, \alpha_{iklmn}, \ldots$ are called thermomagnetic coefficients. The ρ and K coefficients of corresponding order are tensors of same rank and kind. Similarly, the α and β coefficients of corresponding order are tensors of same rank and kind. The Onsager relations in the presence of a magnetic field have been given in equations (17). As already pointed out, in the case of $\rho_{ik}(H)$ and $K_{ik}(H)$ the symmetric and antisymmetric parts are given by the even power and odd power terms in their series development. We have already dealt with terms up to second order in H. However, for the sake of completeness we shall systematically enumerate the effects of various orders.

Zero order effects and tensors of second rank

The tensors $\rho_{ik}^0, K_{ik}^0, \alpha_{ik}^0, \beta_{ik}^0$ represent the zero order effects. They are the corresponding transport properties in the absence of magnetic fields.

First order effects and tensors of third rank

The tensors ρ_{ikl}, K_{ikl} represent the Hall effect and the Leduc–Righi effect. As a result of their intrinsic symmetry they are each equivalent to a second rank polar tensor. They are called the Hall tensor and the Leduc–Righi tensor, respectively. α_{ikl} and β_{ikl} which may be called the Nernst tensor and the Ettingshausen tensor, respectively, are of third rank which relate a second rank polar tensor and an axial vector.

Second order effects and tensors of fourth rank

ρ_{iklm} is the magnetoresistance tensor. Its intrinsic symmetry has already been discussed. K_{iklm} which has identical intrinsic symmetry represents what may be called magnetothermal conductivity, and does not appear to have been studied as extensively as ρ_{iklm}. The tensors α_{iklm} and β_{iklm} are symmetric in the suffixes lm but not symmetric with respect to an interchange of i and k. They both relate a second rank polar tensor with a second rank symmetric polar tensor. α_{iklm} is called magnetothermoelectric power.

Third order effects and tensors of fifth rank

ρ_{iklmn} which represents the third order effect of the magnetic field on electrical resistivity can be regarded as second order Hall effect. Similarly, K_{iklmn} can be regarded as second order Leduc–Righi effect. These tensors are antisymmetric in i, k and totally symmetric in lmn.

TABLE XIII

Classification of transport phenomena

	Composite tensor	Zero order component	First order component	Second order component	Third order component	Fourth order component
Galvanomagnetic effects	$\rho_{ik}(H)$	Electrical resistivity $\rho_{ik}{}^{\circ}$	Hall effect ρ_{ikl}	Magneto-resistance ρ_{iklm}	Second order Hall effect ρ_{iklmn}	Second order magneto-resistance ρ_{iklmnp}
	$\beta_{ik}(H)$	No name $\beta_{ik}{}^{\circ}$	Ettingshausen effect β_{ikl}	No name β_{iklm}	Second order Ettingshausen effect β_{iklmn}	No name β_{iklmnp}
Thermomagnetic effects	$K_{ik}(H)$	Thermal conductivity $K_{ik}{}^{\circ}$	Leduc–Righi effect K_{ikl}	Magnetothermal conductivity K_{iklm}	Second order Leduc–Righi effect K_{iklmn}	Second order magneto-thermal conductivity K_{iklmnp}
	$\alpha_{ik}(H)$	Thermoelectric power $\alpha_{ik}{}^{\circ}$	Nernst effect α_{ikl}	Magnetothermo-electric power α_{iklm}	Second order Nernst effect α_{iklmn}	Second order magneto-thermoelectric power α_{iklmnp}

They relate an antisymmetric tensor of second rank to a totally symmetric third rank tensor.

α_{iklmn} and β_{iklmn}, on the other hand, relate a second rank general tensor with a totally symmetric third rank tensor. They can be regarded as second order Nernst effect and second order Ettingshausen effect, respectively.

Fourth order effects and tensors of sixth rank

ρ_{iklmnp} represents the second order magnetoresistance. Similarly K_{iklmnp} represents the second order magnetothermal conductivity. They both relate a second rank symmetric tensor with a fourth rank totally symmetric tensor (totally symmetric in suffixes $lmnp$).

α_{iklmnp} and β_{iklmnp} relate a second rank general tensor with a fourth rank totally symmetric tensor.

In Table XIII are given the galvanomagnetic and thermomagnetic coefficients, conveniently tabulated under columns and giving properties of increasing order effects in H.

17.6 Effect of Symmetry on the Galvanomagnetic and Thermomagnetic Coefficients

The galvanomagnetic and thermomagnetic properties of a crystal depend on its point group symmetry. The effect of symmetry is obtained, as in the case of other physical properties, by the application of Neumann's principle. The numbers of non-vanishing independent components calculated by the group theoretical methods for the various galvanomagnetic and thermomagnetic properties are given in Table VIII(b).

We give below the schemes of non-vanishing components for tensors. The Hall tensor ρ_{ikl} and the Leduc–Righi tensor K_{ikl} have identical schemes of non-vanishing components under the various point group symmetries. The schemes for ρ_{ikl} are as follows.

(i) TRICLINIC SYSTEM

$$
\begin{array}{ccccccccc}
0 & \rho_{121} & \rho_{131} & 0 & \rho_{122} & \rho_{132} & 0 & \rho_{123} & \rho_{133} \\
-\rho_{121} & 0 & \rho_{231} & -\rho_{122} & 0 & \rho_{232} & -\rho_{123} & 0 & \rho_{233} \\
-\rho_{131} & -\rho_{231} & 0 & -\rho_{132} & -\rho_{232} & 0 & -\rho_{133} & -\rho_{233} & 0
\end{array}
$$

(ii) MONOCLINIC SYSTEM

$$
\begin{array}{ccccccccc}
0 & 0 & \rho_{131} & 0 & 0 & \rho_{132} & 0 & \rho_{123} & 0 \\
0 & 0 & \rho_{231} & 0 & 0 & \rho_{232} & -\rho_{123} & 0 & 0 \\
-\rho_{131} & -\rho_{231} & 0 & -\rho_{132} & -\rho_{232} & 0 & 0 & 0 & 0
\end{array}
$$

(iii) ORTHORHOMBIC SYSTEM

$$
\begin{array}{ccccccccc}
0 & 0 & 0 & 0 & 0 & \rho_{132} & 0 & \rho_{123} & 0 \\
0 & 0 & \rho_{231} & 0 & 0 & 0 & -\rho_{123} & 0 & 0 \\
0 & -\rho_{231} & 0 & -\rho_{132} & 0 & 0 & 0 & 0 & 0
\end{array}
$$

(iv) (a) TETRAGONAL, TRIGONAL, HEXAGONAL SYSTEMS: CLASSES 4, $\bar{4}$, 4/m, 3, $\bar{3}$, 6, $\bar{6}$, 6/m

$$
\begin{array}{ccccccccc}
0 & 0 & \rho_{131} & 0 & 0 & \rho_{132} & 0 & \rho_{123} & 0 \\
0 & 0 & -\rho_{132} & 0 & 0 & \rho_{131} & -\rho_{123} & 0 & 0 \\
-\rho_{131} & \rho_{132} & 0 & -\rho_{132} & -\rho_{131} & 0 & 0 & 0 & 0
\end{array}
$$

(iv) (b) TETRAGONAL, TRIGONAL, HEXAGONAL SYSTEMS: CLASSES 422, 4mm, $\bar{4}2m$, 4/mmm, 32, 3m, $\bar{3}m$, 622, 6mm, $\bar{6}m2$, 6/mmm

$$
\begin{array}{ccccccccc}
0 & 0 & 0 & 0 & 0 & \rho_{132} & 0 & \rho_{123} & 0 \\
0 & 0 & -\rho_{132} & 0 & 0 & 0 & -\rho_{123} & 0 & 0 \\
0 & \rho_{132} & 0 & -\rho_{132} & 0 & 0 & 0 & 0 & 0
\end{array}
$$

(v) CUBIC SYSTEM AND ISOTROPIC MEDIUM

$$
\begin{array}{ccccccccc}
0 & 0 & 0 & 0 & 0 & \rho_{132} & 0 & -\rho_{132} & 0 \\
0 & 0 & -\rho_{132} & 0 & 0 & 0 & \rho_{132} & 0 & 0 \\
0 & \rho_{132} & 0 & -\rho_{132} & 0 & 0 & 0 & 0 & 0
\end{array}
$$

The Nernst tensor α_{ikl} and the Ettingshausen tensor β_{ikl} have identical schemes of non-vanishing components under the various point group symmetries. We give below the schemes for α_{ikl}.

(i) TRICLINIC SYSTEM

$$
\begin{array}{ccccccccc}
\alpha_{111} & \alpha_{121} & \alpha_{131} & \alpha_{112} & \alpha_{122} & \alpha_{132} & \alpha_{113} & \alpha_{123} & \alpha_{133} \\
\alpha_{211} & \alpha_{221} & \alpha_{231} & \alpha_{212} & \alpha_{222} & \alpha_{232} & \alpha_{213} & \alpha_{223} & \alpha_{233} \\
\alpha_{311} & \alpha_{321} & \alpha_{331} & \alpha_{312} & \alpha_{322} & \alpha_{332} & \alpha_{313} & \alpha_{323} & \alpha_{333}
\end{array}
$$

(ii) MONOCLINIC SYSTEM

$$
\begin{array}{ccccccccc}
0 & 0 & \alpha_{131} & 0 & 0 & \alpha_{132} & \alpha_{113} & \alpha_{123} & 0 \\
0 & 0 & \alpha_{231} & 0 & 0 & \alpha_{232} & \alpha_{213} & \alpha_{223} & 0 \\
\alpha_{311} & \alpha_{321} & 0 & \alpha_{312} & \alpha_{322} & 0 & 0 & 0 & \alpha_{333}
\end{array}
$$

(iii) ORTHORHOMBIC SYSTEM

$$\begin{array}{ccccccccc}
0 & 0 & 0 & 0 & 0 & \alpha_{132} & 0 & \alpha_{123} & 0 \\
0 & 0 & \alpha_{231} & 0 & 0 & 0 & \alpha_{213} & 0 & 0 \\
0 & \alpha_{321} & 0 & \alpha_{312} & 0 & 0 & 0 & 0 & 0
\end{array}$$

(iv) (a) TETRAGONAL, HEXAGONAL SYSTEMS: CLASSES 4, $\bar{4}$, 4/m, $\bar{6}$, 6, 6/m

$$\begin{array}{ccccccccc}
0 & 0 & \alpha_{131} & 0 & 0 & \alpha_{231} & \alpha_{113} & \alpha_{123} & 0 \\
0 & 0 & \alpha_{231} & 0 & 0 & \alpha_{131} & \alpha_{123} & \alpha_{113} & 0 \\
\alpha_{311} & \alpha_{321} & 0 & \alpha_{321} & \alpha_{311} & 0 & 0 & 0 & \alpha_{333}
\end{array}$$

(iv) (b) TETRAGONAL, HEXAGONAL SYSTEMS: CLASSES 4mm, $\bar{4}2m$, 422, 4/mmm, $\bar{6}m2$, 6mm, 622, 6/mmm

$$\begin{array}{ccccccccc}
0 & 0 & 0 & 0 & 0 & \alpha_{231} & 0 & \alpha_{123} & 0 \\
0 & 0 & \alpha_{231} & 0 & 0 & 0 & \alpha_{123} & 0 & 0 \\
0 & \alpha_{321} & 0 & \alpha_{321} & 0 & 0 & 0 & 0 & 0
\end{array}$$

(v) (a) TRIGONAL SYSTEM: CLASSES 3, $\bar{3}$

$$\begin{array}{ccccccccc}
\alpha_{111} & \alpha_{121} & \alpha_{131} & -\alpha_{121} & -\alpha_{111} & -\alpha_{231} & \alpha_{113} & \alpha_{123} & 0 \\
\alpha_{121} & -\alpha_{111} & \alpha_{231} & -\alpha_{111} & -\alpha_{121} & \alpha_{131} & -\alpha_{123} & \alpha_{113} & 0 \\
\alpha_{311} & \alpha_{321} & 0 & -\alpha_{321} & \alpha_{311} & 0 & 0 & 0 & \alpha_{333}
\end{array}$$

(v) (b) TRIGONAL SYSTEM: CLASSES 3m, 32, $\bar{3}m$

$$\begin{array}{ccccccccc}
\alpha_{111} & 0 & 0 & 0 & -\alpha_{111} & -\alpha_{231} & 0 & \alpha_{123} & 0 \\
0 & -\alpha_{111} & \alpha_{231} & -\alpha_{111} & 0 & 0 & -\alpha_{123} & 0 & 0 \\
0 & \alpha_{321} & 0 & -\alpha_{321} & 0 & 0 & 0 & 0 & 0
\end{array}$$

(vi) (a) CUBIC SYSTEM: CLASSES 23, m3

$$\begin{array}{ccccccccc}
0 & 0 & 0 & 0 & 0 & \alpha_{321} & 0 & \alpha_{231} & 0 \\
0 & 0 & \alpha_{231} & 0 & 0 & 0 & \alpha_{321} & 0 & 0 \\
0 & \alpha_{321} & 0 & \alpha_{231} & 0 & 0 & 0 & 0 & 0
\end{array}$$

(vi) (b) CUBIC SYSTEM: CLASSES $\bar{4}3m$, 432, m3m, AND ISOTROPIC MEDIUM

$$\begin{array}{ccccccccc}
0 & 0 & 0 & 0 & 0 & -\alpha_{231} & 0 & \alpha_{231} & 0 \\
0 & 0 & \alpha_{231} & 0 & 0 & 0 & -\alpha_{231} & 0 & 0 \\
0 & -\alpha_{231} & 0 & \alpha_{231} & 0 & 0 & 0 & 0 & 0
\end{array}$$

The schemes of non-vanishing components of the magnetoresistance tensor ρ_{iklm} and of the magnetothermal conductivity tensor K_{iklm} are identical with each other and are the same as those for the photoelasticity tensor. These also represent a symmetric tensor–symmetric tensor relation. In the two-suffix notation, they are given as stress-optical coefficients (q's) in Chapter 16. A similar notation for the suffixes has to be adopted to express the coefficients ρ_{iklm}. As for q's, we have the relations for ρ's given below.

$$\rho_{iklm} = A_{pq} \text{ when } p \text{ is 1 to 6 and } q \text{ is 1, 2 or 3.}$$

$$2\rho_{iklm} = A_{pq} \text{ when } p \text{ is 1 to 6 and } q \text{ is 4, 5 or 6.}$$

Identification of the magnetoresistance tensor with the q schemes of photoelasticity in the short notation implies that we choose the products $H_1 H_1, H_2 H_2, H_3 H_3, H_2 H_3, H_3 H_1, H_1 H_2$ in the place of the stresses τ_{ij}.

The second order Hall effect and the second order Leduc–Righi effect are effects of third order in the magnetic field. They are represented by tensors of fifth rank ρ_{iklmn} and K_{iklmn}, respectively, each of which is antisymmetric in the first two suffixes i and k and totally symmetric in the last three suffixes l, m and n. They can be interpreted as relating an antisymmetric tensor of second rank with a totally symmetric tensor of third rank. An antisymmetric tensor of second rank is equivalent to an axial vector and has only three independent components. We have here chosen the components bearing suffixes $23, 31, 12$ as independent. A polar tensor of third rank which is totally symmetric in the suffixes has only 10 independent components. We have here chosen the components bearing suffixes $111, 112, 113, 122, 123, 133, 222, 223, 233, 333$ as independent. The schemes of the second order Hall tensor and second order Leduc–Righi tensor are therefore presented here as 3×10 matrices with the components $23, 31, 12$ of the second rank antisymmetric tensor denoting 3 rows and the 10 components of the totally symmetric third rank tensor denoting the columns. In the schemes given below, the letters denoting the particular tensor, i.e. ρ and K, are omitted as the suffixes are too many and only the suffixes of the non-vanishing components are given.

The schemes for the magnetothermoelectric power tensor α_{iklm} are given in the Appendix, as they are somewhat lengthy and the applications thereof are likely to be of interest only in special problems.

17.7 Piezogalvanomagnetic Effects

The effects of elastic stress on the electrical resistivity in the presence of a magnetic field may be called piezogalvanomagnetic effects. From the point of view we have been adopting here, it amounts to a study of the effect of elastic stress on the various coefficient tensors in the expansion of $\rho_{ik}(H)$ as power series in H. The zero order term or the coefficient independent of H is ρ_{ik}^0 which is the ordinary electrical resistivity. The effect of elastic stress τ_{ik} on ρ_{ik}^0 is called piezoresistance, which has been studied in some detail by Smith.[†] τ_{ik} and ρ_{ik}^0 are both second rank symmetric tensors. Piezo–Hall effect relates a general second rank tensor to which Hall tensor ρ_{ikl} reduces and the elastic stress τ_{ik}. The numbers of independent components of such tensors have already been given in columns (4) and (5) in Table VIII(b). Piezomagnetoresistance relates the magnetoresistance tensor ρ_{iklm} with elastic stress τ_{ik}. The character of a general symmetry element in the representation formed by such a tensor and the numbers of independent components are shown in Tables VII(b) and VIII(b) against No. 10.

(i) TRICLINIC SYSTEM: CLASSES 1, $\bar{1}$

23111	23112	23113	23122	23123	23133	23222	23223	23233	23333
31111	31112	31113	31122	31123	31133	31222	31223	31233	31333
12111	12112	12113	12122	12123	12133	12222	12223	12233	12333

(ii) MONOCLINIC SYSTEM: CLASSES m, 2, 2/m

23111	23112	0	23122	0	23133	23222	0	23233	0
31111	31112	0	31122	0	31133	31222	0	31233	0
0	0	12113	0	12123	0	0	12223	0	12333

(iii) ORTHORHOMBIC SYSTEM: CLASSES 2mm, 222, mmm

23111	0	0	23122	0	23133	0	0	0	0
0	31112	0	0	0	0	31222	0	31233	0
0	0	12113	0	0	0	0	12223	0	12333

(iv) (a) TETRAGONAL SYSTEM: CLASSES 4, $\bar{4}$, 4/m

23111	23112	0	23122	0	23133	23222	0	23233	0
−23222	23122	0	−23112	0	−23233	23111	0	23133	0
0	0	12113	0	0	0	0	12113	0	12333

(iv) (b) TETRAGONAL SYSTEM: CLASSES 4mm, $\bar{4}$2m, 422, 4/mmm

23111	0	0	23122	0	23133	0	0	0	0
0	23122	0	0	0	0	23111	0	23133	0
0	0	12113	0	0	0	0	12113	0	12333

(v) (a) TRIGONAL SYSTEM: CLASSES 3, $\bar{3}$

3(23122)	$-\tfrac{1}{2}$(31111)	23113	23122	−31223	23133	−31111	−23113	23233	0
+31111	23122	−31223	−23112	−23113	−23233	3(23122)	31223	23133	0
12111	−12222	12113	−12111	0	0	12222	12113	0	12333

[†] Smith, C. S., Macroscopic Symmetry and Properties of Crystals, "Solid State Physics", Vol. 6. Academic Press, New York (1958).

(v) (b) TRIGONAL SYSTEM: CLASSES $3m$, 32, $\bar{3}m$

3(23122)	0	0	23122	−31223	23133	0	0	0	0
0	23122	−31223	0	0	0	3(23122)	31223	23133	0
0	−12222	12113	0	0	0	12222	12113	0	12333

(vi) (a) HEXAGONAL SYSTEM: CLASSES $\bar{6}$, 6, $6/m$

3(23122)	0	0	23122	0	23133	−31111	0	23233	0
31111	23122	0	−23112	0	−23233	3(23122)	0	23133	0
0	0	12113	0	23133	0	0	12113	0	12333

(vi) (b) HEXAGONAL SYSTEM: CLASSES $\bar{6}m2$, $6mm$ 622, $6/mmm$

3(23122)	0	0	23122	0	23133	0	0	0	0
0	23122	0	0	0	0	3(23122)	0	23133	0
0	0	12113	0	0	0	0	12113	0	12333

(vii) (a) CUBIC SYSTEM: CLASSES 23, $m3$

23111	0	0	23122	0	23133	0	0	0	0
0	23133	0	0	0	0	23111	0	23122	0
0	0	23122	0	0	0	0	23133	0	23111

(vii) (b) CUBIC SYSTEM: CLASSES $\bar{4}3m$, 432, $m3m$

23111	0	0	23122	0	23122	0	0	0	0
0	23122	0	0	0	0	23111	0	23122	0
0	0	23122	0	0	0	0	23122	0	23111

CHAPTER 18

Single Crystal Illustrations

18.1 Galvanomagnetic Coefficients in Cubic Crystals

As already pointed out, conventional measurements of galvanomagnetic phenomena in single crystals often seek to establish the directional dependence of these properties only. However, straightforward determinations of the galvanomagnetic coefficients is to be preferred particularly in crystal systems of higher symmetry, because the conventional classifications can become ambiguous due to intermixing of voltages from Hall effect and magnetoresistance. As an illustration, we give here the arrangements which enable one to obtain the galvanomagnetic tensor components in cubic crystals.

We shall first deal with the cubic class $m3m$. Germanium and silicon are typical representatives of this class. There is only one independent coefficient in the first order Hall effect tensor and 3 and 2 coefficients, respectively, in the magnetoresistance and second order Hall effect tensors. Detailed schemes in conformity with the notation already adopted in the earlier Chapters are given below.

CLASS $m3m$: SCHEME FOR FIRST ORDER HALL TENSOR

$$
\begin{array}{ccccccccc}
0 & 0 & 0 & 0 & 0 & \rho_{132} & 0 & -\rho_{132} & 0 \\
0 & 0 & -\rho_{132} & 0 & 0 & 0 & \rho_{132} & 0 & 0 \\
0 & \rho_{132} & 0 & -\rho_{132} & 0 & 0 & 0 & 0 & 0
\end{array}
$$

CLASS $m3m$: SCHEME FOR MAGNETORESISTANCE TENSOR

$$
\begin{array}{cccccc}
A_{11} & A_{12} & A_{12} & 0 & 0 & 0 \\
A_{12} & A_{11} & A_{12} & 0 & 0 & 0 \\
A_{12} & A_{12} & A_{11} & 0 & 0 & 0 \\
0 & 0 & 0 & A_{44} & 0 & 0 \\
0 & 0 & 0 & 0 & A_{44} & 0 \\
0 & 0 & 0 & 0 & 0 & A_{44}
\end{array}
$$

CLASS $m3m$: SCHEME FOR SECOND ORDER HALL TENSOR

	111	112	113	122	123	133	222	223	233	333
23	P	0	0	$-Q$	0	$-Q$	0	0	0	0
31	0	$-Q$	0	0	0	0	P	0	$-Q$	0
12	0	0	$-Q$	0	0	0	0	$-Q$	0	P

We shall further designate the single first order Hall coefficient ρ_{132} by R. P and $-Q$ stand for the two second order Hall coefficients ρ_{23111} and ρ_{23122}, respectively. It is convenient to write out the explicit expressions for the field and current relations appropriate to this point group. They are as follows:

$$E_1 = \rho_{11}j_1 + \rho_{12}j_2 + \rho_{13}j_3$$

$$E_2 = \rho_{21}j_1 + \rho_{22}j_2 + \rho_{23}j_3$$

$$E_3 = \rho_{31}j_1 + \rho_{32}j_2 + \rho_{33}j_3 \tag{1}$$

where

$$\rho_{11} = \rho_{11}^0 + \rho_{111}H_1 + \rho_{112}H_2 + \rho_{113}H_3 + A_{11}H_1^2 + A_{12}H_2^2 + A_{13}H_3^2$$
$$+ A_{14}H_2H_3 + A_{15}H_3H_1 + A_{16}H_1H_2 + \rho_{11111}H_1^3 + 3\rho_{11112}H_1^2H_2$$
$$+ 3\rho_{11113}H_1^2H_3 + 3\rho_{11122}H_1H_2^2 + 6\rho_{11123}H_1H_2H_3 + 3\rho_{11133}H_1H_3^2$$
$$+ \rho_{11222}H_2^3 + 3\rho_{11223}H_2^2H_3 + 3\rho_{11233}H_2H_3^2 + \rho_{11333}H_3^3 \tag{2}$$

and similar expressions for ρ_{12}, ρ_{13}, etc. It is now possible to write out the expressions for E_1, E_2 and E_3 using the schemes appropriate to the class $m3m$ and evaluating ρ_{11}, ρ_{12}, etc. They are

$$E_1 = (A_{11}H_1^2 + A_{12}H_2^2 + A_{12}H_3^2)j_1$$
$$+ [-\rho_{132}H_3 + A_{44}H_1H_2 - 3Q(H_1^2H_3 + H_2^2H_3) + PH_3^3]j_2$$
$$+ [\rho_{132}H_2 + A_{44}H_3H_1 + 3Q(H_1^2H_2 + H_2H_3^2) - PH_2^3]j_3. \tag{3}$$

$$E_2 = [\rho_{132}H_3 + A_{44}H_1H_2 + 3Q(H_1^2H_3 + H_2^2H_3) - PH_3^3]j_1$$
$$+ (A_{11}H_2^2 + A_{12}H_1^2 + A_{12}H_3^2)j_2$$
$$+ [-\rho_{132}H_1 + A_{44}H_2H_3 - 3Q(H_1H_2^2 + H_1H_3^2) + PH_1^3]j_3. \tag{4}$$

$$E_3 = [-\rho_{132}H_2 + A_{44}H_3H_1 - 3Q(H_2H_3^2 + H_2H_1^2) + PH_2^3]j_1$$
$$+ [\rho_{132}H_1 + A_{44}H_2H_3 + 3Q(H_2^2H_1 + H_3^2H_1) - PH_1^3]j_2$$
$$+ (A_{11}H_3^2 + A_{12}H_2^2 + A_{12}H_1^2)j_3. \tag{5}$$

It may be noted that E_2 and E_3 do not yield any independent information, because in the case of a cubic crystal they can be easily derived from E_1 by performing an appropriate symmetry operation. For instance, if the cyclic substitution (123) is performed on E_1 in respect of the suffixes of E, H and j, we obtain E_2. By the same operation and in the same manner, we obtain E_3 from E_2 and so on. Equation (3) may be regarded as the basic equation for the cubic classes $\overline{4}3m$, 432 and $m3m$ with the help of which all the galvanomagnetic coefficients up to the third power of the magnetic field may be determined by devising suitable experiments. The coefficients are 6 in number and they are R (first order Hall coefficient), A_{11}, A_{12} and A_{44} (magnetoresistance coefficients) and P and Q (second order Hall coefficients).

If one cuts a cylinder of square cross-section from a cubic crystal with the edges parallel to the cube axes, the first simple experiment is to designate the length of the cylinder as the X_3-axis, the two edges of the square cross-section as the X_1- and X_2-axes and measure E_1 for $j_3 = j$ and $H_2 = H$, all other components of j and H being zero. We have from equation (3) that

$$E_1 = (\rho_{132}H - PH^3)j. \tag{6}$$

The measurement of E_1 for a few different values of H will permit the determination of ρ_{132} and P.

We can now consider other alternatives in respect of the same crystal sample and write out the following corresponding equations.

$$j_3 = j; \quad H_1 = H_3 = H; \quad E_1 = A_{44}H^2j:$$
$$j_3 = j; \quad H_1 = H_2 = H; \quad E_1 = (\rho_{132}H + 3QH^3)j:$$
$$j_1 = j; \quad H_1 = H; \quad E_1 = A_{11}H^2j:$$
$$j_1 = j; \quad H_2 = H; \quad E_1 = A_{12}H^2j. \tag{7}$$

The components of j and H not explicitly mentioned in (7) are to be regarded as zero. The settings suggested are only illustrative. In all settings, the measurement is of E_1. We can thus obtain experimentally the values of all the 6 coefficients along with a few additional checks. Many other possibilities can be thought of but the essential point relates to the measurement of all the 6 galvanomagnetic coefficients appropriate to the crystal class by working on a single suitably cut sample. The suitably cut sample in this case is therefore a cylinder with its length and the edges of the square cross-section parallel to the three cubic axes.

It is interesting to note that in the two other cubic classes 23 and $m3$, while the first order Hall coefficient remains the same, one additional independent coefficient appears in each of the schemes relating to the magnetoresistance tensor and the second order Hall coefficient tensor.

An immediate consequence of such a situation is that there will be marked and distinguishable differences in the galvanomagnetic properties of the cubic classes 23 and $m3$, on the one hand, and $\overline{4}3m$, 432 and $m3m$, on the other, when we are dealing with the second and higher powers of the magnetic field H. This aspect has neither been realized and pointed out explicitly nor experimentally investigated upon so far in the literature. However, this difference will be dealt with more fully when we discuss the analogous photoelasticity tensor in a following section.

18.2 Some Crystal Classes with Lower Symmetry

We shall now choose another group of crystal classes which includes the class $3m$ of which antimony is an example. Juretschke† made a detailed study of this case in particular. Table XIV summarizes the features of the crystal classes chosen.

TABLE XIV

Magnetic properties of some crystals

Example crystal	Symmetry symbol	Number of independent coefficients		
		Hall effect first order	Magneto-resistance	Hall effect second order
Antimony	$3m$ (C_{3v})	2	8	6
Bismuth	$\overline{3}m$ (D_{3d})	2	8	6
Tin	$4/mmm$ (D_{4h})	2	7	5
Zinc Cadmium }	$6/mmm$ (D_{6h})	2	6	4

In the case of antimony with the symmetry $3m$, the schemes picked out from Chapters 16 and 17 are reproduced below. The same schemes apply to $\overline{3}m$ which is the symmetry class appropriate to bismuth. Modifications necessary for making the schemes applicable to $4/mmm$ and $6/mmm$ are also indicated at the appropriate places.

CLASS 3m: SCHEME FOR FIRST ORDER HALL TENSOR

$$
\begin{matrix}
0 & 0 & 0 & 0 & 0 & \rho_{132} & 0 & \rho_{123} & 0 \\
0 & 0 & -\rho_{132} & 0 & 0 & 0 & -\rho_{123} & 0 & 0 \\
0 & \rho_{132} & 0 & -\rho_{132} & 0 & 0 & 0 & 0 & 0
\end{matrix}
$$

The same scheme as above applies to $4/mmm$ and $6/mmm$.

† Juretschke, H. J., *Acta cryst.* **8**, 716 (1955).

CLASS 3m: SCHEME FOR MAGNETORESISTANCE TENSOR

$$
\begin{array}{cccccc}
A_{11} & A_{12} & A_{13} & A_{14} & 0 & 0 \\
A_{12} & A_{11} & A_{13} & -A_{14} & 0 & 0 \\
A_{31} & A_{31} & A_{33} & 0 & 0 & 0 \\
A_{41} & -A_{41} & 0 & A_{44} & 0 & 0 \\
0 & 0 & 0 & 0 & A_{44} & 2A_{41} \\
0 & 0 & 0 & 0 & A_{14} & (A_{11}-A_{12})
\end{array}
$$

By putting $A_{14} = A_{41} = 0$ and replacing $A_{11} - A_{12}$ by A_{66} in the above scheme, the number of coefficients becomes 7 instead of 8 and we get the scheme appropriate to $4/mmm$. Similarly, by just putting $A_{14} = A_{41} = 0$, the number becomes 6 instead of 8 and we get the scheme appropriate to $6/mmm$.

CLASS 3m: SCHEME FOR SECOND ORDER HALL TENSOR

	111	112	113	122	123	133	222	223	233	333
23	$3T_{112}$	0	0	T_{112}	$-T_{224}$	T_{113}	0	0	0	0
31	0	T_{112}	$-T_{224}$	0	0	0	$3T_{112}$	T_{224}	T_{113}	0
12	0	$-T_{322}$	T_{331}	0	0	0	T_{322}	T_{331}	0	T_{333}

In the above scheme, if we put $T_{224} = \rho_{31223} = 0$ and $T_{322} = \rho_{12222} = 0$, we have only 4 independent constants left and the resulting Table is appropriate to the class $6/mmm$. Further, if in the positions 23111 and 31222 where $3T_{112}$ is appearing, we substitute the coefficient $\rho_{23111} = T_{111}$, the resulting Table will have 5 independent constants and is appropriate to the class $4/mmm$.

A procedure for assigning the subscripts to T has been followed in the above Table with a view to bringing the notation in line with what has been adopted by Juretschke. The five-digit subscript is condensed into a three-digit one by replacing the first two digits by the absent third digit, retaining the middle digit unchanged and by replacing the last two digits by the appropriate single digit in the one-suffix notation. As examples, we may note that 23122 becomes 112 and 31223 becomes 224. We may also note that in deriving the three schemes given in the foregoing Tables for the class 3m, in addition to taking the 3-fold axis as X_3, one of the three reflection planes containing the 3-fold axis is assumed to induce the transformation $1 \to -1, 2 \to 2, 3 \to 3$. This is equivalent to regarding the X_2X_3-plane as the reflection plane under consideration.

We can now write out the expressions for E_1, E_2 and E_3 using the schemes for the class 3m and with the help of equations (1) and (2), adopting the same procedure as for the cubic crystals. We have

$$E_1 = [A_{11} H_1^2 + A_{12} H_2^2 + A_{13} H_3^2 + A_{14} H_2 H_3] j_1$$

$$+ [\rho_{123} H_3 + A_{14} H_3 H_1 + (A_{11} - A_{12}) H_1 H_2$$

$$+ T_{322}(H_2^2 - 3H_1^2) H_2 + 3T_{331}(H_1^2 + H_2^2) H_3 + T_{333} H_3^3] j_2$$

$$+ [\rho_{132} H_2 + A_{44} H_3 H_1 + 2A_{41} H_1 H_2 - 3T_{112}(H_1^2 + H_2^2) H_2$$

$$+ 3T_{224}(H_1^2 - H_2^2) H_3 - 3T_{113} H_2 H_3^2] j_3. \tag{8}$$

$$E_2 = [- \rho_{123} H_3 + A_{14} H_3 H_1 + (A_{11} - A_{12}) H_1 H_2$$

$$- T_{322}(H_2^2 - 3H_1^2) H_2 - 3T_{331}(H_1^2 + H_2^2) H_3 - T_{333} H_3^3] j_1$$

$$+ [A_{12} H_1^2 + A_{11} H_2^2 + A_{13} H_3^2 - A_{14} H_2 H_3] j_2$$

$$+ [- \rho_{132} H_1^2 + A_{41}(H_1^2 - H_2^2) + A_{44} H_2 H_3$$

$$+ 3T_{112}(H_2^2 + H_1^2) H_1 + 3T_{113} H_1 H_3^2 - 6T_{224} H_1 H_2 H_3] j_3. \tag{9}$$

$$E_3 = [- \rho_{132} H_2 + A_{44} H_3 H_1 + 2A_{41} H_1 H_2$$

$$+ 3T_{112}(H_1^2 + H_2^2) H_2 - 3T_{224}(H_1^2 - H_2^2) H_3 + 3T_{113} H_2 H_3^2] j_1$$

$$+ [\rho_{132} H_1 + A_{41}(H_1^2 - H_2^2) + A_{44} H_2 H_3$$

$$- 3T_{112}(H_1^2 + H_2^2) H_1 + 6T_{224} H_1 H_2 H_3 - 3T_{113} H_1 H_3^2] j_2$$

$$+ [A_{31}(H_1^2 + H_2^2) + A_{33} H_3^2] j_3. \tag{10}$$

These expressions are the same as those obtained by Juretschke but for some minor differences of notation. In order to make the correspondence evident, we note that, in accordance with the procedure already explained,

$$\rho_{23122} = T_{112}; \quad \rho_{12311} = T_{331}; \quad \rho_{12222} = T_{322};$$

$$\rho_{23133} = T_{113}; \quad \rho_{12333} = T_{333}; \quad \rho_{31223} = T_{224}.$$

Equations (8), (9) and (10) are applicable as such to $\bar{3}m$ (bismuth) and can be made applicable to the classes $4/mmm$ and $6/mmm$ by making suitable alterations as indicated below each of the schemes for the class 3m. For instance, by putting $A_{14} = A_{41} = 0$, we get the magneto-resistance part of the equations modified as to become appropriate to the class $6/mmm$ and so on.

Juretschke has considered a number of possible alternatives for working with samples of rectangular cross-section, the length and the edges being chosen as the axes of reference. One of the more important choices is described here.

We shall choose j perpendicular to c and H perpendicular to j. Crystallographic axis c is the unique axis (axis of 3-fold symmetry, etc.) and is parallel to X_3 which is numbered 3 in our notation. The directions of j and H with respect to crystallographic axis c are indicated in

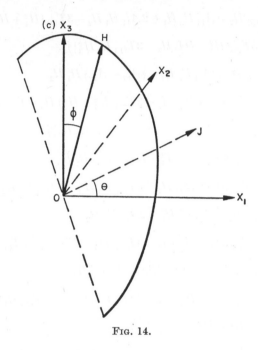

Fig. 14.

Fig. 14. θ is the angle between j and the X_1-axis. ϕ is the angle between H and the X_3-axis in the plane normal to j, and is positive in the direction $c \times j$. ϕ, as indicated in Fig. 14, should therefore be regarded as negative.

In terms of these angles, the components of j and H are

$$j_1 = j \cos \phi \quad H_1 = -H \sin \theta \sin \phi$$

$$j_2 = j \sin \phi \quad H_2 = H \cos \theta \sin \phi$$

$$j_3 = 0 \quad H_3 = H \cos \phi. \tag{11}$$

In this arrangement the most convenient directions of the lateral faces are those parallel and normal to the c-axis. Therefore, the electric fields of interest are

$$E_j = E_1 \cos \theta + E_2 \sin \theta$$

$$E_c = E_3$$

$$E_{c \times j} = -E_1 \sin \theta + E_2 \cos \theta. \tag{12}$$

The fields (12) are determined by substituting the components (11) of H and j in the general expressions (8), (9) and (10) and then forming the appropriate combinations of E_1, E_2 and E_3. We have

$$E_j = jH^2(A_{12} \sin^2 \phi + A_{13} \cos^2 \phi + A_{14} \cos 3\theta \sin \phi \cos \phi)$$

$$E_c = -jH\rho_{132} \sin \phi - jH^2 A_{41} \sin 3\theta \sin^2 \phi$$

$$+ jH^3(3T_{112} \sin^3 \phi + 3T_{113} \sin \phi \cos^2 \phi$$

$$+ 3T_{224} \cos 3\theta \sin^2 \phi \cos \phi)$$

$$E_{c \times j} = -jH\rho_{123} \cos \phi - jH^2 A_{14} \sin 3\theta \sin \phi \cos \phi$$

$$- jH^3(T_{322} \cos 3\theta \sin^3 \phi$$

$$+ 3T_{331} \sin^2 \phi \cos \phi + T_{333} \cos^3 \phi). \tag{13}$$

Equations (13) are again the same as those obtained by Juretschke except for minor notational differences. For a given sample, θ is fixed, while ϕ can be varied at will. The various coefficients are separated by an analysis of the H- and ϕ-dependence of the experimental voltages. By suitable choice of θ, 12 of the 16 galvanomagnetic coefficients can be determined in this manner. Other orientations can be conceived of so as to obtain the remaining coefficients or checks on the ones already obtained.

Freedman and Juretschke† later performed a systematic series of experiments on oriented single crystals of antimony but measured only the two first order Hall coefficients and eight magnetoresistance coefficients besides the two principal zero field electrical resistance coefficients. Thus they limited the experimental work to the second order in the magnetic field and did not extend it to the third order. They also made an elaborate calculation of the galvanomagnetic coefficients for a model with 9 adjustable parameters and adjusted the parameters so as to obtain the best possible fit with experiment. Reference may be made to their original publication for further details. Knowledge of the galvanomagnetic coefficients in chosen substances has lately assumed importance in the study of solid state physics and data are now being collected; copper, bismuth, bismuth selenide, etc. being among the crystals that have been studied.

† Freedman, S. J. and Juretschke, H. J., *Phys. Rev.* **124**, 1379 (1961).

18.3 Photoelastic Coefficients in Cubic Crystals

The scheme for the photoelastic tensor in respect of the crystal classes 23 and $m3$ is taken from Chapter 16 and reproduced below.

CLASSES 23, $m3$: SCHEME FOR PHOTOELASTIC TENSOR

$$
\begin{array}{cccccc}
q_{11} & q_{12} & q_{13} & 0 & 0 & 0 \\
q_{13} & q_{11} & q_{12} & 0 & 0 & 0 \\
q_{12} & q_{13} & q_{11} & 0 & 0 & 0 \\
0 & 0 & 0 & q_{44} & 0 & 0 \\
0 & 0 & 0 & 0 & q_{44} & 0 \\
0 & 0 & 0 & 0 & 0 & q_{44}
\end{array}
$$

If q_{13} is replaced by q_{12}, the same scheme applies to the three other classes $\bar{4}3m$, 432 and $m3m$ in the cubic system. Let us now write down the expressions for the indices B that occur in the refractive index ellipsoid. We have

$$ B_{11} = B^0_{11} - q_{11}\tau_{11} - q_{12}\tau_{22} - q_{13}\tau_{33} $$

and similar expressions for B_{22}, B_{33}, B_{23}, etc.

If one cuts a rectangular parallelepiped out of the cubic crystal with its edges parallel to the cube axes, we can consider several special cases, designed to experimentally determine the tensor coefficients. One of them is as follows:

$$ \tau_{33} = \tau; \quad \tau_{11} = \tau_{22} = 0 $$

$$ B_{11} - B^0_{11} = \frac{1}{n_1^2} - \frac{1}{n_0^2} = -q_{13}\tau $$

$$ B_{22} - B^0_{22} = \frac{1}{n_2^2} - \frac{1}{n_0^2} = -q_{12}\tau $$

$$ B_{33} - B^0_{33} = \frac{1}{n_3^2} - \frac{1}{n_0^2} = -q_{11}\tau. \tag{14} $$

Subtracting the third equation from the first equation in (14), we get (15). Similarly by subtracting it from the second, we get (16).

$$ \frac{1}{n_1^2} - \frac{1}{n_3^2} = \frac{2(n_3 - n_1)}{n_0^3} = (q_{11} - q_{13})\tau. \tag{15} $$

$$ \frac{1}{n_2^2} - \frac{1}{n_3^2} = \frac{2(n_3 - n_2)}{n_0^3} = (q_{11} - q_{12})\tau. \tag{16} $$

In bringing (15) and (16) to the form in which they are given, we have assumed that the refractive indices n_1, n_2 and n_3 differ from n_0 only by small amounts. Difference in refractive indices caused by a given τ is a directly measurable quantity, and hence $q_{11} - q_{13}$ and $q_{11} - q_{12}$ may be evaluated. In the three cubic classes where $q_{12} = q_{13}$, these two differences are not distinguishable from each other. This distinction between the classes 23 and $m3$, on the one hand, and the classes $\overline{4}3m$, 432 and $m3m$, on the other, in regard to photoelasticity was first made by the

TABLE XV
Photoelastic constants

	Barium nitrate	Lead nitrate	Ammonium alum	Potassium alum	Fluorite
$-(q_{11}-q_{12})$	23·84	19·13	5·93	5·21	1·45
$-(q_{11}-q_{13})$	17·13	11·84	5·25	4·64	1·45
$-q_{44}$	1·69	1·39	1·15	0·63	−0·70

author. Table XV contains some experimental results of interest. The first four substances belong to the crystal class $m3(\mathrm{T_h})$ and the fifth belongs to the crystal class $m3m(\mathrm{O_h})$. Two substances, namely sodium chlorate and sodium bromate, crystallizing in the class 23(T) have also been studied and found to exhibit four independent photoelastic constants as may be expected from symmetry considerations. Results are somewhat complicated in these cases as the crystals are also optically active and are not included in Table XV. Values given are in 10^{-13} c.g.s. units.

TABLE XVI
Prism cuts in cubic crystals

Edges	Cut No.		
	I	II	III
X_1	[100]	[01$\overline{1}$]	[110]
X_2	[010]	[$\overline{2}$11]	[$\overline{1}$10]
X_3	[001]	[111]	[001]

In order to determine q_{44}, we have to cut a prism with its edges parallel to [111], [$\overline{2}$11] and [01$\overline{1}$]. A pressure can be applied along the [111] direction and the birefringence, i.e. the difference in the refractive indices for incident light with vibrations parallel to the direction of stress and with vibrations parallel to either of the other two edges, should be measured. q_{44} values given in the foregoing Table have been determined in this manner.

In respect of cubic crystals, Table XVI contains three most useful cuts for the purpose of studying photoelasticity. The length of the prism is denoted by X_3 and the edges of the rectangular cross-section by X_1 and X_2. Expressions for optical path differences in each case, a quantity which can be directly measured by any of the usual instruments like a Babinet compensator, are given in Table XVII. The expressions are appropriate to the crystal classes 23 and $m3$.

TABLE XVII
Path difference for different settings

No.	Direction of pressure	Direction of observation	Path difference $\times 2/n_0^3$
1	[001]	[100]	$q_{11} - q_{12}$
2	[001]	[010]	$q_{11} - q_{13}$
3	[001]	[110] ⎫	
4	[001]	[$\bar{1}$10] ⎬	$q_{11} - \frac{1}{2}(q_{12} + q_{13})$
5	[111]	[01$\bar{1}$] ⎫	
6	[111]	[$\bar{2}$11] ⎬	q_{44}

Settings 1, 2 and either 5 or 6 have already been mentioned as the appropriate ones while dealing with the results given in Table XV. If in Table XVII, q_{12} is put equal to q_{13}, the resulting expressions become applicable to the three other cubic classes, namely, $\bar{4}3m$, 432 and $m3m$. For further details in regard to this subject, reference may be made to a number of publications by the author.†

Similar results may be expected in regard to magnetoresistance as the tensor schemes for photoelasticity and magnetoresistance are identical. However, measurements in this field are more difficult and involved as they get mixed up with Hall voltages, etc., and data do not exist for cubic crystals of the classes 23 and $m3$ in particular.

18.4 Piezoelectricity of Quartz Crystals

We shall briefly deal with another property, namely, piezoelectricity, and choose quartz as an example in view of the important part it plays in several appliances. α-Quartz belongs to the crystal class 32 or D_3 and the appropriate scheme of non-vanishing piezoelectric coefficients is given below.

CLASS 32: SCHEME FOR PIEZOELECTRICITY TENSOR

$$\begin{matrix} d_{11} & -d_{11} & 0 & d_{14} & 0 & 0 \\ 0 & 0 & 0 & 0 & -d_{14} & -2d_{11} \\ 0 & 0 & 0 & 0 & 0 & 0 \end{matrix}$$

† Bhagavantam, S., In "Advanced Methods of Crystallography", ed. by G. N. Ramachandran, p. 97. Academic Press, London (1964).

We may also note from Section 14.4 that $P_i = d_{il}\tau_l$ where i runs from 1 to 3 and l runs from 1 to 6.

On explicitly writing out P_1, P_2 and P_3, equations (17) follow.

$$P_1 = d_{11}\tau_1 - d_{11}\tau_2 + d_{14}\tau_4$$

$$P_2 = -d_{14}\tau_5 - 2d_{11}\tau_6; \quad P_3 = 0. \tag{17}$$

It is at once apparent that no kind of stress can cause a piezoelectric polarization along the 3-fold axis which will be called X_3 according to our convention. Similarly, one cannot obtain a piezoelectric polarization even along the X_1- and X_2-axes by the application of a pure tensile

TABLE XVIII

Piezoelectric constants of some crystals

Crystal	Class	Constants	Values
Quartz	32	d_{11}	2·3
		d_{14}	−0·7
Zinc blende	$\bar{4}$3m	d_{14}	−3·2
Tourmaline	3m	d_{15}	3·6
		d_{22}	−0·3
		d_{31}	0·3
		d_{33}	1·8

stress τ_3 parallel to the 3-fold axis. We can, however, generate a piezo-electric moment parallel to either X_1 or X_2 by the application of a suitable tensile stress along an axis in the X_1X_2-plane. A similar effect may be produced by the application of a shearing stress either in the X_1X_2-plane or in a plane containing X_3. One of the useful applications of the tensor schemes given in this book for various crystal classes in respect of different groups of physical properties is to enable an experimenter to visualize such consequences. Moreover, if one wants to determine by experiment the two non-vanishing piezoelectric coefficients d_{11} and d_{14} for a quartz crystal or for any other crystal in the class 32, it is obvious that one has to perform two experiments. They consist in measuring P_1 caused by the successive applications of a stress, either τ_1 or τ_2 and τ_4. This may be done with what is conventionally called an X-cut plate, its length and breadth being parallel to the X_2- and X_3-axes, respectively, and the thickness being parallel to the X_1-axis. In such a case, the application of an electric field in the thickness direction causes an expansion or contraction of the thickness itself and a shearing stress in the plane of the plate. One can also conceive of other well-known cuts, like the Y-cut and so on, for obtaining further checks on the measurement of d_{11} and d_{14}. In Table XVIII, the results on piezoelectricity for quartz along with those for two other naturally occurring crystals, namely, tourmaline and zinc blende (ZnS), are given in units of 10^{-12} coulomb/newton.

Many other substances, artificial and natural, with piezoelectric constants several hundred times larger, have been studied and are available for specific usages such as frequency control, wave filtering and so on. In all cases, a study of the single crystal in relation to the piezoelectric tensor scheme of the crystal class is of great help in choosing appropriate cuts to produce the desired effects.

Appendix

The Magnetothermoelectric Power Tensor α_{iklm}

(α is omitted in each case. Only the suffixes are given)

(i) TRICLINIC SYSTEM

1111	1122	1133	1123	1131	1112
2211	2222	2233	2223	2231	2212
3311	3322	3333	3323	3331	3312
2311	2322	2333	2323	2331	2312
3111	3122	3133	3123	3131	3112
1211	1222	1233	1223	1231	1212
3211	3222	3233	3223	3231	3212
1311	1322	1333	1323	1331	1312
2111	2122	2133	2123	2131	2112

(ii) MONOCLINIC SYSTEM

1111	1122	1133	0	0	1112
2211	2222	2233	0	0	2212
3311	3322	3333	0	0	3312
0	0	0	2323	2331	0
0	0	0	3123	3131	0
1211	1222	1233	0	0	1212
0	0	0	3223	3231	0
0	0	0	1323	1331	0
2111	2122	2133	0	0	2112

(iii) ORTHORHOMBIC SYSTEM

1111	1122	1133	0	0	0
2211	2222	2233	0	0	0
3311	3322	3333	0	0	0
0	0	0	2323	0	0
0	0	0	0	3131	0
0	0	0	0	0	1212
0	0	0	3223	0	0
0	0	0	0	1331	0
0	0	0	0	0	2112

(iv) TETRAGONAL SYSTEM: CLASSES 4, $\bar{4}$, 4/m

1111	1122	1133	0	0	1112
1122	1111	1133	0	0	-1112
3311	3311	3333	0	0	0
0	0	0	1331	-1323	0
0	0	0	3123	3131	0
1211	1222	1233	0	0	1212
0	0	0	3131	-3123	0
0	0	0	1323	1331	0
-1222	-1211	-1233	0	0	1212

Note: If 1112, 1323, 3123, 1211, 1222, 1233 are put equal to zero, the scheme applies to classes $4mm$, $\bar{4}2m$, 422 and $4/mmm$ as well.

(v) TRIGONAL SYSTEM: CLASSES 3, $\bar{3}$

1122 $+ 2(1212)$	1122	1133	-2223	1131	$-\frac{1}{2}\begin{pmatrix} 2111 \\ +1211 \end{pmatrix}$
1122	1122 $+ 2(1212)$	1133	2223	-1131	$\frac{1}{2}\begin{pmatrix} 2111 \\ +1211 \end{pmatrix}$
3311	3311	3333	0	0	0
-2322	2322	0	1331	-1323	-1311
3111	-3111	0	3123	3131	-3222
1211	-2111	1233	-1131	-2223	1212

(v) *Contd.*

−3222	3222	0	3131	−3123	−3111
1311	−1311	0	1323	1331	−2322
2111	−1211	−1233	−1131	−2223	1212

Note: If 1131, 2111, 1211, 1323, 1311, 3111, 3123, 1233 are put equal to zero, the scheme applies to classes $3m$, 32 and $\bar{3}m$ as well.

(vi) HEXAGONAL SYSTEM: CLASSES $\bar{6}$, 6, $6/m$

1122 +2(1212)	1122	1133	0	0	0
1122	1122 +2(1212)	1133	0	0	0
3311	3311	3333	0	0	0
0	0	0	1331	−1323	0
0	0	0	3123	3131	0
1211	−2111	1233	0	0	1212
0	0	0	3131	−3123	0
0	0	0	1323	1331	0
2111	−1211	−1233	0	0	1212

Note: If 1323, 3123, 1211, 2111, 1233 are put equal to zero, the scheme applies to classes $\bar{6}m2$, $6mm$, 622 and $6/mmm$ as well.

(vii) CUBIC SYSTEM: CLASSES 23, $m3$

1111	1122	1133	0	0	0
1133	1111	1122	0	0	0
1122	1133	1111	0	0	0
0	0	0	1212	0	0
0	0	0	0	1212	0
0	0	0	0	0	1212
0	0	0	1331	0	0
0	0	0	0	1331	0
0	0	0	0	0	1331

Note: If 1122 is put equal to 1133 and 1212 is put equal to 1331, the scheme applies to classes $\bar{4}3m$, 432 and $m3m$ as well.

Subject Index

A

Antiferromagnetism, 174

C

Cartesian systems, right-handed and left-handed, 4–5
Cauchy relations, 138
Characters of
  complementary operations in tensor representations, 86, 90
  group elements, 33–34
  symmetry operations in tensor representations, 85, 88–89
Compliances, 101, 125
Congruence, 35
Conjugate
  class, 29
  elements, 28
Cross effects, 104
Crystal lattices
  rotational symmetry of, 41
  translational symmetry of, 40
Crystallographic restriction, 41

D

Deformation, 109
  finite, 140
Determinant of transformation, 3–4
Dielectric constant tensor, 117, 158
Direct inspection method, 76
Dummy suffix, 2

E

Effective elastic constants, 152
Elastic coefficients, 134–136
  third order, 146–147
Electrical conductivity tensor, 192
Electrocaloric effect, 158
Enantiomorphism, 67
Entropy parameters, 107
Ettingshausen effect, 200
  second order, 204
  tensor, 205–206
Eulerian angles, 5

F

Ferromagnetic classes, 177
Ferromagnetism, 174
  weak, 176
Free suffix, 2

G

Galvanomagnetic coefficients in cubic crystals, 210–211
Galvanomagnetic effects, 196–200
  classification of, 202–203
Groups, 26
  Abelian, 26
  commutative, 26
  crystallographic, 35
  crystallographic cyclic, 44
  cyclic, 26
  dihedral, 44–45
  direct product, 29
  finite, 28
  full orthogonal, 27
  homomorphous, 29
  infinite, 28
  isomorphous, 29
  matrix, 28
  octahedral, 44, 46
  permutation, 30
  point, 38
  postulates, 26
  rotation, 27
  sub-, 28
  symmetric, 31
  tetrahedral, 44–45
Gyration tensor, 188–189

H

Hall effect, 197
  classes $3m$, $\bar{3}m$, $4/mmm$, $6/mmm$, 213
  cubic classes, 210–212
  second order, 202, 207
Hall tensor, 204–205
  second order, 207–209
Higher order effects, 71
Hooke's law—generalized, 125

227